Receptors and
Recognition

Series B Volume 10

Neurotransmitter Receptors

Part 2
Biogenic Amines

Edited by
H. I. Yamamura

Professor of Pharmacology, University of Arizona
Health Sciences Center, Tucson, Arizona

and

S. J. Enna

Professor of Pharmacology and Neurobiology,
University of Texas Medical School at Houston

LONDON AND NEW YORK

CHAPMAN AND HALL

First published 1981
by Chapman and Hall Ltd
11 New Fetter Lane, London EC4P 4EE

Published in the U.S.A. by
Chapman and Hall
in association with Methuen, Inc.,
733 Third Avenue, New York 10017

© 1981 Chapman and Hall

Printed in Great Britain at the
University Press, Cambridge
)

ISBN 0 412 23130 1

British Library Cataloguing in Publication Data

Receptors and recognition.
 Series B. Vol.10: Neurotransmitter receptors.
 Part 2: Biogenic amines
 1. Cell interaction
 I. Cuatrecasas, Pedro   II. Greaves, Melvyn Francis
 III. Enna, S.J.   IV. Yamamura, H.I.
 V. Neurotransmitter receptors. Part 2:
 Biogenic amines
 574.8'76   QH604.2   80-40942

 ISBN 0-412-23130-1

Receptors and Recognition

General Editors: P. Cuatrecasas and M. F. Greaves

About the series

Cellular recognition – the process by which cells interact with, and respond to, molecular signals in their environment – plays a crucial role in virtually all important biological functions. These encompass fertilization, infectious interactions, embryonic development, the activity of the nervous system, the regulation of growth and metabolism by hormones and the immune response to foreign antigens. Although our knowledge of these systems has grown rapidly in recent years, it is clear that a full understanding of cellular recognition phenomena will require an integrated and multidisciplinary approach.

This series aims to expedite such an understanding by bringing together accounts by leading researchers of all biochemical, cellular and evolutionary aspects of recognition systems. This series will contain volumes of two types. First, there will be volumes containing about five reviews from different areas of the general subject written at a level suitable for all biologically oriented scientists (Receptors and Recognition, series A). Secondly, there will be more specialized volumes (Receptors and Recognition, series B), each of which will be devoted to just one particularly important area.

Advisory Editorial Board

Receptors and Recognition

Series A

Published

Series B

Published

The Specificity and Action of Animal, Bacterial and Plant Toxins (B1)
edited by P. Cuatrecasas (Burroughs Wellcome, North Carolina)

Intercellular Junctions and Synapses (B2)
edited by J. Feldman (London), N.B. Gilula (Rockefeller University, New York)
and J.D. Pitts (University of Glasgow)

Microbial Interactions (B3)
edited by J.L. Reissig (Long Island University, New York)

Specificity of Embryological Interactions (B4)
edited by D.R. Garrod (University of Southampton)

Taxis and Behavior (B5)
edited by G.L. Hazelbauer (University of Uppsala)

Bacterial Adherence (B6)
edited by E.H. Beachey (Veteran's Administration and Hospital and University
of Tennessee, Memphis, Tennessee)

Virus Receptors Part 1 Bacterial Viruses (B7)
edited by L.L. Randall and L. Philipson (University of Uppsala)

Virus Receptors Part 2 Animal Viruses (B8)
edited by K. Lonberg-Holm (Du Pont, Delaware) and L. Philipson (University of
Uppsala)

Neurotransmitter Receptors Part 1 Amino Acids, Peptides and Benzodiazepines (B9)
edited by S.J. Enna (University of Texas at Houston) and H.I. Yamamura
(University of Arizona)

In Preparation

Membrane Receptors: Methods for Purification and Characterization (B11)
edited by S. Jacobs and P. Cuatrecasas (Burroughs Wellcome, North
Carolina)

Purinergic Receptors (B12)
edited by G. Burnstock (University College, London)

Receptor Regulation (B13)
edited by R.J. Lefkowitz (Duke University, North Carolina)

Transplantation Antigens (B14)
edited by P. Parham and J. Strominger (Harvard University)

Contents

Contributors

Ian Creese, Department of Neurosciences, University of California, San Diego School of Medicine, La Jolla, California, U.S.A.

Henry J. Haigler, Department of Pharmacology, Emory University School of Medicine, Atlanta, Georgia, U.S.A.

Kenneth P. Minneman, Department of Pharmacology, Emory University School of Medicine, Atlanta, Georgia, U.S.A.

Elliott Richelson, Departments of Psychiatry and Pharmacology, Mayo Foundation, Rochester, Minnesota, U.S.A.

John E. Taylor, Departments of Psychiatry and Pharmacology, Mayo Foundation, Rochester, Minnesota, U.S.A.

Gregory J. Wastek, Departments of Pharmacology and Psychiatry, University of Arizona, Health Services Center, Tucson, Arizona, U.S.A.

Henry I. Yamamura, Departments of Pharmacology and Psychiatry, University of Arizona, Health Services Center, Tucson, Arizona, U.S.A.

Contents of *Neurotransmitter Receptors Part 1 Amino Acids, Peptides and Benzodiazepines*

Preface

Since the discovery that neuronal transmission can be chemically mediated, a large number of compounds have been found in the mammalian central nervous system which appear to function as neurotransmitter agents. Recently, electrophysiological and biochemical methods have been developed which have enabled neuroscientists to classify better the myriad of neurotransmitter receptor sites in brain and to study their properties in finer detail. As a result of these investigations, a significant number of new discoveries have been made about the mechanisms involved in neurotransmitter receptor interactions, the role neurotransmitters play in the actions of pharmacological agents and in the pathogenesis of various neuropsychiatric disorders.

The present two volume text was compiled to summarize the information relating to the physiological, biochemical, pharmacological and functional characteristics of neurotransmitter receptor sites. While emphasis is placed on neurotransmitter receptors in the mammalian central nervous system, the characteristics of these receptors in other species, both vertebrate and invertebrate, are also discussed where appropriate. While these books cover the major classes of putative neurotransmitters – amino acids, peptides and biogenic amines – and are therefore broad in scope, each is discussed in a concise fashion to highlight the major points of historical and contemporary interest. In addition to outlining data, each chapter addresses current theories relating to the various aspects of receptor properties and function in an attempt to reveal the directions of future research and as a stimulus for other workers in the field. This work can serve not only as an introductory text for young neuroscientists, but should also be a valuable resource for more senior investigators as both a reference and research guide.

May, 1980
H.I. Yamamura
S.J. Enna

1 Serotonergic Receptors in the Central Nervous System

HENRY J. HAIGLER

Acknowledgements

Supported in part by National Institute on Drug Abuse grant no. 1-R01-DA01344-04.

Neurotransmitter Receptors Part 2
(*Receptors and Recognition*, Series B, Volume 10)
Edited by H.I. Yamamura and S.J. Enna
Published in 1981 by Chapman and Hall, 11 New Fetter Lane, London
EC4P 4EE

1.1 INTRODUCTION

There are numerous definitions of the term receptor. One definition is that a receptor is a specific component of a cell to which a neurotransmitter or hormone binds. The combination of the neurotransmitter or hormone with the receptor produces a chain of events that lead to the expression of a physiological event (Bockaert, 1978; Moran, 1975).

The concept of receptors is based on the following criteria (Moran, 1975). First there should be high degree of specificity in that minor differences of molecular configuration will alter the activity of the drug. Secondly, the interaction of drug with the receptor should produce a biological response. Thirdly, there should be a quantitative relationship between the concentration of drug and biological response that can be expressed using concentration–response curves. Fourthly, there should be complete reversibility of the effect of the drug indicating that the drug combines reversibly with the receptor. Fifthly, there should be selective antagonists that will block the biological response presumably by competing with the drug and blocking the reaction of the drug with the receptor.

These criteria imply that a molecular interaction occurs between the drug and the membrane of the effector cell (Moran, 1975). The effector cells throughout this chapter will be either the serotonin (5-hydroxytryptamine; 5-HT)-containing neurons or those neurons that receive an input from 5-HT neurons.

1.1.1 Historical review

From the above, it is obvious that the definition of a receptor is intimately associated with the neurotransmitter that acts on that receptor. The study of receptors in the brain is complicated because these receptors are not as readily accessible as the receptors are in the periphery. In the periphery a change in a physiological parameter such as heart rate is used to measure the effects of a drug on a receptor. Similarly, in the brain a change in the rate of neuronal firing is used as an indicator that a drug is acting on a receptor. The technique of microiontophoresis has made it possible to study the pharmacology of receptors *in vivo* in the brain because compounds can be administered into the immediate vicinity of a neuron while changes in its activity are monitored (Curtis, 1964). When a drug or putative neurotransmitter alters spontaneous neuronal activity without affecting the amplitude of the action potential, the compound is assumed to be acting on receptors on the neuronal membrane.

A receptor is characterized by the neurotransmitter that acts on it and the physiological effect produced by the combination of the neurotransmitter with the receptor. When 5-HT is administered microiontophoretically, it produces either inhibition or an acceleration of neuronal firing in almost every area of the brain studied, indicating that 5-HT receptors are widespread (Bloom *et al.*, 1972). However, the primary emphasis in this chapter will concern the 5-HT receptors that are associated with the synaptic action of 5-HT. Presumably to have a synaptic action, endogenous 5-HT is released from presynaptic terminals and diffuses across the synapse to act on receptors located on the membrane of the post-synaptic cell. Thus, to study the action of 5-HT on receptors associated with the synaptic action of 5-HT, it is necessary to establish that 5-HT is a neurotransmitter in the CNS.

The various criteria that are used in the identification of neurotransmitters in the autonomic and peripheral nervous systems are stressed by numerous authors (see Hebb, 1970). The criteria that a substance should meet to be considered a neurotransmitter are as follows: (1) the putative transmitter, an inactivating enzyme or re-uptake system, and enzymes associated with the synthesis of the neurotransmitter should all be present; (2) microiontophoretic administration of the transmitter should mimic the action of the endogenous neurotransmitter; and (3) drugs that block the putative neurotransmitter should also block the actions of the endogenously released neurotransmitter (Hebb, 1970; Werman, 1966).

Fluorescence histochemistry has been used to demonstrate that brain 5-HT is primarily a constituent of nerve cells. Prior to histochemical work Heller *et al.* (1962) and Heller and Moore (1965) showed that lesioning the medial forebrain bundle (MFB) produced a depletion of 5-HT in the forebrain. The rate of 5-HT depletion corresponds to the rate of neuronal degeneration implying that 5-HT neuronal pathways are present in the brain. The direct demonstration of the existence and localization of 5-HT neurons was accomplished by means of the formaldehyde-condensation histochemical method of Falck *et al.* (1962) applied to freeze-dried brain tissue (Carlsson *et al.*, 1962). With this method, the location of 5-HT-containing neuronal perikarya (Dahlström and Fuxe, 1965), terminals (Aghajanian *et al.*, 1973; Fuxe, 1965), and pathways (Anden *et al.*, 1968) were mapped. The perikarya of these neurons are almost exclusively located in the brain stem raphe nuclei; fibres from the raphe nuclei project to other portions of the brain stem, to the spinal cord, and to the forebrain. Of special interest is the fact that almost the entire 5-HT input to the forebrain derives from the midbrain raphe nuclei, and the 5-HT input to the spinal cord is primarily derived from the medullary pontine raphe nuclei (MPR; raphe magnus, obscurus, and pallidus).

On the basis of the histochemical mapping of 5-HT (serotonergic) pathways in the brain, it was possible to test 5-HT against the above criteria important for establishing that a substance is a neurotransmitter. By selectively placing lesions in the raphe nuclei, it has been possible to ascertain whether the biochemical machinery for the synthesis, storage, and metabolism of 5-HT is contained within the raphe projections. Destruction of the midbrain raphe nuclei has the following anatomical and biochemical consequences: (1) a degeneration of histochemically identified 5-HT terminals in the forebrain (Aghajanian *et al.*, 1969; Kuhar *et al.*, 1972a); (2) a selective reduction in forebrain 5-HT content (Heller and Moore, 1965; Jouvet, 1967; Kostowski *et al.*, 1968; Rosecrans and Sheard, 1969); (3) a selective decrease in forebrain tryptophan hydroxylase activity (Kuhar *et al.*, 1971); and (4) a loss of high-affinity 5-HT uptake in synaptosomes from the forebrain (Kuhar *et al.*, 1972b). All of these effects are selective, because other putative transmitters and their associated enzymes are not significantly altered by raphe destruction. Thus raphe projections are distinguished by their content of 5-HT and by the fact that they possess the means for 5-HT synthesis, storage, and high-affinity uptake; the last process could well serve as a means of terminating the synaptic actions of 5-HT in its presumed role as a neurotransmitter.

Knowledge about the location of 5-HT neurons and pathways in brain has served to provide evidence for establishing another neurotransmitter criterion, that of release upon nerve stimulation. Electrical stimulation of the nucleus linearis rostralis in the cat, which is in the vicinity of ascending serotonergic fibers, causes a release of 5-HT as measured in perfusates from the anterior horn of the lateral ventricle (Holman and Vogt, 1972). The release of 5-HT resulting from this stimulation is selective in that there is no concomitant release of acetylcholine (Ashkenazi *et al.*, 1972). These data form an extension of previous experiments showing that selective stimulation of the midbrain raphe nuclei produces an increase in the synthesis and turnover of 5-HT in the forebrain, a region that receives projections from the raphe (Aghajanian *et al.*, 1967; Kostowski *et al.*, 1969; Sheard and Aghajanian, 1968; Shields and Eccleston, 1972). Electrical stimulation of the dorsal raphe nucleus (DR) of the midbrain produces an inhibition of neuronal firing in the amygdala, an effect mimicked by the microiontophoretic administration of 5-HT (Wang and Aghajanian, 1977).

This latter point partially meets Werman's (1966) criterion of identical actions although he advocates intracellular recording to determine if the substance has the same effect on ionic conductance channels as the natural transmitter. However, intracellular recording is difficult to perform in the CNS and extensive experiments comparing the effects of stimulation of the raphe nucleus and the effects of microiontophoretic administration of 5-HT have not yet been carried out.

The above biochemical, histochemical and neurophysiological studies have set the stage for studying 5-HT neurotransmission from a physiological standpoint. If 5-HT is in fact a neurotransmitter, it should be possible to show that neurons that receive a serotonergic input respond to 5-HT in a fashion that mimics stimulation of the natural pathway (i.e. the raphe system). Furthermore, drugs that might block or mimic the action of 5-HT on postsynaptic receptors (i.e. receptors on cells that receive a serotonergic input) should block or mimic in an identical fashion the response to raphe stimulation and applied 5-HT. All of these approaches simply represent a continuation of the basic theme of attempting to match 5-HT against the classical criteria that should be met by any putative transmitter substance. However, it is obviously much more technically difficult to carry out such an experimental program in the brain than in the periphery, where specific neuroeffector junctional tissue can be isolated and directly visualized. Thus when one is applying 5-HT to a neuron deep in the brain and monitoring its physiological response, how can it be known that the neuron in question does in fact receive a serotonergic input? A further complication is the possibility that there are neurons which may respond to 5-HT but which do not naturally receive a serotonergic input. A high proportion of neurons in many parts of the brain are responsive to the local, microiontophoretic application of 5-HT (see below). Does this mean that all of these cells have 5-HT receptors? If 'receptor' is defined in the broad sense as meaning the presence of 'receptivity' or 'responsivity', then 5-HT receptors are to be found anywhere a response to 5-HT can be made to occur. The narrower definition of '5-HT receptor' would count receptors only at those sites that normally receive a 5-HT input. The latter definition is closely linked with the concept of 5-HT as a neurotransmitter substance. According to this view, one would focus attention on the properties of 5-HT 'receptors' that occur in association with sites of established serotonergic transmission.

1.1.2 Techniques

The characteristics of 5-HT receptors in the CNS vary depending on the technique used to study the receptors. Data from experiments using different techniques will be presented so that the reader can compare the similarities and differences in the characteristics of the 5-HT receptors. Some attempt will be made to resolve the differences in the data derived from *in vitro* and *in vivo* techniques. Data from studies using two neurochemical *in vitro* techniques; two neurophysiological microiontophoretic techniques and techniques involving the behavioral response of an animal to nociceptive stimuli, will be reviewed.

One *in vitro* approach used to study receptors is the technique developed by Pert and Snyder (1973) in which a radioactive form of a drug is incubated with brain homogenates and then rapidly filtered. The radioactive drug is trapped on the filter because it is bound to the receptor. Thus, the amount of radioactivity trapped in the filter is a function of the amount of drug attached to the receptor. When the binding of one drug (e.g. LSD) is measured alone and then in the presence of varying concentrations of another drug (e.g 5-HT) the decrease in binding of the first drug is an indication of the relative binding affinities for both drugs. If at low concentrations, drug A can reduce the binding of drug B, an assumption is that both drugs bind to the same site (receptor) on the membrane.

A second *in vitro* approach uses the activation of a 5-HT-sensitive adenylate cyclase as a measure of the presence of a 5-HT receptor (Bockaert, 1978). The adenylate cyclase has a non-uniform distribution in the CNS indicating that it may be associated with 5-HT synapses. If cAMP is a second messenger mediating the 'machine language' of neurons (Bloom, 1973) then alterations in adenylate cyclase activity may mediate the synaptic actions of 5-HT by altering intracellular levels of cAMP.

One neurophysiological technique that has been used to study receptors in the CNS is the technique of microiontophoresis. This technique involves the recording of neuronal activity from one barrel of a multibarrel micropipette during the ejection of drugs from one of the adjacent barrels. In an operational sense the receptor is the most proximal step or steps of a sequential reaction; where detailed steps are not known, the receptor is then defined as the entire sequence (Moran, 1975). Thus if a drug is ejected microiontophoretically in the brain and there is an alteration in neuronal firing rate, the assumption is that the drug produces this effect by acting on a particular receptor. Most of the current data available are based on extracellular recordings in the brain. Alterations in spontaneous neuronal firing or blockade of an increase in firing that is evoked by a stimulus is accepted as evidence that the drug is acting on a receptor. However, it is possible that drugs produce an inhibition of firing without acting on specific receptors. Instead, at high concentrations they may dissolve in the membrane causing it to swell and block the Na^+ channels and thus produce a local anesthetic effect. Local anesthetic effects are assumed to be present when there is a decrease in action potential size during the microiontophoretic administration of a drug (Fig. 1.1). When a drug is present in the vicinity of the cell in high enough concentration to dissolve in the membrane and produce a local anesthetic effect, this concentration is higher than that necessary for the drug to act on specific receptors. Thus when there is a decrease in action potential size as a consequence of the iontophoretic administration of a drug, the assumption is that specific receptors for that drug are not present on the cell.

A second neurophysiological technique that has been used to study 5-HT receptors is to stimulate an area known to contain 5-HT cell bodies while

CIN 10

30 s

Fig. 1.1 Local anesthetic effect produced by the iontophoretic administration of cinanserin. The horizontal bar above the trace indicates the duration of the iontophoretic administration of cinanserin (CIN) at an ejection current of 10 nA. The decrease in action potential size increases the width of each spike so that it appears that there is an increase in rate of firing, there is actually a decrease in firing as the action potential size decreases. This decrease is apparent at 30–45 s after the onset of iontophoresis. An ejection current of 5 nA had no effect on the firing of this cell. This cell is located in MRF and is a cell included in the data of a previous study (Haigler and Aghajanian, 1974b).

recording the neuronal firing in an area that receives a serotonergic input. In this way the effect of the release of the putative neurotransmitter produced by the electrical stimulation can be compared to the effect of the neurotransmitter ejected microiontophoretically.

Unfortunately, the data derived from the *in vitro* studies sometimes are not apparently compatible with data from experiments in which the technique of microiontophoresis is used. After the sections on the *in vitro* and *in vivo* experiments, an attempt to resolve the differences between these two sets of data will be presented.

Behavioral techniques used to study 5-HT receptors attempt to alter the amount of 5-HT reaching the receptor and measure the resulting behavioral effects. Levels of 5-HT at the receptor are manipulated using electrolytic and neurotoxic lesions of the serotonergic system, 5-HT agonists and antagonists, drugs that alter the synthesis of 5-HT and electrical stimulation of the serotonergic system. Some behavioral endpoint is used to determine how the effects of alterations in 5-HT will alter this behavior. Two of the more common endpoints used to measure the behavioral effects of alterations in the 5-HT system are nociception and analgesia. Obviously the interaction of morphine, a narcotic analgesic drug, with the serotonergic system will be significant in this context.

Frequently, the 5-HT antagonists or agonists that are used are drugs that have been shown to mimic or block the effects of 5-HT on smooth muscle.

The assumption is that because these drugs block or stimulate 5-HT receptors in smooth muscle, they will have the same effect on 5-HT receptors in the CNS. Both microiontophoretic studies and behavioral studies have been used to determine the effects that peripheral 5-HT antagonists have on the CNS. The data concerning the effects of 5-HT antagonists in the brain which are presented are based primarily on microiontophoretic studies. The data concerning the effects of 5-HT antagonists in the spinal cord are presented in the context of nociception and morphine because the data are so intertwined and interrelated. The relationship of 5-HT to the analgesic effects of morphine will also be included because much of the available data suggests that blockade of 5-HT receptors can block the analgesic effects of morphine. Conversely, 5-HT injected intrathecally can mimic the analgesic effects of morphine. Although the serotonergic system that descends to the spinal cord from the MPR seems to be intimately involved with the analgesic effects of morphine, the ascending (or forebrain) serotonergic system does not appear to be involved in the expression of morphine analgesia.

1.1.3 Relationship between LSD and 5-HT

D-Lysergic acid diethylamide (LSD) contains an indoleamine nucleus and is consequently a structural analog of 5-HT. Thus, LSD has typically been used to help classify 5-HT receptors. There is considerable evidence that LSD produces significant alterations in the biochemistry and physiology of serotonergic neurons in brain. The hypothesis that LSD might produce its effects on behavior by interacting with 5-HT was originally proposed by Gaddum (1953) and Wooley and Shaw (1954). They suggested that LSD might antagonize or disrupt the normal function of 5-HT in the central nervous system. This concept, which was advanced years prior to the discovery of serotonergic neurons in brain (Dahlström and Fuxe, 1965), was based on some of the following observations: (1) LSD and 5-HT are structural analogues in that both contain an indolethylamine nucleus; (2) LSD antagonizes the effects of 5-HT on certain smooth muscle preparations (Gaddum, 1953; Wooley and Shaw, 1954); and (3) 5-HT is present in the brain (Amin *et al.*, 1954; Twarog and Page, 1953). The hypothesis that the behavioral effects of LSD result from a central antagonism of 5-HT was questioned by the finding that 2-brom-LSD(BOL) was as potent as LSD in antagonizing 5-HT in peripheral systems, but had little behavioural effect (Cerletti and Rothlin, 1955). However, it was later found that LSD, particularly at low concentrations, has a 5-HT-like action in various peripheral systems (Costa, 1956; Mansour, 1957; Shaw and Wooley, 1956; Welsh, 1957). Moreover, there are two tryptamine serotonergic receptors in the guinea-pig ileum. The M receptors are apparently located on *nervous* tissue, and blocked by morphine; D receptors are apparently located on *muscle* tissue and blocked by LSD (Gaddum and Picarelli, 1957). Although there are apparently two types of serotonergic receptors in the periphery, there is no apparent basis for the assumption that central (CNS) and peripheral 5-HT receptors have any of the same pharmacological characteristics. Thus the number and characteristics of peripheral and central 5-HT receptors may be unrelated.

1.2 BIOCHEMICAL STUDIES ON INTERACTIONS BETWEEN LSD AND BRAIN 5-HT

Following the earlier work on LSD-5-HT interactions in the periphery, studies were initiated to investigate the influence of LSD on the metabolism of 5-HT in the brain (Freedman, 1961; Freedman and Giarman, 1962). LSD was found to produce a small but reproducible *increase* in the concentration of 5-HT in the brain. This increase could be interpreted as resulting from either increased synthesis or decreased breakdown in 5-HT. More recent work has shown that the concentration of 5-hydroxyindoleacetic acid, the principal metabolite of 5-HT in the brain, is decreased after the administration of LSD (Freedman *et al.*, 1970; Rosecrans *et al.*, 1967). In addition, the rate of synthesis of 5-HT from labeled precursor (L-tryptophan) is also decreased (Lin *et al.*, 1969; Schubert *et al.*, 1970). Taken together, these results indicate that LSD reduces the rate of 5-HT turnover in brain.

Electrical stimulation of the midbrain raphe nuclei causes an increase in 5-HT turnover (Aghajanian *et al.*, 1967). It was suggested that LSD might reduce 5-HT turnover by depressing the firing of raphe neurons (Aghajanian and Freedman, 1968). A similar suggestion was made by Anden *et al.* (1968), who found that when 5-HT synthesis is inhibited, LSD markedly reduces the usual rate of 5-HT depletion in the brain and spinal cord. It was reasoned by analogy that the LSD-induced decrease in 5-HT turnover might result from a decrease in the activity of central 5-HT neurons because an interruption of descending serotonergic nerve impulses by a spinal transection reduces the rate of 5-HT turnover in the distal cord. It was also surmised that LSD could cause such a reduction in the activity of 5-HT neurons by stimulating postsynaptic 5-HT receptors, setting into motion a compensatory neuronal feedback inhibition of the serotonergic (i.e. presynaptic) neurons.

1.2.1 *In vitro* binding

Many of the neurochemical *in vitro* studies on 5-HT binding sites use D-LSD to displace 5-HT or vice versa. The reasons for using D-LSD are numerous. One reason is that D-LSD is structurally similar to 5-HT and has a behaviourally inactive stereoisomer (L-LSD). A second reason is the strong interest in determining the mechanism by which D-LSD produces its hallucinogenic effect. Other drugs (e.g. 5-HT antagonists) are also evaluated for their ability to block the saturable, specific binding of either 5-HT or D-LSD to particulate fractions derived from brain homogenates.

Early attempts to isolate and characterize the 5-HT receptor *in vitro* were initially inconclusive. Binding sites in the synaptosomal fraction isolated from rat brain have a high affinity for 5-HT ($K_D = 2 \times 10^{-6}$ M). These binding sites are localized mainly in the rhinencephalon, subcortical and midbrain regions. Low concentrations of D-LSD displace 5-HT from these binding sites (Marchbanks, 1966, 1967). However, the non-hallucinogenic form of LSD, L-LSD, also displaces 5-HT at this binding site as effectively as D-LSD (Marchbanks, 1967). Another characteristic of this binding site is that reserpine, a drug that has a vague structural similarity to LSD, also effectively displaces 5-HT from its high-affinity binding site (Fiszer and DeRobertis, 1969; Marchbanks, 1967). In a microiontophoretic study, when compared to 5-HT, reserpine and D-LSD have only a minimal inhibitory effect on neuronal activity in the lateral geniculate (Curtis and Davis, 1962). In subsequent microiontophoretic experiments, D-LSD has a relatively weak inhibitory effect in the ventral lateral geniculate of the rat (see below; Aghajanian, 1976; Haigler and Aghajanian, 1974a). Thus, this particular binding site is apparently not associated with the site that mediates the hallucinogenic effect of D-LSD or even interacts with the physiologically relevant 5-HT receptor.

A different binding site for D-LSD can be isolated. Using an equilibrium dialysis method synaptosomes and synaptic membranes isolated from cerebral cortex (but not other areas of the rat brain) specifically bind D-LSD with a high affinity ($K_D = 9 \times 10^{-9}$ M) (Farrow and Van Vunakis, 1972, 1973). As the authors point our, the characteristics of the 5-HT binding sites isolated from cerebral cortical homogenates are different from those isolated from the rhinencephalon, subcortical and midbrain regions described by Marchbanks (1966, 1967). This latter binding site has the following characteristics: a $K_D = 5 \times 10^{-7}$ M; destroyed by freezing, room temperature, proteolytic enzymes and acid pH, and it can be extracted (with retention of binding activity) using *n*-butanol (Marchbanks, 1966). In contrast, the high-affinity binding site in the cerebral cortex has *none* of the above characteristics. Instead this binding site has the following characteristics: a $K_D = 9 \times 10^{-9}$ M; *not* destroyed by freezing or room temperature, a proteolytic enzyme or acid pH and *cannot* be extracted using *n*-butanol. A critical difference is that *only* the cerebral cortical binding sites show stereospecificity in that D-LSD and not L-LSD, is effective in blocking the binding of 5-HT (Farrow and Van Vunakis, 1973; Marchbanks, 1967). Thus the cortical binding sites are candidates for the receptors that mediate the hallucinogenic effects of D-LSD. When the raphe nucleus is lesioned there is no loss of binding indicating that these receptors are located on cells receiving a 5-HT input, not on the 5-HT-containing neurons (Bennett and Aghajanian, 1974; Bennett and Snyder, 1975).

Preliminary results indicate that synaptosomal fractions isolated from cortical *and* subcortical regions known to receive a 5-HT input (e.g. striatum and diencephalon) contain a specific D-LSD binding site (Bennett and Aghajanian, 1974). However, this binding site is absent in the cerebellum, which does not receive a documented 5-HT input (Dahlström and Fuxe, 1965). The binding site described by Bennett and Aghajanian (1974) is very similar to that described by Farrow and Van Vunakis (1973). For instance, 5-HT is the most effective putative neurotransmitter in displacing D-LSD from its binding site. The binding site is highly stereospecific for D-LSD and drugs structurally related to LSD also show a high affinity for the binding site. Furthermore, slight modifications of the molecular structure of LSD change the affinity for the binding site remarkably.

Other characteristics of the binding site described by Bennett and Aghajanian (1974) are as follows. First the phenothiazines (chlorpromazine and promethazine) reduce the stereospecific binding of D-[^{3}H]-LSD binding. However, promethazine has no antipsychotic action. Secondly, the tricyclic antidepressants (imipramine, desimipramine) are also potent in reducing the binding of D-LSD. Until recently, drugs in this class were thought to exert their effects by blocking the re-uptake of 5-HT and not acting on the 5-HT receptor. In a recent microiontophoretic study, long-term treatment (4–7 days) with tricyclic antidepressant drugs (e.g. iprinole, desimipramine) enhanced the response of neurons in the forebrain to the inhibitory effects of 5-HT (Montigny and Aghajanian, 1978). The chronic administration of desimipramine does not produce any consistent effect on serotonergic binding densities in the cortex. It is possible that the enhancement of the inhibitory effect of 5-HT is mediated by some alteration other than an increase in the number of receptors (Bergstrom and Kellar, 1979).

In a later study on 5-HT and LSD binding sites, also using the rapid filtration method, *two* types of indoleamine receptors were isolated from membrane preparations of rat brain (Bennett and Snyder, 1976). The LSD and 5-HT binding sites are remarkably similar (Bennett and Snyder, 1976). First, 5-HT has the highest affinity for *both* sites when compared to other transmitters. Second, the relative potencies of the two drugs are similar for the two binding sites. Third, the regional and developmental patterns are similar for both 5-HT and LSD binding.

Although the above evidence suggests that LSD and 5-HT are both binding to the same site several striking differences in 5-HT and LSD binding suggest that these sites are different. For example, 5-HT has a 100 times greater affinity for the 5-HT binding site in comparison to the LSD binding site. However, putative 5-HT antagonists (methysergide, cyproheptadine methiothepin, and mianserin) have 3–100 times greater affinity for LSD sites in comparison to 5-HT sites. Based on the above data, there are two binding sites; 5-HT binds to the agonist binding site and D-LSD binds to *both* the agonist and antagonist sites (Bennett and Snyder, 1976).

It is possible that the binding sites are related such that one type can be converted into the other type or, alternatively, there are two completely independent binding sites (Bennett and Snyder, 1976). In any case both of these binding sites appear to be associated with postsynaptic cells because lesions of the raphe nuclei do not produce a decrease in LSD and 5-HT binding (Bennett and Aghajanian, 1974; Bennett and Snyder, 1976).

There may be a disassociation between the D-LSD sites and 5-HT synapses in the cerebral cortex of the monkey. In the cortex where D-[^{3}H]-LSD binding is the highest, the presynaptic 5-HT terminal density, judged by the distribution of high-affinity 5-HT uptake into synaptosomes, is only intermediate (Bennett and Snyder, 1976). Thus it is possible that LSD binding sites are associated with binding sites that are not related to 5-HT binding sites.

Although the potency of a variety of lysergic acid derivatives in blocking the binding of D-LSD correlates to a certain extent with their psychedelic potency, there is a major exception (Bennett and Snyder, 1975). BOL is equipotent with D-LSD in displacing D-[^{3}H]-LSD from its binding site (Bennett and Snyder, 1975). However, only very large doses (>64 µg kg^{-1}) of BOL induce a partial LSD-like syndrome (Bertino *et al.*, 1959; Isbell *et al.*, 1959; Schneckloth *et al.*, 1957). Similarly, BOL administered i.v. typically produces an incomplete inhibition of firing in neurons in DR even at doses as high as 1.2 to 2.0 mg kg^{-1}; LSD administered i.v. at a dose of 10–20 µg kg^{-1} readily produces an inhibition of firing (cf. Figs. 2, 3 Aghajanian *et al.*, 1970). Furthermore, BOL does not block the inhibitory effect of LSD (Aghajanian *et al.*, 1970) as one might expect if it were a agonist–antagonist. When administered microiontophoretically BOL produces an incomplete inhibition of firing and does not block the inhibition of firing produced by 5-HT (Aghajanian, 1976). The binding site for D-LSD described by Bennett and Snyder (1975) is not related to the 5-HT receptor that mediates an inhibition of neuronal firing. Thus, the binding of D-[^{3}H]-LSD to membranes may not be a reliable index of physiologically relevant receptors (Aghajanian, 1976).

The lack of agreement in binding studies makes interpretation difficult. For instance, in one binding study using membranes derived from the caudate of bovine brain, Whittaker and Seeman (1978) found that the specific binding for [^{3}H]-5-HT was higher (K_D = 2 mM) than found for the

Table 1.1

Drug	IC_{50} (mM)		
	Whittaker and Seeman (1978)	Bennett and Snyder (1975)	
	5-HT binding	5-HT binding	D-LSD binding
D-LSD	9.5	10	8
5-HT	2.5	10	1 000
Bufotenin	6	20	300
Methysergide	16	300	100
Tryptamine	270	1 000	5 000
Psilocin	250	1 000	1 000
Mianserin	230	10 000	100
Dimethyltryptamine	220	2 000	2 000

LSD or 5-HT binding site described by Bennett and Snyder (1975) in which the lowest K_D for LSD binding was 5.7 and the lowest for 5-HT was 8.3. The binding sites in these two studies do not appear to be the same because the IC_{50} for a variety of drugs differ remarkably (Table 1.1). There are numerous explanations that may explain the divergent results in these two studies. For instance it is possible that 5-HT receptors in bovine brain are different from those in rat brain. Another possibility is that the 5-HT binding site in bovine brain underwent a post-mortem change because the caudates were removed within 2 h after death (Whitaker and Seeman, 1978). In contrast, the rats were decapitated and their brains rapidly removed and dissected on ice (Bennett and Snyder, 1975).

However, even the 5-HT and LSD binding sites isolated by very similar methods have different characteristics. For instance, in one study the affinity of 5-HT for the LSD binding site is high; the ED_{50} for 5-HT to displace LSD was 0.2 μM (Bennett and Aghajanian, 1974). In another study, 5-HT is much less potent in displacing bound D-[^{3}H]-LSD; its ED_{50} for maximal displacement is 3 μM (Bennett and Snyder, 1975).

1.2.2 LSD and Dopamine

The binding of D-LSD may not only be related to 5-HT binding sites. For instance, LSD is displaced by dopamine (DA) agonists (Bennett and Snyder, 1976). Furthermore, LSD, 5-HT, other tryptamines and 5-HT antagonists compete for high-affinity dopamine binding sites in the striatum (Burt *et al.*, 1976). Because there is a chapter on DA elsewhere in this book, the effects of LSD and DA receptors will be reviewed there.

Although binding specificity is a necessary condition for the identification of a receptor it is not definitive evidence that the binding sites are functional receptors (Bockaert, 1978). Furthermore, using 'binding' studies alone it is not possible to determine if a drug is an agonist or antagonist (Bockaert, 1978). A receptor is a membrane constituent that triggers a physiological effect when an agonist attaches to it. Thus it is necessary to determine the physiological effects that the binding of a drug to a receptor produces before one can conclude that a binding site is a physiologically significant receptor (Bockaert, 1978; Moran, 1975). One way to determine if the attachment of a drug to a membrane binding site is a physiologically significant receptor is to measure the effects on adenylate cyclases (Bockaert, 1978). The adenylate cyclases do not lose their biological activity as a consequence of the homogenization procedure and the topographical distribution of adenylate cyclase coupled with different neurotransmitters, including 5-HT, can be determined (Bockaert, 1978). The topographical distribution of the 5-HT sensitive adenylate cyclase should be related to the distribution of the neurotransmitter (5-HT) to which they are specifically sensitive if these enzymes play a role in synaptic transmission (Bockaert, 1978). Furthermore this should indicate whether or not the pharmacological properties of the receptor are the same throughout the brain (Bockaert, 1978).

In the new-born rat the apparent affinity of the adenylate cyclase for 5-HT was 10^{-6} M in all brain structure considered (Enjalbert *et al.*, 1978). The activity was maximal in hypothalamus and the superior and inferior colliculi and showed decreased activity in the following structures: spinal cord $\cong$ brain stem $>$ hippocampus $\cong$ striatum $>$ cerebral cortex $>$ cerebellum (Enjalbert *et al.*, 1978; Von Hungen *et al.*, 1975). There is no correlation between the distribution of the DA and 5-HT sensitive adenylate cyclases indicating that these cyclases are localized on different synapses (Enjalbert *et al.*, 1978). Like the binding sites, the 5-HT adenylate cyclase is localized postsynaptically because electrolytic lesions of presynaptic fibers did not alter its activity (Enjalbert *et al.*, 1978). The DA and 5-HT adenylate cyclases may be very similar because neuroleptics *and* putative 5-HT antagonists [metergoline (or methergoline), methiothepin, cyproheptadine cinanserin, mianserin] inhibit the 5-HT- and DA-sensitive adenylate cyclase (Enjalbert *et al.*, 1978). These data conflict with a binding site that found neuroleptics (fluphenazine, chlorpromazine promethazine haloperidol) and 5-HT antagonists have a low affinity for the 5-HT binding site although they have a somewhat higher affinity for the LSD binding site (Bennett and Snyder, 1976). Another binding study found that the neuroleptics had a very low potency in producing displacement of 5-HT and had a much higher affinity for 5-HT ($K_D = 2 \times 10^{-9}$ M) (Whittaker and Seeman, 1978) than the other binding study ($K_D = 8 \times 10^{-9}$ M) or the adenylate cyclase ($K_D(?) = 1 \times 10^{-6}$ M).

1.2.3 Microiontophoretic and *in vitro* studies: are they compatible?

When one compares the data from microiontophoretic studies it is difficult to resolve the differences. One is puzzled as to why the receptor on the DR (5-HT$_1$) cannot be demonstrated *in vitro* but in an *in vivo* autoradiographic [³H]-LSD binds to neurons in the DR as well as other subcortical neurons (Diab *et al.*, 1971). This observation coupled with data from microiontophoretic experiments which demonstrate that LSD is more potent in producing inhibition of firing in the DR than it is in affecting postsynaptic cells makes one wonder about the significance of binding studies.

Even if the *in vitro* studies are demonstrating only post-synaptic receptors there are still problems. It is not clear why LSD, BOL and 5-HT have similar affinities for a binding site *in vitro* but LSD and BOL have no effect on the inhibition produced by 5-HT. If the binding site is a physiologically relevant receptor, BOL or LSD, even if they are inactive (i.e. have no intrinsic activity), they should block the inhibitory effect of 5-HT because they would prevent 5-HT from attaching to the receptor. An easy answer to this problem is that the binding sites are not physiologically relevant receptors. This possibility is supported by the observation that some of the binding sites are unaffected by extreme conditions indicating that they may not be components of the cell membrane. However, most of the *in vitro* data are convincing enough to make it worthwhile to try to resolve the differences between data derived from *in vitro* experiments and those derived from *in vivo* microiontophoretic experiments using a simple model described later in this chapter.

When the order of inhibitory potency of some of the indoleamines is compared to the order of potency according to the IC$_{50}$ of the drug in blocking D-[³H]-LSD there appears to be an inverse correlation (Table 1.2).

This inverse correlation is not perfect (e.g. tryptamine). Interestingly there is *no* apparent correlation of the inhibitory potency ratio with the order of potency based on the binding to the [³H]-5-HT binding site. If the order of potency of LSD and 5-HT binding are combined, it is difficult to see any relationship to the order of potencies derived from the microiontophoretic experiments. However, one tentative conclusion that one can reach is that the more strongly a drug is bound to the LSD receptor, the less potent the drug is in producing an inhibition of firing in postsynaptic neurons when it is administered microiontophoretically. LSD is also less potent in producing inhibition in the postsynaptic neurons when it is administered systemically (Haigler and Aghajanian, 1974a).

Table 1.2 Comparison of binding and inhibitory potencies

Rank order of indoleamines according to IC_{50} values for LSD binding site (from Bennett and Snyder, 1976) IC_{50} D-[^{3}H]-LSD (nM)		Rank order of indoleamines according to inhibitory potencies on postsynaptic neurons in the serotonergic system* (from Aghajanian and Haigler, 1975) Inhibitory potencies† (%)	
LSD	8	5-HT	100
Bufotenin	300	Tryptamine	100
5-HT	1 000	Bufotenin	82
Psilocin	1 000	DMT	79
DMT	2 000	Psilocin	68
Tryptamine	5 000	D-LSD	36

* Neurons are located in the amygdala and ventral lateral geniculate (VLG).
† Inhibitory potencies are an average from both areas; drugs are typically slightly more potent in the VLG. All of these indoleamines were equipotent with 5-HT in producing inhibition in presynaptic neurons in the dorsal raphe.

The postsynaptic 5-HT receptor may have two sites, one to which 5-HT binds and one to which LSD binds (as suggested by Bennett and Snyder). It is possible that these two binding sites have a membrane component located between them such that when a molecule is bound to (attached to) one receptor, it cannot attach to the other receptor (see Section 1.3.6). Thus as the apparent affinity for the LSD binding site decreases and/or the affinity for the 5-HT binding site increases, the probability that the molecule will attach to the 5-HT receptor and produce an inhibition of neuronal firing will increase. Affinity for the LSD binding site and hallucinogenic potency would increase as the molecule became increasingly more complex relative to the 5-HT molecule and as the affinity for the LSD binding site increases. Thus it is possible that a bulky molecule with a high affinity for the LSD binding site will have a higher hallucinogenic potency than will a smaller, more flexible molecule, that has a lower affinity for the LSD receptor (e.g. psilocin and DMT). According to this proposal the bulky molecule will act on the presynaptic autoreceptor (5-HT), but *not* on the postsynaptic receptor, to produce an inhibition of neuronal firing. This will produce an acceleration of firing in the postsynaptic cells that may be the basis for the hallucinogenic effect of drugs in the indolethylamine class. Thus the hallucinogenic effects of LSD may arise because it has a differential effect on presynaptic and postsynaptic 5-HT receptors (see Section 1.3.5).

1.3 MICROIONTOPHORETIC STUDIES

1.3.1 Background

When 5-HT is administered microiontophoretically it may or may not act on receptors associated with a functional synapse. For instance, when 5-HT is administered microiontophoretically it produces an effect on neuronal firing in almost every area of the brain studied (Bloom *et al.*, 1972). There should be some areas of the brain that do not receive a serotonergic input. Thus, the primary emphasis will be on data derived from areas of the brain where there is evidence for the existence of a serotonergic synapse and where the effects of 5-HT administered microiontophoretically have been shown to match the effects of stimulation of the raphe nuclei.

Using the technique of fluorescent histochemistry, Dahlström and Fuxe (1964) determined the distribution of 5-HT- and catecholamine-containing neurons in the brain; the fluorescent condensation product of 5-HT is yellow and for catecholamines it is green. Serotonin-containing neurons were found in the raphe nuclei of the pons and medulla (raphe magnus, pallidus, obscurus) and mesencephalon (dorsal and median raphe). The use of fluorescent histochemistry also allowed a localization of 5-HT terminals in the brain. Thus fluorescent histochemistry provides a color-coded 'wiring diagram' of the brain. This 'wiring diagram' can then be used as a map to guide a detailed examination (using electrophysiological and microiontophoretic techniques) of the neural circuits associated with monoamines (5-HT and the catecholamines).

1.3.2 5-HT receptors located on serotonin-containing neurons

Cells in the dorsal and median raphe (DR and MR, respectively) of the mesencephalon contain 5-HT (Dahlström and Fuxe, 1964). The DR, where 5-HT containing cells are densely packed, and MR project to areas in the forebrain, sending their fibers forward primarily in the medial forebrain bundle (MFB). Cells in the DR have a characteristic slow firing rate in both the anesthetized and locally anesthetized animals and in animals rendered pain-free by brain transection (Aghajanian *et al.*, 1972; Haigler 1978a; Haigler and Aghajanian, 1974a). Cells in the DR have this same slow firing rate when recordings are made *in vitro* from brain slices, suggesting that the slow firing rate may be an inherent characteristic of neurons in the DR (Mosko and Jacobs, 1976). The action potentials recorded extracellularly are positive, usually have an inflection point and a duration of 1 ms (Fig. 1.2).

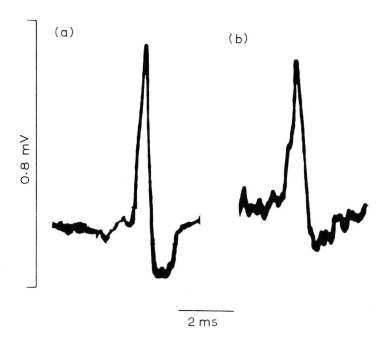

Fig. 1.2 Action potentials recorded from (a) the DR and (b) the MR. Both action potentials have a duration of about 1 ms. Reprinted from Haigler (1978b) with permission from Elsevier/North-Holland Biomedical Press.

1.3.3 5-HT and LSD

One of the first hypotheses concerning 5-HT was that LSD had its effect by interacting with 5-HT in the CNS (see Section 1.1.3). The densely packed 5-HT containing neurons in the DR provided an ideal target for an electrophysiological study to test the hypothesis derived from neurochemical studies and studies on smooth muscle that LSD would alter the neuronal firing of these 5-HT-containing cells. Low doses (10–20 μg kg^{-1}) LSD administered systemically produce an inhibition of firing in the DR and MR (Aghajanian *et al.*, 1969). Only 5-HT-containing neurons contain tryptophan hydroxylase and can convert the non-fluorescent L-tryptophan (L-TP) into the highly fluorescent 5-HT (Aghajanian and Asher, 1971). Cells in the DR that are inhibited by low doses of LSD (Fig. 1.3) become intensely fluorescent after L-TP is iontophoresed from the recording electrode (Fig. 1.4). Thus, cells in the DR that are inhibited by LSD contain 5-HT. Two explanations used to explain the inhibitory effects of LSD in

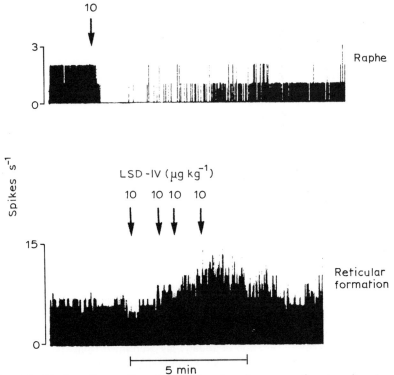

Fig. 1.3. Single-cell recordings from a dorsal raphe neuron (top trace) and a neuron in the midbrain reticular formation (lower trace). The raphe neuron shows a typical inhibitory response to a small i.v. dose of LSD (10 μg kg^{-1}). On the other hand, the reticular formation neuron shows little response to 10 μg kg^{-1} of LSD, but accelerates temporarily at higher doses. Reprinted from Aghajanian and Haigler (1974) by permission of Elsevier/North-Holland Biomedical Press.

the midbrain raphe nuclei are the following: (1) LSD acts directly on these neurons to produce an inhibition of firing; and (2) LSD mimics 5-HT on the postsynaptic cell and thus activates a negative feedback system that inhibits neuronal firing in the raphe (Aghajanian *et al.*, 1969). Thus, in response to an apparent excess of 5-HT, the postsynaptic cell would send a feedback signal to inhibit the firing in the DR in order to produce a decrease in the release of 5-HT.

Microiontophoresis is the best method available to determine the effects of drugs or compounds on neurons in the brain, especially those that do not cross the blood–brain barrier (e.g. 5-HT). When a drug that is administered i.v. produces a particular effect, it is possible that the observed effect arises

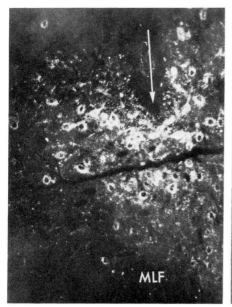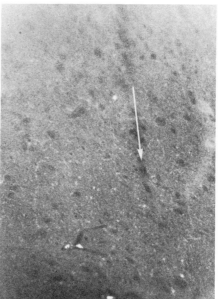

Fig. 1.4. Histofluorescence following L-TP ejection from recording electrodes in dorsal raphe nucleus (left panel) or midbrain reticular formation (right panel). Increased fluorescence can be seen surrounding tip of electrode tract (arrow) in the ventral lobe of dorsal raphe (see text for details). No increase in fluorescence can be seen at tip of electrode tract in reticular formation. In both cases, L-TP was ejected from recording micropipette for a period of 4 min at a negative current of 10 μA. Reprinted from Aghajanian and Haigler (1974) by permission of Elsevier/North-Holland Biomedical Press.

from an action on neurons in areas distant from the recording site. The value of the microiontophoretic approach is illustrated by the finding that mescaline administered i.v. will also produce an inhibition of firing in DR neurons (Aghajanian *et al.*, 1969) but administered iontophoretically it had no effect (Haigler and Aghajanian, 1973). When LSD and 5-HT are administered microiontophoretically on neurons in the DR, LSD and 5-HT both produce an inhibition of firing (Aghajanian *et al.*, 1972; Bramwell and Gonye, 1976). LSD administered i.v. in low doses produced an inhibition of firing in the same cells that were inhibited by the microiontophoretic administration of 5-HT and LSD. If a dose of LSD was administered that did not produce a complete inhibition of firing (e.g. 5 μg kg^{-1}), a submaximal ejection current of 5-HT would produce a complete inhibition of firing (Haigler and Aghajanian, unpublished observation). Furthermore if the ejection currents of 5-HT and LSD that alone produce a 50% decrease in firing are used together, a total inhibition of firing is produced (Aghajanian *et al.*, 1972). Once an ejection current that produced a complete inhibition of firing was determined for both drugs, any fraction of that ejection current for 5-HT could be used with any fraction of the ejection current for LSD to produce a desired degree of inhibition (personal observation). Therefore, the effect of the iontophoretic administration of 5-HT and LSD on neuronal firing in the DR appears to be additive.

Thus, there appears to be a 5-HT receptor that is presynaptic or an 'autoreceptor' (i.e. a receptor mediating the response of a neuron to its own neurotransmitter; Carlsson, 1975). Both 5-HT and LSD act on this receptor to produce an inhibition of firing. The presence of this receptor (labeled 5-HT_1 for convenience) on the DR and MR indicate that 5-HT neurons may receive input from other 5-HT neurons. This possibility receives further support from the following data.

Studies using electron microscopic autoradiography have shown that nerve terminals in the pontine raphe nuclei (Bloom *et al.*, 1972) and DR (Aghajanian and Bloom, 1967) have a high-affinity uptake system for $[^3H]$-5-HT. The presence of such high-affinity uptake systems is usually presumptive evidence that the nerve terminal contains that neurotransmitter. Based on studies using HRP, cells in the median raphe project to the DR (Aghajanian and Wang, 1978; Mosko *et al.*, 1977). However, cells in the MR that project to the DR have not been shown to contain 5-HT.

Further evidence supporting the existence of 5-HT collaterals is that stimulation of the major ascending 5-HT pathway at the level of the ventromedial tegmentum (VMT) produces an inhibition of firing in DR neurons that is linearly related to the stimulus intensity (Aghajanian and Wang, 1978). Chlorimipramine, a 5-HT uptake blocker, potentiated the post-stimulus depression and the iontophoretic administration of 5-HT on these 5-HT-containing cells invariably produced inhibition (Aghajanian and Wang, 1978). Thus, 5-HT receptors are apparently part of a synapse involving collaterals *from* 5-HT-containing neurons *to* 5-HT-containing neurons.

In apparent contradiction to the above evidence, a preliminary study using EM autoradiography has failed to find any evidence of 5-HT terminals associated within classical synaptic junctions (Baraban and Aghajanian, 1979). This latter finding indicates that interactions between raphe neurons may be dendrodendritic (Aghajanian, personal communication). Further research is needed before a conclusion can be reached concerning the existence of projections from 5-HT neurons *to* 5-HT neurons.

There is another function that 5-HT_1 receptors may serve. If 5-HT_1 receptors are distributed over the entire membrane of the 5-HT neuron and its processes (e.g. terminals of the 5-HT neuron) the presence of 5-HT in the synapse might serve as a negative feedback signal to inhibit the continued release of 5-HT from the nerve terminal. This possibility is supported by the observation that LSD blocks the release of $[^3H]$-5-HT from isolated brain slices (Chase *et al.*, 1967).

1.3.4 5-HT receptors in the forebrain

Even though there are 5-HT_1 receptors that are associated with the 5-HT-containing neurons in the DR, one would expect that there would be another 5-HT receptor associated with the 5-HT synapse between the raphe and cells in areas that receive a dense serotonergic input (e.g. VLG, cortical and basolateral nucleus of the amygdala). The 5-HT receptor located on non-serotonergic cells in areas receiving a dense serotonergic input will be called 5-HT_2 receptors for convenience.

The evidence that the midbrain raphe nuclei project to discrete areas of the forebrain is as follows: lesions in the midbrain raphe nuclei result in a disappearance of 5-HT-containing, yellow fluorescent axons and terminals that is associated with a decrease in synaptosomal uptake of 5-HT, a decrease in 5-HT content of the forebrain and a decrease in tryptophan hydroxylase activity in discrete regions of the forebrain (Kuhar *et al.*, 1972a). The serotonergic input to the amygdala has also been shown to be primarily derived from the DR by using the horseradish peroxidase retrograde tracing technique (Wang and Aghajanian, 1977). Furthermore stimulation of the DR produces an inhibition of firing in cells in the amygdala that is mimicked by the iontophoretic administration of 5-HT (Wang and Aghajanian, 1977).

In postsynaptic areas (e.g. amygdala and VLG) where cells are surrounded by 5-HT terminals, 5-HT produces an inhibition of firing at ejection currents that are in the same range as those that produce an inhibition of firing in DR neurons (Fig. 1.5). Thus 5-HT seems to have an equal potency when acting on the 5-HT_1 or 5-HT_2 receptor. In contrast, LSD produces inhibition at lower ejection currents in DR cells than on the postsynaptic cells (Figs. 1.5 and 1.6). This difference in sensitivity is also apparent when LSD is given i.v. because the systemic administration of $20\ \mu g\ kg^{-1}$ of LSD produces an inhibition of firing in the DR but consistently produces an acceleration of firing in the postsynaptic (non-serotonergic) cells (Fig. 1.5; Table 1.3). Thus LSD, a structural analog of 5-HT has a differential effect on the 5-HT_1 and 5-HT_2 receptor, being more potent on 5-HT_1 than 5-HT_2.

Structurally, LSD differs from 5-HT in the following ways: it (1) lacks the 5-hydroxyl group on the phenyl ring; and (2) has a complete ring structure attached to both the terminal amino group and the 4 position of the indole nucleus of 5-HT. Either of these changes could alter the ability of LSD to activate the 5-HT_2 receptor and produce an inhibition of firing.

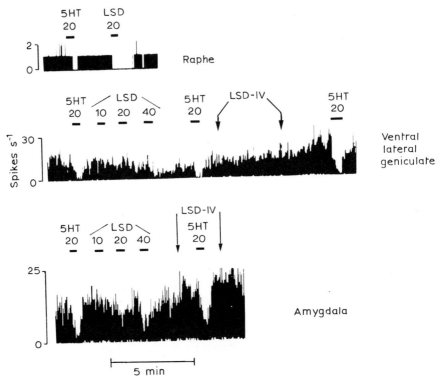

Fig. 1.5 Comparison of the response of a neuron in the dorsal raphe nucleus with that of neurons in the ventral lateral geniculate and the basolateral nucleus of the amygdala to the microiontophoretic administration of 5-HT and LSD. In the top trace a raphe cell is completely inhibited by the microiontophoresis of both 5-HT and LSD for 30 s at the ejection current of 20 nA. In the second trace a cell in the ventral lateral geniculate is inhibited by 5-HT given for 30 s at an ejection current of 20 nA. However, LSD has little effect at 10 or 20 nA but produces a partial inhibition at 40 nA. LSD intravenously (20 μg kg^{-1} at each arrow) produces an acceleration of firing in the cell. After the intravenous LSD, 5-HT at 20 nA is still capable of producing the same absolute amount of inhibition. In the bottom trace the postsynaptic cell in the amygdala is inhibited by 5-HT (20 nA). The cell is unaffected by LSD at 10 nA and slightly by 20 and 40 nA of ejection current. After 20 μg kg^{-1} of LSD intravenously (indicated by the first arrow), the cell shows an acceleration of firing. However, 5-HT (20 nA) is still capable of producing the same absolute amount of a decrease in firing. In this and all subsequent figures of recordings, the horizontal bar indicates the duration of the ejection current; the number above the bar indicates the ejection current in nA. Arrows indicate the time of intravenous injection of drugs. The ordinate represents the integrated rate of firing in spikes per second unless otherwise indicated. Reprinted from Haigler and Aghajanian (1974a) by permission of the Williams and Wilkins Co, Baltimore, USA.

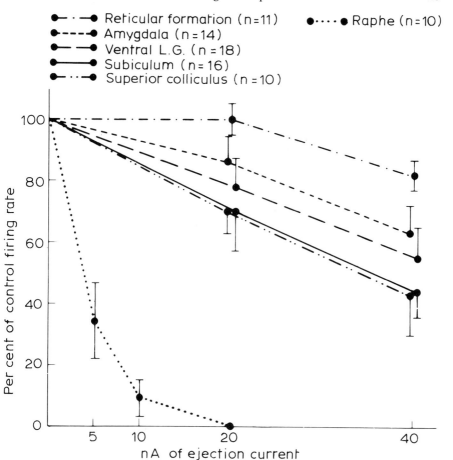

Fig. 1.6 Effect of LSD on dorsal raphe neurons and postsynaptic neurons when applied microiontophoretically. This is a graphical presentation of the difference in sensitivity to LSD between dorsal raphe cells (presynaptic cells) and cells that receive a 5-HT input (postsynaptic cells) in the amygdala, ventral lateral geniculate, subiculum and optic tectum (superior colliculus). The response of cells in the reticular formation (an area receiving a sparse 5-HT input) to directly applied LSD is also shown. The vertical bars show the S.E.M. The percentage of control firing rate was determined by taking the mean of the firing rate for 10 s in a control period and also at the 25 to 35 s interval after the onset of the ejection current. The mean firing rate in the ejection current period was divided by the firing rate during the control period and converted into a percentage. Reprinted from Haigler and Aghajanian (1974a) by permission of the Williams and Wilkins Co, Baltimore, USA.

Table 1.3 Response of dorsal raphe (presynaptic) and postsynaptic neurons to intravenous LSD

Area	No. of cells	Intravenous dose of LSD (μg kg^{-1})	% change from control firing rate*
Presynaptic area			
Dorsal raphe nucleus	7	11.6 ± 1.3†	-100
Postsynaptic areas			
Superior colliculus	12	20	$+49 \pm 11$‡
Ventral lateral geniculate	8	20	$+40 \pm 15$§
Subiculum	12	20	$+23 \pm 9$
Amygdala	10	20	$+15 \pm 5$‡

* The mean control and postdrug firing rates were determined as described in Fig 1.6. The postdrug firing rate was determined at the 30–40 s interval after the i.v. administration of LSD since inhibition of the raphe would have occurred within 30 s. These data were evaluated statistically using the Student *t*-test for paired data on the mean of the firing rates before they were converted into the percentage shown.

† This is the mean dose $\pm$ S.E.M. which produced a total inhibition of firing of the raphe neuron for at least 30 s.

‡ $P < 0.01$

§ $P < 0.05$

Reprinted from Haigler and Aghajanian (1974a) by permission of The Williams and Wilkins Company, Baltimore, USA.

Because LSD has a lower affinity for 5-HT$_2$ receptors than it does for 5-HT$_1$ receptors, it is possible that other 5-HT analogs might also have a differential effect on 5-HT$_1$ and 5-HT$_2$ receptors. As pointed out in Section 1.1, one of the ways to characterize receptors is to determine if modification of the molecular structure alters the activity on one receptor without affecting the activity on another receptor. The differential effect of LSD suggested that the structure–activity relationship (SAR) was not the same for 5-HT$_1$ as for 5-HT$_2$ receptors for the following six structural analogs of 5-HT that were tested: tryptamine; 4-hydroxytryptamine (4-HT); bufotenin (5-hydroxy-*N*, *N*-dimethyltryptamine); *N*, *N*-dimethyltryptamine (DMP); and LSD. As the 5-HT analogs become less like 5-HT and more like LSD, the difference in their potency on the pre- and postsynaptic receptors also increases (Table 1.2). As groups are added to the nitrogen on the side chain, the resulting compounds are more potent on the 5-HT$_1$ than on the 5-HT$_2$ receptor (Fig. 1.7). If 4-hydroxylation of the indole ring is combined

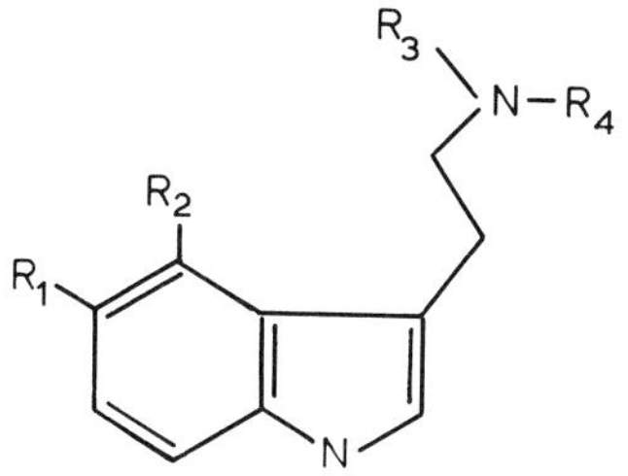

	R_1	R_2	R_3	R_4	Potency ratio $\dfrac{\% \text{ Presynaptic inhibition}}{\% \text{ Postsynaptic inhibition}}$
5-HT	OH	H	H	H	1.00
Tryptamine	H	H	H	H	1.00
4-HT	H	OH	H	H	1.22
Bufotenine	OH	H	CH_3	CH_3	1.27
DMT	H	H	CH_3	CH_3	1.47
Psilocin	H	OH	CH_3	CH_3	1.90
LSD	H	Complex ring structure		CH_3	2.74

Fig. 1.7 Comparison of the structures of seven indoleamines with the ratio of their potency on the presynaptic:postsynaptic receptors. The potency ratio was obtained by dividing the percent inhibition in the raphe by the average percent inhibition in the two postsynaptic areas that are presented in Table 1.1. As substituents are added to the terminal amino group and to the four position (R_2) of the indoleamine, the potency ratio increases. An ejection current of 5-HT that produced 100 per cent inhibition was always used as a standard in these comparisons. For further details see Aghajanian and Haigler, 1975. Reprinted from Federation Proceedings 36: 2159–2164 (1977) by permission of Federation Proceedings.

with *N,N*-dimethylation, to yield psilocin, one has a compound that, next to LSD, shows the greatest change in potency between the 5-HT$_1$ and 5-HT$_2$ receptors and is one of the most potent indoleamines to be tested on human subjects (Wolbach *et al.*, 1962). Psilocin resembles LSD in that it also has ring substitution on the 4 position and carbon containing groups attached to the terminal amino group of the indole molecule (Fig. 1.7). Furthermore, conformation and molecular orbital analysis indicate that psilocin can approximate the A, B and C rings of LSD (Kang *et al.*, 1973; Snyder and Richelson, 1968). Thus, the ability of psilocin and LSD to discriminate between 5-HT$_1$ and 5-HT$_2$ receptors may arise because of their similarities in molecular structure. It appears that *N,N*-dimethylation of the side chain *and* hydroxylation of the indole ring at the 4 position makes a compound more potent on the 5-HT$_1$ receptor than on the 5-HT$_2$ receptor.

These data are consistent with the hypothesis that LSD and other indoleamines, like psilocin and DMT, are hallucinogenic because they are more potent on the 5-HT$_1$ receptor than they are on the 5-HT$_2$ receptor. According to this hypothesis, a hallucinogenic compound inhibits the firing of the presynaptic cells and allows the postsynaptic cells to escape from a tonic inhibition. LSD and psilocin, two powerful hallucinogens, have the greatest differential effect on the 5-HT$_1$ and 5-HT$_2$ receptors. Another powerful hallucinogen, psilocybin (4-phosphoryl-*N,N*-dimethyltryptamine) probably produces its effect because it is rapidly converted into psilocin (Horita, 1963). DMT, which has a weaker differential effect, produces a hallucinogenic effect similar to LSD but is less potent. Bufotenin has little hallucinogenic activity even at high doses and discriminates poorly between the 5-HT$_1$ and 5-HT$_2$ receptors. However, bufotenin does not readily penetrate the brain (Sanders and Bush, 1967) and this could also contribute to its lack of hallucinogenic activity. Thus the data concerning SAR indicate that the 5-HT$_1$ receptors and the 5-HT$_2$ receptors differ in their basic structures.

1.3.5 LSD: a possible mechanism of action

Although the above hypothesis concerning the mechanism of action of LSD is supported by most available data, data from recent experiments may require a major revision of this hypothesis.

The most serious challenge to this hypothesis is that lisuride, an ergoline derivative that is structurally similar to LSD, produces an inhibition in DR neurons in rats but does not produce hallucinations in man (Rogawski and Aghajanian, 1979). However, if lisuride is like 5-HT and does not discriminate between 5-HT$_1$ and 5-HT$_2$ receptors and consequently, produces a depression of firing in the postsynaptic neurons as readily as it does in the DR, the potency ratio for lisuride should be close to one. According to this hypothesis, lisuride would not be expected to be hallucinogenic. If on the other hand, lisuride is like LSD and is more potent on 5-HT$_1$ than on 5-HT$_2$ receptors it will be necessary to modify the hypothesis that LSD acts principally by acting on the serotonergic system. One possible explanation is that drugs like lisuride may share properties in common with drugs that inhibit raphe firing indirectly (e.g. tricyclic antidepressants, MAO inhibitors) (Rogawski and Aghajanian, 1979). The effects of lisuride on *postsynaptic* neurons in the serotonergic system need to be tested to resolve these questions.

LSD may produce hallucinations not only by acting on the 5-HT system but also by acting on other neurotransmitter systems such as the dopamine (DA) system. For instance, LSD administered systemically produces an abrupt inhibition of firing in the substantia nigra. However, this inhibitory effect lasts less than 30 s and tolerance develops rapidly to this effect (Christoph *et al.*, 1978). Furthermore the dose of LSD (50 μg kg^{-1}) is higher than the dose that will produce an inhibition of firing in the DR. Tolerance does not readily develop to the inhibitory effects of LSD in the DR, and the duration of the inhibition produced by a low dose (20 μg) of LSD is at least 15 min (cf. Fig. 1; Aghajanian *et al.*, 1972).

LSD also blocks the stimulation of cerebral adenyl cyclase activity that is produced by a combination of noradrenalin and dopamine (von Hungen *et al.*, 1974). However, this effect is apparently not related to the hallucinogenic effect of LSD because BOL, a non-hallucinogenic congener of LSD, also produces the same effect as LSD.

LSD may also have a direct effect on cells in the visual cortex, independent of a release from a tonic inhibition by 5-HT (Fox and Dray, 1979). However, the lack of a consistent effect of LSD on these cells and a clearer explanation of the mechanism of action of LSD on these neurons requires further study. Another objection to the 5-HT-LSD hypothesis is that lesions of the midbrain raphe nuclei should produce behavioral effects similar to those of LSD (Bramwell and Gonye, 1976). However, because adaptation may develop, comparing the effects of brain lesions to the acute effects of LSD may be inappropriate.

1.3.6 Comparison of neurochemical and neurophysiological data

One difficulty with the above data is that in neurochemical binding studies, some 5-HT agonists (e.g. LSD) have a higher affinity for the 5-HT$_2$ receptor than does 5-HT. This apparent contradiction can be resolved by the following model. Suppose that the 5-HT$_1$ and 5-HT$_2$ receptors both have two active sites that need to be occupied in order to produce an effect (e.g. inhibition of firing). If the main difference between the 5-HT$_1$ and 5-HT$_2$ receptors is that the 5-HT$_2$ receptor has a protrusion between sites X and Y (Fig. 1.8) such that only molecules with equal affinities for both sides have an equal potency on both 5-HT$_1$ and 5-HT$_2$ receptors.

If an alteration in molecular structure increased the affinity for site X or Y, only the activity on the 5-HT$_2$ receptor would be affected. As the affinity for one site (site Y) increased, a bulky molecule such as LSD might be attached to site Y so strongly that site X would not be occupied because the part of the molecule with an affinity for site X could not attach to this site (Fig. 1.8). Thus as the affinity for site Y on the 5-HT$_2$ receptor increased, the ability of the drug to produce an inhibition of firing in the postsynaptic cells should decrease.

A second possible explanation for the apparent contradiction between

(a) 5-HT₁ Receptor

PRE - SYNAPTIC

| X | LSD binding site |
| Y | 5-HT binding site |

(b) 5-HT₂ Receptor

POST - SYNAPTIC

1. Drug has high affinity for LSD binding site;
   low affinity for 5-HT binding site.

2. Drug has equal affinity for both 5-HT and LSD binding sites.

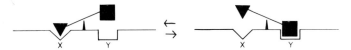

3. Drug has high affinity for 5-HT binding site;
   low affinity for LSD binding site.

Fig. 1.8 A representation of a possible difference between 5-HT₁ and 5-HT₂ receptors. (a) On the 5-HT₁ receptor a difference in affinities for the two binding sites would not alter the physiological activity. (b) If the 5-HT₂, postsynaptic, receptor has the same two binding sites arranged so that when one part of a molecule (▼) is attached to site X, another part of the molecule (■) cannot attach to the site Y. If site Y must be occupied to produce a physiological effect, then as the affinity for X increased the physiological activity of the molecule would decrease. It is possible that a small flexible molecule with a high affinity for both sites would produce inhibition of firing at both 5-HT₁ and 5-HT₂ receptors.

the binding data and the microiontophoretic data is that high-affinity ligands act on site Y to produce a secondary conformational change such that site X is not available for binding to the drug molecule. Perhaps one way to select between these two hypotheses is to test a simple molecule (relative to the bulky LSD molecule) that has a high affinity for the 5-HT binding sites (the 5-HT$_2$ receptor?) isolated from the cortex. According to this proposal, if a simple molecule has a high affinity for the 5-HT$_2$ receptor but has the same weak action on the postsynaptic receptor as LSD, it produces a conformational change that masks site X. On the other hand, if a simple molecule with a high affinity for the binding sites in the cortex has an effect on the 5-HT$_2$ receptor like 5-HT (i.e. potency on 5-HT$_1$ equal to that of 5-HT$_2$) this would support the hypothesis that the difference in binding is caused by the protrusion between sites X and Y. The basic assumption from the above proposal is that during the homogenization of the tissue, the 5-HT$_2$ receptor is disrupted such that its configuration is not different from that of the 5-HT$_1$ receptor.

The value of the above model is that it allows a reconciliation of the data derived from neurochemical binding studies with that derived from neurophysiological, microiontophoretic studies. Thus as the affinity for the binding sites from the cortex increases, the potency ratio (see Fig. 1.5) should increase.

1.3.7 A 5-HT receptor mediating excitatory effects on neuronal firing

There appear to be at least two types of 5-HT receptors that mediate inhibition. A third type of 5-HT receptor, 5-HT$_3$, mediates an increase in neuronal firing in response to the microiontophoretic administration of 5-HT (Fig. 1.9). Because this response to 5-HT is typically found in areas where 5-HT terminals are sparse or have a non-uniform distribution (e.g. MRF and thalamus, respectively) the 5-HT$_3$ receptor, if it exists, is located on cells in these areas. This acceleration in firing produced by 5-HT is blocked by LSD (Haigler and Aghajanian, 1974a); the effects of both 5-HT and LSD closely resemble the effects reported by Boakes *et al.* (1970) and (Roberts and Straughan, 1967). In addition to being blocked by LSD, the 5-HT acceleration is also blocked by five peripheral 5-HT antagonists (Haigler and Aghajanian, 1974; also see Section 1.3.10). Thus the 5-HT$_3$ receptor differs from the other two 5-HT receptors in that it (1) mediates excitation; (2) is blocked by LSD; (3) is blocked by peripheral 5-HT antagonists; and (4) is found in areas where 5-HT terminals are sparsely distributed. Even though the terminals are sparsely distributed, the majority of responses to 5-HT in these areas is inhibitory (Haigler and Aghajanian, 1974a).

When the pH of 5-HT solutions is less than pH 4, the percentage of

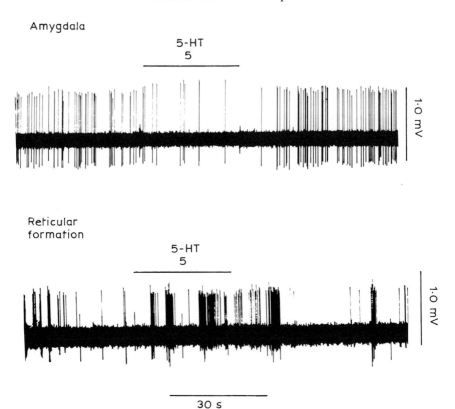

Fig. 1.9 Recordings of extracellular action potentials from two cells, one in the amygdala and one in the reticular formation, showing the effects of 5-HT on the rate of neuronal firing and action potential size. In the amygdala (top trace) 5-HT slows and inhibits the cell; there is an increase in the size of the action potential in association with the decrease in rate. In contrast, a cell in the reticular formation is accelerated by 5-HT with little change in action potential size. The accelerated firing continues in bursts which are greater than control for between 15 and 45 s. Reprinted from Haigler and Aghajanian (1974b) by permission of Springer-Verlag New York, Inc., USA.

cells excited by 5-HT is increased (Fredrickson *et al.*, 1972; Jordan *et al.*, 1972). However, in the MRF, microiontophoresis of 5-HT at pH 4 produces an acceleration in firing (Haigler and Aghajanian, 1974b). The acceleration in firing produced by a low pH is characterized by a sudden increase in the firing rate and the sudden appearance of a spike-like positive action potential that replaces the normal biphasic action potential as described previously (Curtis *et al.*, 1961). The effects of the ejection of a positive current from an NaCl solution with a pH of 1.5 on the extracellu-

Na Cl 60 ; pH 2

Fig. 1.10 Effect of low pH on firing rate and action potential size. When NaCl is ejected with a positive current at 60 nA at pH 2, after 27 s the action potential suddenly decreases in size and there is a remarkable increase in firing. A short burst of firing seen 10 s before the decrease in size is the only symptom of the impending shift in the action potential. Higher ejection currents of NaCl (100 nA) at pH 5, do not produce any change in the action potential or firing (personal observation).

larly recorded action produces an effect similar to that described by Curtis *et al.* (1961) (Fig. 1.10). The effects on the action potential produced by a low pH are not seen when 5-HT was iontophoresed in the MRF (compare Fig. 1.9 with 1.10).

Even if the acceleration in firing produced by 5-HT is not a pH artefact, the question remains as to whether it represents a physiologically relevant effect. When 5-HT is administered iontophoretically it produces either an inhibition or acceleration of neuronal firing in almost every area of the brain studied (Bloom *et al.*, 1972). However, the predominant action of 5-HT appears to be inhibitory because stimulation of the midbrain raphe nuclei, where most ascending serotonergic projections originate, has a predominantly inhibitory effect on neuronal firing in the suprachiasmatic nucleus (Bloom *et al.*, 1972) and amygdala (Wang and Aghajanian, 1977) where 5-HT terminals from the raphe are dense. Midbrain raphe stimulation also produces an inhibition of firing in the reticular formation (RF) (Nakamura, 1975) and hippocampus (Segal, 1975); 5-HT terminals in these areas are less dense or have a patchy distribution, respectively (Table 1.4). Furthermore, even in the RF and hippocampus, 5-HT administered iontophoretically typically produces inhibition (Haigler and Aghajanian, 1974a; Segal, 1975).

All of the above data suggest that the synaptic action of 5-HT is inhibitory and that the excitatory response produced by 5-HT is not

Table 1.4 Density and pattern of distribution of 5-HT terminals in rat midbrain and forebrain

Area	Density	Distribution
Midbrain		
Optic tectum	+++	Uniform
Linearis caudalis nucleus	+++	Uniform
Substantia nigra, zona reticulata	++	Uniform
Reticular formation	+ to 0	—
Medial geniculate	0	—
Red nucleus	0	—
Inferior colliculus	0	—
Nuclei III and IV	0	—
Limbic forebrain		
Amygdala, cortical and basolateral nuclei	+++	Uniform
Amygdala, medial and lateral nuclei	+++ to ++	Patchy
Hippocampus	++ to +	Patchy
Subiculum	++ to +	Patchy
Septal and diagonal band nuclei	+++ to 0	Patchy
Cingulate gyrus	++ to +	Patchy
Pyriform cortex	+ to 0	—
Olfactory tubercles*	?	?
Diencephalon		
Ventral lateral geniculate	+++	Uniform
Suprachiasmatic nucleus	+++	Uniform
Pretectal nucleus	+++	Uniform
Reuniens nucleus	++	Uniform
Mammillary body	+++ to +	Patchy
Periventricular nucleus (rotundocellularis)	+++ to +	Patchy
Habenular nuclei	++ to +	Patchy
Preoptic area	++ to +	Patchy
Medial forebrain bundle	+++ to 0	Patchy
Parafascicular nucleus	+	—
Ventromedial and anterior hypothalamic nuclei	+ to 0	—
Ventral, lateral, and medial thalamic nuclei	+ to 0	—
Dorsal lateral geniculate	+ to 0	—
Basal ganglia		
Globus pallidus	++	Uniform
Entopeduncular nucleus	++	Uniform
Caudate-putamen*	?	?
Cerebral cortex		
Molecular layer	+	Uniform

Based on data from Aghajanian *et al*. (1973) and unpublished data of Aghajanian.

* Density and distribution of 5-HT terminals uncertain because of interference by intense dopamine fluorescence.

Reprinted from Aghajanian *et al*. (1975) by permission of Plenum Publishing Corporation.

physiologically relevant. However, 5-HT apparently produces its excitatory effect by enhancing the effects of excitatory neurotransmitters (McCall and Aghajanian, 1979). The excitatory effects of glutamate are enhanced by microiontophoretic administration of 5-HT, stimulation of the motor cortex and the red nucleus. The slow time course for the onset of the enhancement by any of these methods matches the time course seen for the excitatory effects produced by iontophoretic 5-HT. Furthermore, the enhancing effect of 5-HT for excitatory inputs is blocked by methysergide, a peripheral 5-HT antagonist. It remains to be determined if 5-HT enhances the release of an excitatory transmitter from the presynaptic terminal, acts postsynaptically to enhance the binding of the excitatory neurotransmitter or acts to increase the sensitivity of the postsynaptic neuron to the excitatory transmitter (McCall and Aghajanian, 1979). Because stimulation of the DR or iontophoretic administration of 5-HT can enhance the response produced by cortical stimulation, the increase in neuronal firing produced by ionto-5-HT is probably a physiologically relevant effect (McCall and Aghajanian, 1979). Regardless of the site of action the increase in firing produced by 5-HT in the facial nucleus and in other areas of the brain are probably mediated by a postsynaptic receptor distinct from 5-HT_1 and 5-HT_2 (McCall and Aghajanian, 1979). For convenience this receptor will be referred to as the 5-HT_3 receptor. However, remember that the location of this receptor remains to be determined and that it may represent 5-HT serving as a neuromodulator to enhance the affinity of an excitatory neurotransmitter for its receptor (McCall and Aghajanian, 1979).

1.3.8 Summary of 5-HT_1, 5-HT_2 and 5-HT_3 receptors

There appear to be at least three 5-HT receptors in the brain; two that mediate inhibition and one that mediates excitation. The 5-HT_1 receptor is located on the 5-HT containing cells in the midbrain raphe nuclei (the medullary-pontine raphe nuclei will be covered later).

The 5-HT_2 receptors are apparently located on neurons in areas that receive a dense serotonergic input, and mediate an inhibition of neuronal firing. LSD, like 5-HT, produces an inhibition of firing when it acts on (interacts with) the 5-HT_1 receptor. Unlike 5-HT, LSD is less potent on 5-HT_2 receptors producing only a weak inhibitory response. The 5-HT_3 receptors are located on cells in areas where 5-HT terminals are sparse (RF) or have a non-uniform (patchy) distribution (thalamus and hippocampus). However, there apparently is a mixture of 5-HT_2 and 5-HT_3 receptors in these areas because 5-HT produces an inhibition of firing in some cells but an excitation in other cells. The 5-HT_3 receptor which mediates excitation, is blocked by LSD and six 5-HT antagonists that have been studied to date.

1.3.9 5-HT receptors in the medullary-pontine raphe nuclei

It is difficult to interpret most of the studies in the MPR (raphe pallidus, obscurus and magnus) for the following reasons: (1) the identity of a neuron with respect to the neurotransmitter it contains is uncertain; and (2) the neurons and fiber pathways that are activated by electrical stimulation may contain transmitters other than 5-HT. The 5-HT-containing cells in the MPR are not densely packed and appear to have non-fluorescent cells interspersed among them (cf. Figs. 29 and 30, Dahlström and Fuxe, 1965). The interested reader might find it beneficial to compare the scattered 5-HT cells in B-3 (Fig. 30; Dahlström and Fuxe, 1964), to the densely packed 5-HT neurons in the DR (Fig. 1.11). The above uncertain-

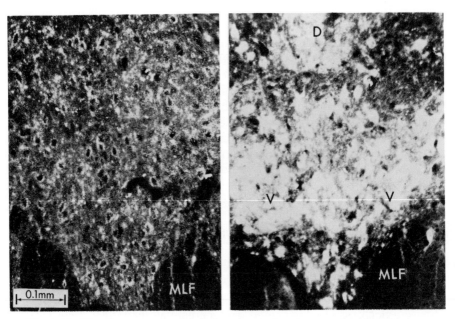

Fig. 1.11 Histofluorescence of dorsal raphe nucleus in control and L-TP loaded animals. In the control (left panel) the fluorescence of raphe neurons is barely discernible and mainly located in the perinuclear zone. Discrimination between fluorescent and non-fluorescent cells is difficult. After L-TP loading (100 mg kg^{-1}, i.p., 1 h prior to removal of brain) the raphe neurons are brilliantly fluorescent and readily distinguished from adjacent non-fluorescent cells. A midline dorsal (D) and two ventral (V) lobes can be seen. MLF: medial longitudinal fasciculus. Reprinted from Aghajanian and Haigler (1974b) by permission of Elsevier/North-Holland Biomedical Press.

ties hamper the interpretation of data derived from experiments in the MPR as illustrated below.

Action potentials recorded in the MPR have the same electrophysiological characteristics as those recorded from 5-HT-containing neurons in the DR (Fig. 1.2). Perhaps all 5-HT-containing neurons have action potentials with similar electrophysiological characteristics. However, only about one-third of the neurons in the MPR are inhibited by 5-HT or LSD (Haigler, 1978). This creates the following problem in interpretation. If all 5-HT-containing neurons have the same type of action potential, there are 5-HT-containing neurons in the MPR that are not inhibited by 5-HT or LSD, and thus do not have a 5-HT_1 receptor on the perikarya. Conversely, if the 5-HT_1 receptor is located on the perikarya of all 5-HT-containing neurons, there are neurons in the MPR with raphe-like action potentials that do not contain 5-HT. The data currently available do not allow a choice between these two alternatives.

In the MPR, there is evidence that all three types of 5-HT receptors are present; 5-HT-containing cells may project to adjacent cells that do not contain 5-HT. There may be 5-HT_1 receptors because some cells are inhibited by both 5-HT and LSD (cf. Table 1, Couch, 1976). There may also be 5-HT_2 receptors in the MPR because there are cells inhibited by 5-HT but they show an increase in firing after the systemic administration of LSD. There is also evidence for 5-HT_3 receptors because some cells are excited by 5-HT but inhibited by LSD. However, the presence of combinations of responses that have not been reported in other areas of the brain (e.g. an increase in firing produced by 5-HT but no effect produced by LSD) indicate that another distinct type of 5-HT receptor might be located in the MPR. Until the receptors in the MPR are adequately defined, this latter possibility cannot be ignored.

The response to morphine administered microiontophoretically also indicates that the 5-HT receptors in the MPR are not identical with those in the forebrain serotonergic system. In the DR, MR and postsynaptic areas in the forebrain, morphine produces a depression in one-third of the neurons studied (see Section 1.5 for further details; Haigler, 1978a). However, in the MPR morphine administered microiontophoretically does not produce an inhibition of firing in any neurons studied (Table 1.5). Furthermore, cells in the MPR are not consistently inhibited by LSD or 5-HT administered microiontophoretically or LSD administered systemically.

Thus receptors in the MPR need to be studied in more detail before they can be classified. However, the interpretation of all data derived from MPR will remain ambiguous until the cells can be identified with greater certainty with respect to their neurotransmitter content.

Table 1.5 Effects on spontaneous firing rates in medullary pontine raphe neurons.

	Drugs administered					
	Microiontophoretically			Intravenously		
	+	−	0	+	−	0
Morphine	4*	0	39	6*	4	5
LSD	0	8	22	0	2	3
5-HT	0	5	12	−	−	−
NE	1	5	9	−	−	−
ACh	2	3	7	−	−	−

+ = acceleration; − = slowing or inhibition; and 0 = no change in spontaneous firing rate
* These are not the same cells.
  Reprinted from Haigler (1978b) by permission of Elsevier/North Holland Biomedical Press.

1.3.10 5-HT antagonists: effects in the brain

The selective blockade of a response by an antagonist is most readily explained by the blockade or occlusion of specific receptors (Moran, 1975). Therefore, if the 5-HT receptors described so far (5-HT$_1$, 5-HT$_2$, and 5-HT$_3$) are distinct entities, drugs that antagonize 5-HT in the periphery would be useful in confirming the existence of three types of 5-HT receptors and perhaps indicate the presence of other types of 5-HT receptors. There are five drugs that have been hypothesized to block the effects of 5-HT in the brain, based on: (1) their ability to block the effects of 5-HT on smooth muscle and on invertebrate neurons [cinanserin cyproheptadine, methysergide (UML) and metergoline (MCE)] and (2) the ability to block the EEG effects of 5-hydroxytryptophan (e.g. methiothepin). For specific references, see Haigler and Aghajanian (1974b).

The putative 5-HT antagonists listed above do *not* block the 5-HT$_1$ and 5-HT$_2$ receptors, thus they are not antagonists at the 5-HT$_1$ and 5-HT$_2$ receptors. Instead they act as 5-HT *agonists* in that they produce an inhibition of firing when given alone or enhance the inhibition produced by 5-HT (Fig. 1.12; Table 1.6). Furthermore, the short latency inhibition of firing produced in the amygdala after stimulation of the DR is not typically blocked by cyproheptadine or methysergide (Wang and Aghajanian, 1977).

There may be another 5-HT receptor type in the cortex because metergoline, a 5-HT antagonist, blocks the short latency inhibition (<100 ms; most cases, 2–5 ms) produced by stimulation of the midbrain raphe *and*

Table 1.6 Effects of putative 5-HT antagonists on excitation and inhibition induced by 5-HT administered microiontophoretically

Drug	Brain areas						
	Raphe	Amygdala	VLG	Optic tectum	Reticular formation	Dorsal hippocampus	Cerebral cortex
Methysergide	A,B[1]	A,B[1]	A,B[1]	A,B[1]	A,B,C[1,5]	A,D[2]	
Cyproheptadine	A,B[1]	A,B[1]	A,B[1]	A,B[1]	A,B,C[1]	A,D[2]	
Cinanserin	A,B[1]	A,B[1]	A,B[1]	A,B[1]	A,B,C[1]	A,B[2]	
Methiothepin	A,B[1]	A,B[1]	A,B[1]	A,B[1]	A,B,C[1]	A,B[2]	
Metergoline	A,B[1]	A,B[1]	A,B[1]	A,B[1]	A C[1]		
LSD	A,B[3,4]	A,B[3,4]	A,B[3,4]	A,B[3]	A,B,C[3,5]	A,D[2]	A,D[6]
BOL	A,B[4]	A,B[4]	A,B[4]		A,B,C[5]	A,D[2]	
Mianserin						A,B[2]	

A. Depressant or inhibitory effects; B. does not block depressant or inhibitory effects of 5-HT; C. blocks acceleration produced by 5-HT; D. blocks depressant or inhibitory effects of 5-HT. [1]Haigler and Aghajanian (1974b); [2]Segal (1976); [3]Haigler and Aghajanian (1974a); [4]Aghajanian (1976); [5]Boakes et al. (1970); [6]Sastry and Phillis (1977).
Reprinted with permission from Federation Proceedings 36: 2159–2164 (1977).

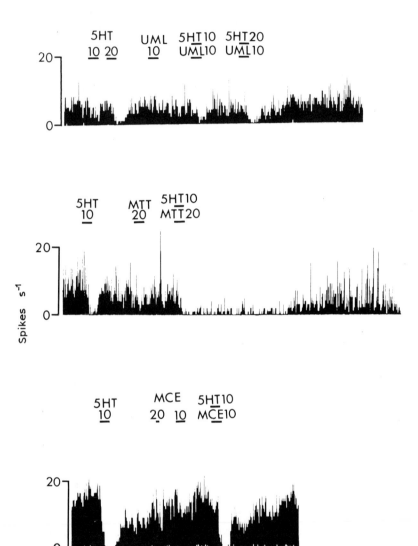

Fig. 1.12 Failure of the putative 5-HT antagonists methysergide (UML),
methiothepin (MTT) and metergoline (MCE) to block the depressant effects
of 5-HT on cells in the ventral lateral geniculate (top two traces) and the
optic tectum (bottom trace). In the top trace a ventral lateral geniculate cell
is partially slowed and inhibited by the microiontophoresis of 5-HT for 30 s
at ejection currents of 10 and 20 nA, respectively. Although methysergide
has little effect by itself at an ejection current of 10 nA, when administered

the inhibitory effect of 5-HT. The presence of a fourth type of 5-HT receptor might be proposed if other 5-HT antagonists are shown to block the inhibitory effects of 5-HT in the cerebral cortex.

There may also be a 5-HT receptor type in the hippocampus (an area where 5-HT terminals have a non-uniform distribution) that does not resemble the 5-HT_1, 5-HT_2 and 5-HT_3 receptors. Some of the 5-HT antagonists act as 5-HT agonists but others block the inhibitory effects produced by electrical stimulation of the midbrain raphe or the microiontophoretic administration of 5-HT (Table 5; Segal, 1975, 1976). Methysergide and cyproheptadine only block the long latency (100–120 ms), not the short latency (5–15 ms), inhibition produced by midbrain raphe stimulation. However, the interpretation of this effect is difficult because raphe stimulation usually produces only a short latency inhibition of neuronal firing in the suprachiasmatic nucleus (Bloom *et al.*, 1972), the mesencephalic reticular formation (Nakamura, 1975), amygdala (Wang and Aghajanian, 1977) and cortex (Sastry and Phillis, 1977). Thus, the long latency inhibition seen in the dorsal hippocampus may arise from activation of polysynaptic pathways. Therefore the blockade of the long latency inhibition of methysergide or cyproheptadine may represent the blockade by a neurotransmitter *other than* 5-HT. The interpretation of the effect of 5-HT antagonists in the hippocampus is difficult because the data are not consistent.

LSD and BOL block the inhibitory effect of 5-HT only in the hippocampus (Segal, 1976). However, LSD and BOL do *not* antagonize either the long or short latency inhibition that is produced by raphe stimulation

---

simultaneously with 5-HT the depression produced is equal to or greater than the depression produced by 5-HT alone. In the second trace, a cell in the ventral lateral geniculate is inhibited by the microiontophoresis of 5-HT for 30 s at an ejection current of 10 nA. Methiothepin (MTT) slows the cell slightly when administered microiontophoretically at an ejection current of 20 nA. When methiothepin and 5-HT are administered simultaneously, a prolonged depression of firing is produced that is longer than the depression produced by 5-HT alone. No change in action potential size was noted during this period. In the bottom trace 5-HT (30 s, 10 nA) inhibits a cell in the optic tectum. At a 20 nA ejection current MCE produces a slight slowing in rate. When 5-HT and MCE (10 and 20 nA, respectively, 30 s) are administered simultaneously, there is no blockade of the inhibitory effect produced by 5-HT; in fact, there is another prolonged depression of firing. The period during which 5-HT was administered by microiontophoresis is indicated by a horizontal line; the number immediately above the line indicates the ejection current in nA. Reprinted from Haigler and Aghajanian (1974b) by permission of Springer-Verlag New York, Inc, USA.

(Segal, 1975). In any case, if the 5-HT antagonists block the inhibitory effect of 5-HT in the hippocampus the 5-HT receptor in the hippocampus, as in the cortex, may represent a 5-HT receptor that is different from 5-HT$_1$, 5-HT$_2$, or 5-HT$_3$. The conclusion that the 5-HT receptor in the hippocampus or cortex is *not* like 5-HT$_2$ awaits confirmation that methysergide, cyproheptadine, metergoline, LSD and BOL antagonize the inhibitory effects of 5-HT in the hippocampus and cortex.

1.4 5-HT RECEPTORS IN THE SPINAL CORD, NOCICEPTION AND MORPHINE

Most of the recent data concerning 5-HT receptors in the spinal cord is derived from experiments designed to study the relationship between 5-HT, nociception, and morphine. Thus, the 5-HT receptors and the effects of 5-HT antagonists in the spinal cord will be discussed in this context.

The data since the early 1970s strongly support the hypothesis that 5-HT projections to the spinal cord play an important role in modulating nociception. The 5-HT projection from the MPR to the spinal cord may be one of the final common pathways through which the analgesic action of morphine is ultimately expressed.

1.4.1 Behavioral and neurochemical studies

Most of the neurochemical and behavioral studies concerning 5-HT and morphine are described below in Section 1.5.3. Only neurochemical studies directly related to 5-HT and spinal cord will be covered in this section. In most of the neurochemical studies, drugs are administered systemically thus many of the effects of a drug affecting 5-HT could arise from an effect on 5-HT receptors in the spinal cord or in the brain.

In the spinal cord, LSD may act as a 5-HT agonist but BOL and methysergide have no effect (Anden *et al.*, 1968). If the 5-HT content in the spinal cord is reduced using the intercerebroventricular injection of 5, 6-dihydroxytryptamine or i.p. administration of *para*chlorophenylalanine (*p*-CPA), the analgesic effect of low doses (1.3–1.6 mg kg^{-1}) of morphine is reduced or abolished in 33–58 per cent of rats tested (Vogt, 1974). The systemic administration of morphine (10 mg kg^{-1}) produces an increase in 5HIAA a 5-HT metabolite (Shiomi *et al.*, 1978). These data indicate that 5-HT is one of the neurotransmitters that provide an important link from the MPR to the spinal cord. Apparently morphine acts through this link to produce analgesia.

When morphine is injected into the periaqueductal gray it produces analgesia that is blocked by the systemic administration of two 5-HT antagonists (methysergide and cinanserin; Yaksh *et al.*, 1976). Furthermore this antinociceptive effect of morphine is also blocked by the intrathecal administration of methysergide (Yaksh, 1979). Intrathecal injection of 5-HT also produces analgesia in rats, rabbits, and cats without detectable changes in voluntary motor function (Yaksh and Wilson, 1979). This effect is potentiated by blockade of monoamine oxidase (an enzyme that breaks down 5-HT) or blockade of 5-HT re-uptake with imipramine. The analgesic effects of 5-HT are antagonized in a surmountable way by two putative 5-HT antagonists, methysergide and cyproheptadine (Yaksh and Wilson, 1979); methysergide also blocks morphine analgesia (Yaksh *et al.*, 1976). Analgesia becomes apparent in 5–10 min after the administration of 5-hydroxytryptophan, (5-HTP) a precursor of 5-HT; analgesia produced by 5-HTP is also antagonized by methysergide (Yaksh and Wilson, 1979). Thus it appears that 5-HTP increases endogenous levels of 5-HT which in turn produce analgesia.

The above data clearly demonstrate that morphine injected into the PAG activates a pathway that increases the firing of 5-HT-containing cells in the MPR. These cells project to the spinal cord (see below) where they act selectively to block the response of cells in the spinal cord to nociceptive stimuli.

It is possible that 5-HT produces analgesia at the spinal cord level by producing an increase in firing of interneurons. These interneurons may act to block the increase in neuronal firing produced by a nociceptive stimulus in laminae 1,2,4, and 5. If the interneurons that are excited by 5-HT contain enkephalin, naloxone should block the analgesia by activation of the descending serotonergic pathway (Oliveras *et al.*, 1977).

Studies apparently designed to test this hypothesis yield mixed results. In cats, naloxone (0.3 mg kg^{-1}) blocks the analgesia produced by electrical stimulation of the MPR (Oliveras *et al.*, 1977). Although stimulation of MPR blocks the increase in neuronal firing in the spinal cord that is produced by a noxious heat stimulus, naloxone ($0.6–1$ mg kg^{-1}) does not alter this effect (Duggan and Griersmith, 1979). Furthermore, in rats, naloxone (2 mg kg^{-1}) does not block the analgesic effect of intrathecally administered 5-HT (Yaksh and Wilson, 1979). Thus there appears to be little evidence that the descending serotonergic pathway activates interneurons that contain enkephalin. However, the descending 5-HT projection may activate interneurons that contain other neurotransmitters. If 5-HT produces an increase in firing of an interneuron, 5-HT$_3$ receptors may mediate this excitation because 5-HT antagonists (e.g. methysergide and cyproheptadine) block the analgesic effect of 5-HT (injected intrathecally) and morphine (injected into the PAG). This hypothesis is difficult to reconcile with the observation that LSD is a 5-HT *agonist* in the spinal cord (Anden *et al.*, 1968). LSD is a 5-HT antagonist at 5-HT$_3$ receptors (see Section 1.3.7). An alternative hypothesis is that 5-HT acts directly on cells in the spinal cord to block their response to a nociceptive stimulus.

1.4.2 Electrophysiological and iontophoretic studies

Electrophysiological and iontophoretic studies are necessary to determine accurately the characteristics of 5-HT receptors in the spinal cord. Stimulation in the area of *DR* (rat) produces analgesia that is blocked by *p*-CPA (Akil and Mayer, 1972); *p*-CPA blocks the synthesis of 5-HT (Koe and Weissman, 1966).

Stimulation in the area of the *DR* in the cat also produces an inhibition of firing of cells responsive to nociceptive stimuli in L4 and 5 of the spinal cord of the cat, and produces analgesia to tooth pulp stimulation (Oliveras *et al.*, 1974). Although LSD blocks the analgesia produced by stimulation in the area of the *DR* (Guilbaud *et al.*, 1973), LSD may have this effect because it decreases the excitability of neurons in the MPR as it does for neurons in the DR and MR (Wang and Aghajanian, 1977). Stimulation of the PAG in the vicinity of the DR may activate neurons in the MPR via a pathway that projects from PAG to MPR (Gallagher and Pert, 1978). Thus the projection from the MPR to the spinal cord could be one of the final common pathways through which morphine acts to produce analgesia.

1.4.3 The MPR link

Although the MPR is apparently one of the final common pathways, morphine does not act directly on these cells. Morphine administered microiontophoretically does not alter the neuronal firing in MPR but morphine

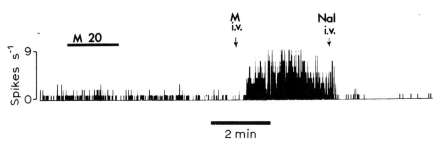

Fig. 1.13 Effects of morphine administered microiontophoretically and i.v. on a neuron in the MPR. Morphine administered microiontophoretically at 20 nA (horizontal bar) does not alter the spontaneous firing rate. In contrast, after morphine (M) is administered i.v. (dose: 4 mg kg^{-1}), there is a marked increase in firing rate. The firing rate abruptly slows after naloxone (Nal), a specific narcotic antagonist, is administered i.v. (dose: 2 mg kg^{-1}). The ordinate represents the integrated rate of firing in spikes s^{-1}. Reprinted from Haigler (1978b) with permission from Elsevier/North-Holland Biomedical Press.

administered systemically produces a marked increase in firing (Fig. 1.13; Table 1.5). In the cat morphine administered systemically depressed 4 cells and excited 6 in the MPR (Anderson *et al.*, 1977).

If serotonergic projections inhibit neuronal firing in the spinal cord, 5-HT must be acting on some receptor in the cord. These 5-HT receptors in the cord can be compared to those in the DR, MPR, and postsynaptic areas with respect to the effects of 5-HT, and putative 5-HT antagonists.

Stimulation of the brainstem raphe nuclei (MPR) inhibits and potentiates the monosynaptic reflexes (MSR) (Proudfit and Anderson, 1973). There is disagreement concerning which of the effects of raphe stimulation on the MSR are mediated by 5-HT (Clineschmidt and Anderson, 1970; Proudfit and Anderson, 1973; Sastry and Sinclair, 1976; Sinclair and Sastry, 1974). In these studies, methysergide blocked 5-HT receptors in the spinal cord in one set of experiments (Proudfit and Anderson, 1973) but not in another set (Sastry and Sinclair, 1976).

Stimulation of the MPR in the cat produces a powerful inhibition of neuronal firing elicited by a nociceptive stimulus in lamina 2 (Duggan and Griersmith, 1979) and lamina 1, 5 and 6 of the spinal cord (Fields *et al.*, 1977). When 5-HT is administered microiontophoretically it selectively reduces the excitation produced by a noxious heat stimulus (Griersmith and Duggan, 1980). Although methysergide blocks this effect of 5-HT when ejected before or during the ejection of 5-HT (Griersmith and Duggan, 1980), it does *not* block the effect of MPR stimulation indicating that this stimulation does not produce a release of 5-HT in the spinal cord (Duggan, personal communication). Thus, in spite of the elegant study by Yaksh and Wilson (1979), it remains to be definitively established that any putative 5-HT antagonists block the synaptic actions of 5-HT in the spinal cord. The disagreement between these two sets of experiments illustrates the necessity of measuring the effects of MPR stimulation on neuronal firing in the spinal cord.

Serotonin-containing neurons located in the MPR project to the anterior, posterior and dorsolateral horns of the spinal cord. However, the distribution in the substantia gelatinosa (SG) is less dense than in the other parts of the cord (Dahlström and Fuxe, 1965). Electrical stimulation of MPR produces analgesia in the cat (Oliveras *et al.*, 1975). The 5-HT projections from the MPR to the spinal cord travel in the dorsolateral funiculus (DLF) of the spinal cord and terminate in laminae 1 and 5 (Fields *et al.*, 1977), although the axons may branch and send a projection down the ventrolateral funiculus (Peacock and Wolstencroft, 1976). However, the main projections apparently travel in the DLF because a lesion of this pathway diminishes the analgesic effects of low doses of morphine (Basbaum *et al.*, 1976) and electrical stimulation of the MPR (Fields *et al.*, 1977).

The apparent contradictions between studies using microiontophoresis

and those using the intrathecal administration of 5-HT need to be resolved
before any firm conclusions can be reached concerning the type of 5-HT
receptor located in the spinal cord. If 5-HT produces an inhibition of
neuronal firing in the spinal cord that is blocked by 5-HT antagonists, this
receptor in the spinal cord is not a 5-HT_2 receptor. The receptor in the
cord may resemble the 5-HT receptor found in the hippocampus and cortex (5-HT_{hc}). However, if 5-HT produces an increase in neuronal firing
that is blocked by the 5-HT antagonists, the receptor would be a 5-HT_3
receptor. Thus the classification of the 5-HT receptors in the spinal cord
awaits further, more definitive microiontophoretic experiments.

1.5 MORPHINE AND 5-HT

1.5.1 Introduction

A current hypothesis is that morphine acts on the serotonergic system in
the brain to produce analgesia. Morphine may act to produce analgesia by
interacting with more than one neurotransmitter to produce its analgesic
effect. One hypothesis is that morphine may activate one, or more, network that ultimately acts to block the ability of nociceptive stimuli to
excite neurons in the spinal cord and the brain. Obviously manipulations of
the levels of the neurotransmitter that are in these circuits may alter the
analgesic effect of morphine. There is evidence that morphine (1) indirectly activates a circuit containing 5-HT; (2) acts *directly* on a serotonergic
system to initiate a sequence of events that ultimately lead to the expression of morphine analgesia; and (3) alters the action of 5-HT on its receptors.

The hypothesis that the serotonergic system is intimately involved with
morphine analgesia grew out of observations that drugs that alter the 5-HT
content of the brain also affect the analgesia produced by morphine. For
instance, treatment with *p*-CPA, an irreversible blocker of 5-HT synthesis
(Koe and Weissman, 1966), antagonizes the analgesia produced by morphine (Lee and Fennessy, 1970; Tenen, 1968). After being blocked by
p-PCA, morphine-produced analgesia was restored by 5-HTP (Gorlitz and
Frey, 1972). Cyproheptadine, a 5-HT antagonist also blocked the morphine analgesia (Gorlitz and Frey, 1972).

A second approach to studying the relationship between morphine and
5-HT is to lesion one or more of the raphe nuclei and subsequently test
the analgesic effects of morphine. Lesions of the raphe nuclei (DR and
MR and MPR) where 5-HT-containing perikarya are located, typically
block the analgesic effects of morphine. Lesions in the DR that reduce the
brain levels of 5-HT and 5-hydroxyindoleacetic acid (5-HIAA), a metab-

olite of 5-HT, also reduce the analgesic activity of morphine
(7.5–10 mg kg^{-1}) using the tail compression and hotplate techniques to
measure analgesia (Samanin and Bernasconi, 1972; Samanin *et al.*, 1970).
Occasionally lesions of the DR make the animals more sensitive to painful
stimuli (Samanin and Bernasconi, 1972; Samanin *et al.*, 1970). However,
the analgesia produced by 30 mg kg^{-1} (Yaksh *et al.*, 1977). Lesions of
meperidine, codeine and propoxyphene) are unaffected by lesions of the
MR that produce a marked depletion of forebrain 5-HT (Samanin *et al.*,
1973). It is not clear if the differential effects of narcotic analgesic drugs
will also be apparent when the DR is lesioned.

The above evidence indicates that the DR and MR are important components of a circuit involved in morphine analgesia. There is also evidence
that contradicts this hypothesis. Lesions of the DR that produce a reduction of forebrain 5-HT do not affect the analgesic effect of morphine
(Blasig *et al.*, 1973; Buxbaum *et al.*, 1973; Harvey *et al.*, 1974). More
recently the analgesic effect of morphine was significantly reduced in rats
lesioned in the *MR* but not the *DR* (Adler *et al.*, 1975).

Lesions of the MPR, DR and MR produce a differential effect on morphine analgesia depending on the dose. A lesion of the MPR blocks the
analgesia produced by a low dose of morphine (3 mg kg^{-1}); attenuates
analgesia produced by a moderate dose (10 mg kg^{-1}) but has no effect on
the analgesia produced by 30 mg kg^{-1} (Yaksh *et al.*, 1977). Lesions of
both the DR and MR have less of an effect on morphine analgesia (Yaksh
et al., 1977). Electrolytic lesions of the DR and MFB as well as the
administration of *p*-CPA, all of which produce a decrease in forebrain
5-HT, do not antagonize the analgesic effects of 10 mg kg^{-1} as measured
on the flinch jump method (Harvey *et al.*, 1974). Lesions of the DR and
MR antagonize morphine analgesia but 5-HTP restores serotonin levels
and the analgesic effect of morphine (Samanin and Bernasconi, 1972).
What is not clear in this study is how 5-HTP restores the analgesic effect
of morphine if substantial numbers of raphe neurons are destroyed by the
electrolytic lesion.

Another technique used to lesion the serotonergic system is to use either
5,7-dihydroxytryptamine (Hole *et al.*, 1976) or 5,6-dihydroxytryptamine
(Bläsig *et al.*, 1973). The compound 5,6-dihydroxytryptamine (5,6-DHT)
produces degeneration of indoleamine (5-HT or 5-HT-like compounds)
containing nerve terminals in rat brain and spinal cord (Baumgarten and
Lachenmayer, 1972) and a decrease in brain content of 5-HT when
injected intracerebroventricularly (Baumgarten *et al.*, 1971). Furthermore,
5,6-DHT depletes 5-HT in the spinal cord to less than 50 per cent of control levels but has no effect on 5-HT in the pons and medulla (Vogt,
1974). However, morphine analgesia was attenuated in only 46 per cent of
the rats that had low levels of 5-HT in the spinal cord.

When p-CPA (320 mg kg^{-1}) is injected systemically it blocks the analgesic effect of only *low* doses (1.33–2.25 mg kg^{-1}) of morphine in all rats tested. In contrast to depletion of 5-HT produced by 5,6-DHT, p-CPA produces a depletion of 5-HT in *both* the spinal cord and pons-/medulla areas (Vogt, 1974). Based on 5-HT content in the spinal cord after 5,6-DHT, only about 13 per cent of the serotonergic fibers survive (Vogt, 1974). However, after p-CPA, all neurons, fibers and terminals are intact but have only 8 per cent of transmitter available for release. Thus, it is not clear if the marginal effect that 5,6-DHT has on morphine analgesia arises because 13 per cent of the serotonergic axons in the cord survive with normal amounts of 5-HT available for release *or* because 5,6-DHT fails to damage neurons in the area of the pons/medulla (Vogt, 1974). It is noteworthy that neither p-CPA nor 5,6-DHT completely block morphine analgesia; with high doses the analgesic effect of morphine may not be impaired (Vogt, 1974).

In another study, 5,6-DHT and lesions of the DR and MR that deplete forebrain 5-HT have no effect on morphine analgesia. In contrast, 6-OH-dopamine blocks morphine analgesia at doses that reduce brain catecholamines remarkably but have *no* effect on 5-HT levels (Bläsig *et al.*, 1973). The dose of morphine (10 mg kg^{-1}) used in the latter study (Bläsig *et al.*, 1973) was ten times higher than in prior study (Vogt, 1974). Thus it is possible that the antagonism of morphine analgesia produced by damage to the serotonergic system can be demonstrated only at low doses, and that at high doses, other circuits and mechanisms are involved that are not dependent on 5-HT.

Another neurotoxin, 5,7-DHT, produces a specific lesion of the ascending serotonergic pathway. The 5-HT neurons and their neuropil are destroyed and there is a decrease in the uptake of [^{3}H]-5-HT in synaptosomes from the cortex and hypothalamus (Hole *et al.*, 1976). The analgesia (using the hot-plate method) produced by morphine (7.5–10 mg kg^{-1}) is *not* attenuated in rats treated with 5,7-DHT. Thus damage to the serotonergic system, especially the descending one, attenuates the analgesia produced by low doses of morphine (1–1.5 mg kg^{-1}). However, damage to the ascending serotonergic system has no apparent effect on the analgesia produced by high doses (7.5–10 mg kg^{-1}) of morphine. The interpretation and comparison of the above three studies remains tenuous because of differences in the methods used to measure analgesia, the dose of morphine, the measures of damage to the serotonergic system, the sites of injection, and the neurotoxic agent used to lesion the serotonergic system.

One difficulty with some of the above studies is that after lesions in the serotonergic system, animals may become *more* sensitive to nociceptive stimuli. Thus, morphine may still produce the same absolute increase in nociceptive threshold – but after lesion of the 5-HT system the end point for nociception, with or without morphine, is lower. This could incorrectly be interpreted as an antagonism of morphine analgesia. Examples of studies concerned with this problem are given below; even in these studies there is little agreement.

Although p-CPA decreases the pain threshold it also attenuates the magnitude of the analgesic effect of morphine when foot pinch is used as the nociceptive stimulus (Gorlitz and Frey, 1972). In one of the most thorough studies of this possibility there is no significant increase in sensitivity to nociceptive stimuli and the analgesic effect of morphine is *not* blocked by a variety of lesions in and around the DR nucleus (Harvey *et al.*, 1974). In another paper, lesions of the MR produce an antagonism of morphine analgesia, and produce a slight increase in sensitivity to nociception on the tail compression test (cf. Table 4, Samanin and Bernasconi, 1972).

It appears that lesions of raphe nuclei affect nociception as a function of the test used to measure analgesia. Animals with DR lesions are more sensitive than controls on the tail compression test, but not when tested on the tail shock or hot-plate tests (Samanin *et al.*, 1970). It appears that 5-HT may be involved in some, but not all aspects of nociception.

1.5.2 Electrical stimulation of the serotonergic system

Another approach to studying the relationship between 5-HT and morphine analgesia is to stimulate areas of the serotonergic system electrically to determine if the electrical stimulation (1) will produce analgesia alone, or (2) will alter the analgesic effect of morphine. Electrical stimulation of the PAG in the vicinity of the DR produces analgesia that in some cases is additive with morphine analgesia (Akil and Mayer, 1972; Oliveras *et al.*, 1975; Reynolds, 1969; Samanin and Valzelli, 1971). A logical problem with this finding is that a serotonergic projection from the DR to the MPR has not been demonstrated (Ungerstedt, 1971). However, a fiber pathway presumably non-serotonergic, detected by HRP tracing techniques, projects from the PAG to the MPR (Gallagher and Pert, 1978). When neuronal activity in the PAG is increased by the microinjection of glutamate there is a concomitant increase in firing in the MPR and also a concomitant analgesic effect (Behbehani and Fields, 1979). Stimulation in the area of the MPR in cats produces analgesia (Oliveras *et al.*, 1975). The fibers from the MPR to the cord apparently travel in the dorsolateral funiculus because lesions of this pathway reduce the analgesia produced by morphine administered either systemically (Hayes *et al.*, 1978) or injected into the PAG (Murfin *et al.*, 1976). The systemic administration of morphine produces an acceleration of firing in MPR neurons but has no direct effect on these neurons (Fig. 1.13; Table 1.5). Thus morphine may act like glutamate to increase neuronal firing in the PAG, and produce an increase in firing in the MPR. Unfortunately, this has not been demonstrated. Instead morphine and levorphanol, administered microiontophoretically, produce inhibition of firing in 29–47 per cent of the neurons recorded in the PAG (Haigler, 1978a); neither drug produces an acceleration of firing in the PAG (personal observation).

It is possible to reach two contradictory conclusions based on the above data. Morphine may produce an increase in firing of the MPR in one of the following two ways. It may *inhibit* cells in certain areas of the brain (e.g. PAG) and release cells in the MPR from a tonic inhibition. Alternatively morphine may *excite* cells in certain areas of the brain (e.g. PAG) and produce an increase in firing of cells in the MPR. The resolution of this apparent contradiction may shed more light on how morphine interacts with the descending serotonergic system to produce analgesia. In any case, morphine apparently produces some of its analgesic effects by increasing the neuronal firing in the MPR and causing an increase in the release of 5-HT in the spinal cord.

However, the analgesic effects of morphine may also arise by acting on the ascending serotonergic system that first ascends into forebrain structures and then projects to the spinal cord via a pathway that has not yet been described (Mayer and Price, 1976). The complexity of such a system should not be evidence against its existence.

1.5.3 Microiontophoretic studies in the forebrain

A more direct way to determine if a drug affects a particular system is to use the technique of microiontophoresis to eject the drug into the vicinity of a neuron while changes in its firing rate are monitored. Thus if morphine has a direct effect on the forebrain serotonergic system the microiontophoretic administration of morphine should alter the firing of neurons in the serotonergic system. In the DR, morphine has little effect on spontaneous or evoked neuronal firing rates in rats anesthetized with chloral hydrate (Haigler, 1976). However, the effect of morphine on firing rates in the DR may have been masked by chloral hydrate.

In a more detailed study the effects of morphine on the ascending serotonergic system was studied in rats in which no general anesthetic was present at the time of the recordings. In this preparation rats still have a normal electroencephalogram (EEG) that could be desynchronized by a nociceptive stimulus (Fig. 1.14).

Because the rat was capable of being aroused (EEG desynchronization) the animal was not in an abnormal physiological state and was not functionally decorticate or decerebrate. Furthermore, the desynchronization of the EEG indicates that the rat was not in a state of tonic arousal and thus was probably not experiencing continuing nociceptive stimuli (i.e. pain).

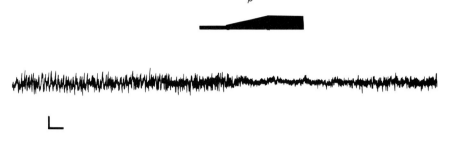

Fig. 1.14 EEG of a rat in absence of general anesthetic showing desynchronization during administration of a nociceptive stimulus. This parietal EEG demonstrates that the EEG of rats can be desynchronized, indicated by a decrease in amplitude when foot pressure (p) indicated by the horizontal bar, is increased from 40, indicated by thickening of the horizontal bar to 400 lb in^{-2} and maintained at this level until release. Notice that synchronization returns after the foot is released. The calibration bars in the left hand corner are 200 μV (vertical) and 5 s (horizontal). Reprinted from Haigler (1978a) by permission of Elsevier/North-Holland Biomedical Press.

The criteria for neurons to be considered part of the 5-HT system of the forebrain (ascending serotonergic system) are as follows. They must either contain 5-HT and be located in the midbrain raphe nuclei (DR and MR the presynaptic neurons) or receive a documented 5-HT input from the DR (based on biochemical, histochemical and tracing techniques) as do the postsynaptic neurons in the cortical and basolateral nuclei of the amygdala (Aghajanian *et al.*, 1973; Wang and Aghajanian, 1977; Table 1.4).

Based on biochemical, histochemical and pharmacological data two other areas, optic tectum and subiculum, receive a uniform and dense 5-HT input from the DR and MR (Aghajanian *et al.*, 1973; Haigler and Aghajanian, 1974a; Table 1.4). Cells in these five areas of the serotonergic system were compared to cells that have a lower probability of receiving a serotonergic input because they are in areas where 5-HT terminals are lower in number and less uniformly distributed (MRF, PAG, cerebral cortex and hippocampus) (Aghajanian *et al.*, 1975; Dahlström and Fuxe 1965; Table 1.4). These are 'comparison areas'. Since electrical stimulation of the raphe nuclei produces an inhibition of neuronal firing in the MRF (Nakamura, 1975), cortex (Sastry and Phillis, 1977) and hippocampus (Segal, 1975), it is possible that some of the comparison areas receive an important serotonergic input and thus may be important components of the serotonergic system. If this is the case, statistical comparisons between cells in the serotonergic and 'comparison areas' with respect to their response to nociceptive stimuli and the effects of morphine and other drugs, would be less likely to detect a significant difference. If morphine acts on the serotonergic systems to produce analgesia, nociceptive stimuli should change the neuronal firing in this system and morphine should block this evoked change in neuronal firing. The neurons in the five areas of the serotonergic system were further characterized in this study by determining their response to a nociceptive stimulus.

(a) Lack of specific narcotic effects of morphine on the forebrain serotonergic system

Morphine administered microiontophoretically slows or inhibits spontaneous neuronal firing in one-third of the serotonergic neurons in the midbrain raphe nuclei (Fig. 1.15) and neurons that receive a 5-HT input located in three postsynaptic areas (Table 1.7). Morphine also prolongs the inhibitory effect of 5-HT on neuronal firing in the subiculum (Fig. 1.16, Table 1.7); in comparison areas (e.g. PAG, MRF), morphine does not prolong 5-HT inhibition ($P < 0.05$). It is possible that morphine produces its analgesic effect by prolonging the inhibitory effect of 5-HT on postsynaptic cells (Fig. 1.16, Table 1.7). This possibility is supported by the observation that naloxone antagonizes the potentiating effect of morphine (Fig. 1.16).

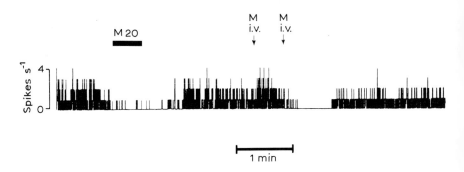

Fig. 1.15 Morphine administered both microiontophoretically and i.v. produces an inhibition of neuronal firing in the dorsal raphe. The microiontophoretic ejection of morphine (M) at 20 nA produces an inhibition that is comparable to the systemic administration of morphine at a cumulative dose of 2 mg kg^{-1}. The slight acceleration seen after the first arrow was only occasionally seen and was not sustained. In this and all subsequent figures, the heavy horizontal bar indicates the duration of the ejection current; the letter indicates the drug and the numbers indicate the ejection current in nA. The isolated arrows indicate the time of intravenous injection of the drug. The ordinate represents the rate of firing in spikes s^{-1}. Reprinted from Haigler (1978a) by permission of Elsevier/North-Holland Biomedical Press.

Table 1.7 Effects of morphine, levorphanol and dextrorphan when administered microiontophoretically

Areas in the serotonergic system*	Drug inhibits spontaneous neuronal firing						Effect of morphine on inhibition produced by serotonin		
	Morphine		Levorphanol		Dextrorphan		Augments†	Blocks	No effect
	Yes	No	Yes	No	Yes	No			
Dorsal raphe	38(32)‡	79(68)	37(42)	51(58)	41(48)	44(52)	1(17)§	0	5(83)
Median raphe	5(22)¶	18(78)‖	3(37)	5(63)	3(25)	9(75)	—	1(50)§	1(50)
Subiculum	14(45)	17(55)	5(71)	2(29)	7(70)	3(30)	7(54)§	1(8)§	5(38)
Optic tectum	7(30)	16(70)	3(25)	9(75)	5(33)	10(67)	0	0	2(100)
Amygdala	6(27)	16(73)	1(9)	10(91)	3(25)	9(75)	—	—	—
Comparison areas									
PAG	13(29)	32(71)	8(47)	9(53)	4(29)	10(71)	0	0	4(100)
MRF	5(56)	4(44)	5(56)	4(44)	2(66)	1(33)	0	1(17)	5(83)
Pontine nuc.	2(25)	6(75)	0	2(100)	0	6(100)	1(33)	0	2(67)
Cerebral cortex	2(18)	9(82)	4(36)	7(64)	5(56)	4(44)	—	—	—
Medial hypothalamus	4(100)	0	—	—	—	—	—	—	—

* Locations of the areas listed in this and other tables are shown in Fig. 2 of Haigler (1978a).
† Morphine augments the inhibitory effect in the serotonergic system more frequently than in other areas ($P < 0.05$).
‡ Numbers in parentheses in this and all subsequent tables represent the percentage of cells tested in each category.
§ In seven of these cells the nociceptive stimulus produced inhibition ($N = 2$), no effect ($N = 4$) and an increase in firing ($N = 1$); morphine potentiated the latter effect. In the other three cells the response to the nociceptive stimulus was not determined.
¶ Four of these cells had raphe-like action potentials.
‖ Eleven of these cells had raphe-like action potentials.
Reprinted from Haigler (1978a) by permission of Elsevier/North Holland Press, Amsterdam.

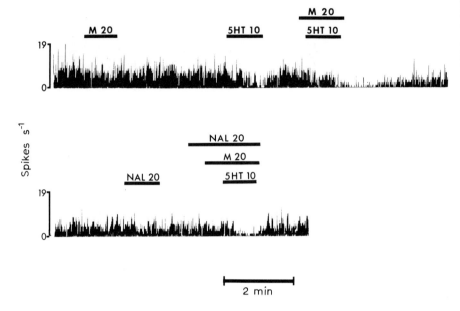

Fig. 1.16 The prolongation of the inhibitory effect of serotonin (5-HT) by morphine. Morphine (M) (20 nA) has no apparent effect on the spontaneous rate of firing on a cell in the subiculum. However, 5-HT at 10 nA produces a decrease in firing. When morphine is administered prior to and during the ejection of 5-HT, there is an increase in the duration of the inhibition produced by 5-HT. This enhancement of the inhibitory effect is evidently a specific narcotic effect because naloxone (Nal) ejected at 20 nA antagonizes this effect when administered with morphine and 5-HT.

This effect must be confirmed in a greater number of cells before it is accepted. However, the nociceptive stimulus rarely affects cells in which morphine promotes the inhibitory effects of 5-HT. Thus even if morphine reliably potentiates the inhibitory effects of 5-HT and this is a specific narcotic effect, this effect may not be related to the analgesic effects of morphine.

Morphine inhibits neuronal firing more consistently in the hypothalamus than in any other areas of the brain studied ($P < 0.05$). However, it remains to be determined if this inhibition is a specific narcotic effect. The specific areas where these neurons were recorded are shown in Fig. 1.17.

Morphine, levorphanol and dextrorphan apparently produce the same amount of inhibition within the serotonergic system as they do in comparison areas (Table 1.7). However, the distribution of cells in the following two categories: 1, all drugs producing the same effect; and 2, dextrorphan

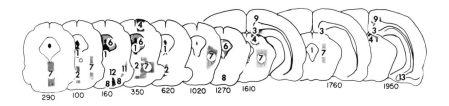

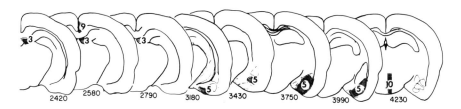

Fig. 1.17 Histological location of recording sites. Numbers and shading indicate boundaries of areas where cells were recorded; in some cases numbers obscure the area of interest. The numbers under each section are anterior (A) or posterior (P) distances of the presented section from a frontal section taken in the zero plane and correspond to the legend in the atlas by König and Klippel (1970). 1, Dorsal raphe; 2, 2a, median raphe (see below); 3, subiculum; 4, optic tectum; 5, cortical and basolateral nuclei of the amygdala; 6, periaqueductal gray (PAG); 7, mesencephalic reticular formation (MRF); 8, pontine nucleus; 9, cereberal cortex (cells were recorded in the lateral area of the cortex shown in A4230 as far anterior as A7020); 10, hypothalamus; 11, lateral lemniscus; 12, longitudinal fasiculus; 13, entrohinal cortex. Hippocampal area not shown but is just lateral to numeral 3 at A2790. 2a, median raphe: eight cells located at P290 are anatomically in the region of the median raphe and are included in this category even though they did not have the electrophysiological characteristics of raphe neurons. If these same cells are put in the MRF category the differences between the serotonergic and non-serotonergic areas does not change because most of these cells are not affected by the nociceptive stimulus or morphine; see Tables 1.7 and 1.8 for further details. The areas are numbered as closely as possible to correspond to the sequence in which the areas are listed in Tables 1.7, 1.8 and 1.9. Reprinted from Haigler (1978a) by permission of Elsevier/North-Holland Biomedical Press.

(differing from morphine and levorphanol) was not the same in the serotonergic system as it was in the comparison areas ($P < 0.05$) (Table 1.8). In the lateral areas of the MRF at P100–A1020 in chloral hydrate-anesthetized rats, dextrorphan has no inhibitory effect.

Like morphine, levorphanol and dextrorphan both produce an inhibition

Table 1.8 Varying patterns of effects of morphine, levorphanol and dextrorphan in five areas of the serotonergic system and comparison areas*

	Dextrorphan produces an effect different from that of morphine or levorphanol†	Morphine, levorphanol and dextrorphan all produce inhibition	Morphine, levorphanol and dextrorphan do not produce inhibition
Serotonergic areas			
Dorsal and median raphe	22(27)	16(22)	37(51)
Subiculum	2(25)	5(63)	1(12)
Optic tectum	4(30)	1(8)	8(62)
Amygdala	1(9)	2(18)	8(73)
Comparison areas			
Cerebral cortex	24(70)	4(12)	6(18)
PAG	5(63)	1(12)	2(25)
Hippocampus	2(29)	1(14)	4(57)
Entrohinal cortex	2(29)	0	5(71)
MRF, medial	0	2(67)	1(33)
MRF, lateral‡	7(47)	0	8(53)

* The difference in the pattern of effects of these three drugs in the serotonergic and comparison areas of the brain was significant ($P < 0.01$) using a 2×3 contingency table analysis.

† Included in this category are cells in which dextrorphan produced an inhibition and morphine or levorphanol produced no effect or vice versa; dextrorphan produced an acceleration and morphine or levorphanol produced no effect or inhibition; dextrorphan produced no effect and levorphanol or morphine produced an inhibition.

‡ These determinations were made in chloral hydrate-anesthetized animals in areas of the MRF more lateral than those shown in Fig. 2 of Haigler (1978a) at levels P100–A1020.

Reprinted from Haigler (1978a) by permission of Elsevier/North Holland Press. Amsterdam.

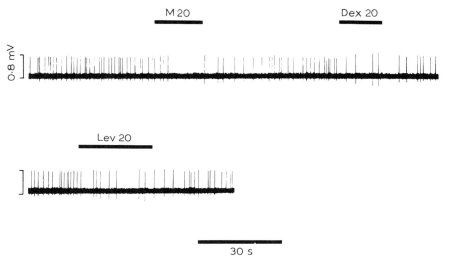

Fig. 1.18 Record from a light beam oscillograph showing that there is no decrease in action potential size when morphine (M), dextrorphan (Dex) and levorphanol (Lev) are administered microiontophoretically. This record differs from previous figures in that it is a direct recording of the action potential and *not* an analog record of firing. When morphine is administered microiontophoretically (20 nA) for 10 s there is an inhibition of neuronal firing. Dextrorphan (20 nA) for 10 s produces a comparable degree of inhibition and slowing is associated with an increase in action potential size. The inhibitory effect of levorphanol (20 nA) is less apparent even though the ejection current is left on for 20 s. The microiontophoretic ejection currents in this figure are shorter than those typically used so that recovery from inhibition is more rapid for the purpose of this record. The amplitude of the action potential is 0.8 mV. Reprinted from Haigler (1978a) by permission of Elsevier/North-Holland Biomedical Press.

of neuronal firing in all areas of the serotonergic system studied (Fig. 1.18; Table 1.7). There is no apparent local anesthetic effect because the amplitude of the action potential is not decreased (Fig. 1.18). When these three drugs are compared to each other using cumulative dose–response curves based on single microiontophoretic application of the drug (Hill and Simmonds, 1973), there is little or no difference in their potency either in the DR or three areas which apparently receive a projection from the DR (Fig. 1.19). All three drugs are compared on the same five cells as in Fig. 1.18. In five additional cells, dextrorphan and levorphanol effects are compared. Dose–response curves based on these ten cells alone are similar to those in Fig. 1.19. The drugs are similar in potency and there is little difference in drug effects between the DR and the postsynaptic areas.

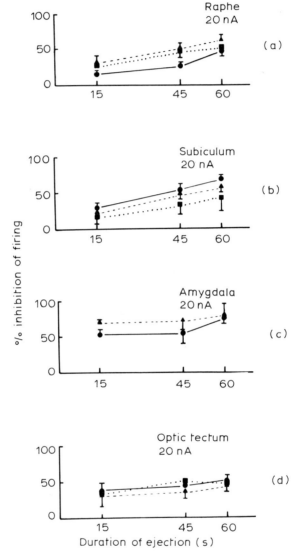

Fig. 1.19 Percentage inhibition of firing rates (ordinate) plotted against linear time (abscissa) comparing responses of morphine (Mor), dextrorphan (Dex), and levorphanol (Lev) in the raphe (a), subiculum (b), amygdala (c), and optic tectum (d). The number of cells used from each area for morphine was 11 (a:raphe), 9 (b:subiculum), 6 (c:amygdala) and 7 (d:optic tectum); for dextrorphan 10 (a), 8 (b), 4 (c), 4 (d); and levorphanol 11 (a), 5 (b), 1 (c) (not plotted), 3 (d). The lower potency for levorphanol is apparent in that it affected fewer cells. Reprinted from Haigler (1978a) by permission of Elsevier/North-Holland Biomedical Press.

Naloxone occasionally blocks the inhibition produced by morphine and levorphanol in the serotonergic system and fails to modify the inhibitory effect produced by dextrorphan (Table 1.8). In contrast, in areas where serotonin terminals are less dense, naloxone blocks the effect of ion-tophoretically applied morphine and levorphanol more consistently ($P < 0.05$). The depressant effects of dextrorphan are not blocked by naloxone in any of these areas. Dextrorphan and dextromethorphan, another dextrorotary isomer of a morphine agonist, have identical inhibitory effects in the serotonergic system when both are administered microiontophoretically ($n = 6$). Thus, the effect of ionotophoretically applied morphine in five areas of the serotonergic system is not related to its analgesic effects because it is not stereospecific and cannot be reliably blocked by naloxone.

(b) *Effect of morphine on changes in neuronal firing evoked by a nociceptive stimulus*

The nociceptive stimulus produces an alteration in firing more frequently in cells in comparison areas than in five areas of the serotonergic system ($P < 0.05$) (Table 1.9). In 9 of 14 cells, the response to the nociceptive stimulus in areas of the serotonergic system studied was not blocked by the microiontophoretic administration of morphine (Fig. 1.20). However, if a cell is accelerated by a nociceptive stimulus, morphine blocks this acceleration in serotonergic areas as often as it does in comparison areas ($P < 0.1$). Morphine blocks the response to the nociceptive stimulus more often in the DR and amygdala (5 of 9) than it does in the subiculum and optic tectum (0 of 5) ($P < 0.05$); the frequency with which morphine blocks the response to the nociceptive stimulus is the same in the DR and amygdala as it is in cells in other areas in this study as well as the cells in the lateral MRF previously reported (Haigler, 1976).

(c) *Systemic administration of drugs*

Morphine administered systemically produces an inhibition of neuronal firing in the serotonergic system approximately as frequently as morphine administered iontophoretically; 3 of 7 (42 per cent) cells are inhibited by morphine administered i.v. ($2-14$ mg kg^{-1}); 4 of 7 (58 per cent) are unaffected ($14-56$ mg kg^{-1}). To link the i.v. and microiontophoretic data, morphine was administered both microiontophoretically and i.v. in six experiments. Neurons not inhibited by morphine administered iontophoretically are not inhibited by morphine administered i.v. in doses as high as 60 mg kg^{-1} ($n = 4$) (Fig. 1.20). In only two cells inhibited by the microiontophoretic administration of morphine was it possible to continue to record from the cells after the i.v. administration of morphine. In these two cells, morphine ($1-10$ mg kg^{-1}) administered systemically produced an inhibition

Table 1.9 Effect of morphine administered microiontophoretically on the change in neuronal firing evoked by a nociceptive stimulus

Areas in the serotonergic system	N	Change evoked by nociceptive stimulus			Morphine blocks change evoked by nociceptive stimulus	
		Acceleration	Slowing	No change	Yes	No
Dorsal raphe	78	11(14)	1(1)	66(85)	3(50)	3(50)
Median raphe	10*	1†(10)	0	9(90)	—	—
Subiculum	20	4(20)	3(15)	13(65)	0	3(100)
Amygdala	29	3(10)	0	26(90)	2(67)	1(33)
Optic tectum	13	2(15)	1(8)	10(77)	0	2(100)
Comparison areas						
PAG	30	2(7)	4(13)	24(80)	1(100)	—
MRF	39	18(46)	3(8)	18(46)	7(50)	7(50)
Pontine nuc.	10	7(70)	0	3(30)	2(33)	4(67)
Lateral lemniscus	3	3(100)	0	0	1(33)	2(67)
Longitudinal fas.	4	4(100)	0	0	2(50)	2(50)

* Four of these cells did not have a raphe-like action potential but were in the area of the median raphe.
† This cell had a raphe-like action potential.

Reprinted from Haigler (1978a) by permission of Elsevier/North Holland Press, Amsterdam.

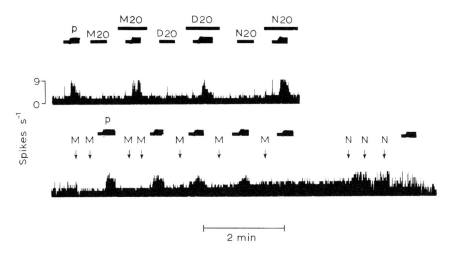

Fig. 1.20 Morphine (M), dextrorphan (D) and naloxone (N) fail to block the acceleration of firing produced by a nociceptive stimulus in a cell in the dorsal raphe and produce no effect on spontaneous firing. The administration of a nociceptive stimulus, pressure (p) delivered to the left foot, produces an increase in firing. The pressure at the beginning of the lighter horizontal line is 40 lb in.$^{-2}$; at the thickening of the bar the pressure is increased from 40 lb in.$^{-2}$ to 400 lb in.$^{-2}$ which takes 14 s. This pressure is maintained for an additional 10 s before the foot is released. Morphine was administered i.v. at each arrow marked M (2 mg kg^{-1}) except at the last arrow (4 mg kg^{-1}). After 12–16 mg kg^{-1} of morphine there is a slow increase in firing until the response to the nociceptive stimulus no longer rises above background. Naloxone (N) (2.5, 2.5, 5.0 mg kg^{-1} at the arrows) reverses the acceleration but the response to the nociceptive stimulus is obscured by the spontaneous bursting activity of the cell. Reprinted from Haigler (1978a) by permission of Elsevier/North-Holland Biomedical Press.

of firing similar to the inhibition of firing produced by the iontophoretic administration of morphine (Fig. 1.15). Thus whatever effect morphine has microiontophoretically is the effect that it will have when administered systemically.

Levorphanol and dextrorphan follow the same pattern as morphine; if they produce an inhibition of firing when administered microiontophoretically, they also produce an inhibition of firing when given i.v. (levorphanol: 0.5–4.0 mg kg^{-1}; $n = 4$) (dextrorphan: 6–10 mg kg^{-1}; $n = 3$). The duration of inhibition produced by these drugs was not usually determined because once an effect became apparent, naloxone was administered to test reversal.

(d) The analgesic effect of serotonin and morphine

Morphine inhibits neuronal firing in 35 per cent of cells in the five areas of the serotonergic system studied. However, this effect does not appear to be related to analgesia for the following reasons. First, the effect of morphine is not stereospecific because both levorphanol and dextrorphan have an equal potency in inhibiting the neuronal firing when given microiontophoretically at the same ejection currents. In contrast, levorphanol and dextrorphan do not have an equal potency in comparison areas where serotonin terminals are less dense and less uniform. In these areas morphine and levorphanol produce an inhibition of firing in cells unaffected by dextrorphan and vice versa. The inhibition produced by morphine, levorphanol and dextrorphan is not a local anesthetic effect because these drugs do not produce a decrease in action potential size when administered microiontophoretically. Furthermore, these drugs apparently have the same effects when administered systemically.

There have been other reports that dextrorphan has an effect similar to morphine. Dextrorphan has an inhibitory effect on neuronal firing comparable to that of morphine when administered to sensory interneurons in the spinal cord (Dostrovsky and Pomeranz, 1976). Dextrorphan and levorphanol occasionally produce a depression of firing on the same cells in the cortex; the frequency with which this occurs in this study is not different from the frequency found in a previous study ($P > 0.1$) (Satoh *et al.*, 1976). Although the raphe nuclei in the midbrain and forebrain areas that receive projections from them do not appear to be areas where morphine acts to produce analgesia, it is still possible that morphine acts at the level of the brainstem raphe (MPR) nuclei to produce analgesia (see Section 1.4.3).

A second reason that the effect of morphine on these five areas of the serotonergic system does not appear to be related to analgesia is that the nociceptive stimulus used in this study did not consistently (<20 per cent) affect the neuronal firing in these areas. If most of the cells in the serotonergic system are not involved with nociception, it is difficult to understand how effects of morphine on this system could produce analgesia. The number of cells that responded to the nociceptive stimulus is significantly *more* prevalent in areas where 5-HT terminals are less dense in this study ($P < 0.05$) as well as in the MRF as previously reported ($P < 0.05$) (Haigler, 1976). The reason that cells in the five serotonergic areas are infrequently accelerated by a nociceptive stimulus might be that they have restricted peripheral receptive fields. This possibility is apparently not the case because cells not accelerated by pressure to the left foot are not accelerated by a hemostat pinch delivered to other parts of the body.

A hypothesis based on the results of several studies that have employed electrical stimulation of the DR and MR to produce morphine-like analgesia (Akil and Mayer, 1972; Mayer *et al*., 1972; Samanin and Valzelli, 1971), is that morphine produces an acceleration of firing in the DR, increases the release of 5-HT and produces an inhibition of firing in cells involved with nociception. This inhibition of firing would then result in analgesia. Although this hypothesis may be valid for neurons in the MPR (Haigler, 1978b), this is clearly not the case in the DR or MR. The data in the above study (Haigler, 1978a) do not support the hypothesis that the DR or MR are sites where morphine acts directly to produce analgesia.

Morphine has pharmacological effects other than analgesia; for example, it produces hypothermia and changes in locomotor behavior, as well as a wide variety of other physiological and behavioral effects. Thus, morphine's effect on the serotonergic system may be related to one or more of these effects rather than analgesia. The serotonergic system seems to be important in thermoregulation (Jahns, 1976; Sawa and Oka, 1976; Weiss and Aghajanian, 1971). Dextrorphan administered i.v. (10 mg kg^{-1}) produces a 1.5–3.5° C drop in body temperature (Haigler, unpublished observation). There also appears to be a relationship between the decrease in locomotor activity produced by morphine and its effects on the serotonergic system (Buxbaum *et al*., 1973; Sawa and Oka, 1976). These, and other 'non-specific' effects of morphine may be shared by dextrorphan and may be a consequence of their action on the serotonergic system. Dextromethorphan, another dextrorotatory isomer of a morphine agonist also had an inhibitory effect in the serotonergic system when administered microiontophoretically.

Chloral hydrate apparently antagonizes the effect of morphine on neurons in the DR because morphine has no effect on neurons in the DR in animals anesthetized with chloral hydrate (Haigler, 1976). In contrast, morphine inhibits one third of the neurons in the DR when chloral hydrate is not used (Haigler, 1978a). This antagonistic relationship may be useful in trying to determine the physiological and biochemical consequences of morphine's action on the 5-HT system.

It appears that morphine definitely has an effect on the five areas of the forebrain serotonergic system. Although this effect is not related to analgesia and is not a specific narcotic effect, it is possibly related to one or more of the other pharmacological actions of morphine such as effects on thermoregulation or locomotor activity. Morphine can also apparently promote the inhibitory effects of 5-HT in the serotonergic system.

Although this effect of morphine may be a specific narcotic effect because it is antagonized by naloxone, it does not appear to be related to the analgesic effects of morphine.

One cannot totally reject the hypothesis that the forebrain serotonergic system is involved in the analgesic effects of morphine because morphine blocked the acceleration produced by the stimulus in 35 per cent of the cells that could be tested ($n = 14$) in five areas of the serotonergic system. If the serotonergic system is involved in morphine analgesia, the DR and amygdala would be areas in which to study this involvement. However, areas in the serotonergic system are apparently less involved in morphine analgesia when compared to other areas (e.g. MRF; lateral lemniscus) where cells are more consistently affected by the nociceptive stimulus.

Considering the above data one is led to the conclusion that cells in the MPR are the ones involved in the analgesic effects of morphine. Thus the ascending serotonergic system appears to have a minimal involvement and the descending serotonergic system (MPR) a maximal involvement.

Morphine may produce analgesia by acting through the MPR to activate a descending serotonergic system that inhibits the neuronal firing in the spinal cord that is evoked by a nociceptive stimulus. However, the ascending serotonergic system, originating in the midbrain raphe nuclei, is apparently *not* involved in the expression of the analgesic effects of morphine. In this system the effects of morphine are not stereospecific and are not reliably blocked by naloxone. However, effects of morphine on the ascending serotonergic system may be related to some non-analgesic effects (e,g. effects on body temperature) of morphine.

1.6 SUMMARY AND CONCLUSION

There are numerous definitions of receptors. The one adopted for this chapter is that a receptor is a specific component of a cell membrane to which a drug molecule attaches and produces a change in the activity of the cell. This definition includes several characteristics useful in classifying receptors; these characteristics are used to classify 5-HT receptors.

The 5-HT receptors isolated using *in vitro* biochemical techniques do not have similar characteristics to those found using *in vivo* techniques. For instance, LSD has a very high affinity for postsynaptic binding sites but very weak physiological activity. However, if the postsynaptic 5-HT$_2$ receptor has two binding sites separated by a protrusion of the membrane, it is possible to reconcile the high affinity of drugs for binding sites with their low physiological activity.

Available evidence indicates there are at least three 5-HT receptors in the CNS. There are receptors on the 5-HT-containing neurons in the midbrain raphe nuclei (5-HT$_1$ receptors); receptors on neurons in areas where 5-HT terminals are dense and where the synaptic action of 5-HT is inhibitory (5-HT$_2$ receptors); and receptors on neurons in areas where there is a paucity or scattered distribution of 5-HT terminals (5-HT$_3$ receptors). These receptors have the following characteristics. When 5-HT and LSD act on 5-HT$_1$ receptors they both produce an inhibition of firing; putative 5-HT antagonists do not block the inhibitory effects of 5-HT at these receptors, instead they enhance it. In contrast to the 5-HT$_1$ receptor, LSD is *less* potent in producing an inhibition of firing when it acts on 5-HT$_2$ receptors. However, 5-HT has the same potency on 5-HT$_1$ and 5-HT$_2$ receptors and putative antagonists enhance the inhibitory effects of 5-HT at 5-HT$_2$ receptors. In contrast, the 5-HT$_3$ receptors produce excitation when 5-HT acts on them. Instead of being a 5-HT agonist at these receptors, LSD blocks the excitatory effects of 5-HT. The excitatory effect of 5-HT at 5-HT$_3$ receptors is also blocked by putative 5-HT antagonists. Although initially considered to be an artefact, recent evidence indicates that this effect of 5-HT may arise from a neuromodulatory role in which 5-HT enhances the effects of excitatory neurotransmitters.

The behavioral effects of LSD may arise from its differential effects on 5-HT$_1$ and 5-HT$_2$ receptors. Because LSD is more potent on 5-HT$_1$ receptors than 5-HT$_2$, the postsynaptic cells escape from inhibition. This escape may account for some of the behavioral effects of LSD. However, new experimental evidence challenges this hypothesis and indicates that the mechanism of action of LSD may include other neurotransmitter systems and may involve a direct action on cells in the visual system.

There may be other 5-HT receptors in the cortex and hippocampus that mediate an inhibition of neuronal firing. These receptors differ from the 5-HT$_1$ and 5-HT$_2$ receptors in that they are blocked by putative 5-HT antagonists. There appears to be a mixture of 5-HT receptor types in the medullary–pontine raphe nuclei (MPR) but the interpretation of data in this area is tenuous because the identity of neurons (with respect to their neurotransmitter) is not clear cut.

There are also 5-HT receptors in the spinal cord that are involved in the expression of the analgesic effects of morphine. These receptors may be like 5-HT$_3$ receptors, like those in the hippocampus and cortex, or an entirely different type. These receptors need to be characterized further before they can be categorized.

Antidepressant drugs *increase* the sensitivity of 5-HT$_1$ and 5-HT$_2$ receptors for 5-HT. This change in sensitivity develops over the same time course that the onset of clinical effects of these drugs develop. These data and data concerning morphine and the spinal cord indicate that knowledge of the 5-HT receptors in the CNS will soon lead to a more complete understanding of drugs that are used clinically.

REFERENCES

Adler, M., Kostowski, W., Recchia, M. and Samanin, R. (1975), *Eur. J. Pharmacol., 32,* 39–45.

Aghajanian, G.K. (1976), *Neuropharmacol.* **15,** 521–528.

Aghajanian, G.K. and Asher, I.M. (1971), *Science,* **172,** 1159–1161.

Aghajanian, G.K. and Bloom, F.E. (1967), *J. Pharmacol. Exp. Ther.,* **156,** 23–30.

Aghajanian, G.K., Bloom, F.E. and Sheard, M.H. (1969), *Brain Res.,* **13,** 266–273.

Aghajanian, G.K., Foote, W.E. and Sheard, M.H. (1970), *J. Pharmacol. Exp. Ther.,* **171,** 178–187.

Aghajanian, G.K. and Freedman, D.X. (1968), in *Psychopharmacology: A Review of Progress* (Efron, D., ed), pp. 1185–1193, Government Printing Office, Washington, D.C.

Aghajanian, G.K. and Haigler, H.J. (1974), *Brain Res.,* **81,** 364–372.

Aghajanian, G.K. and Haigler, H.J. (1975), *Psychopharmacol. Comm., 1,* 619–629.

Aghajanian, G.K., Haigler, H.J. and Bennett, J.L. (1975), in *Handbook of Psychopharmacology,* (Iverson, L.L., Iverson, S.D. and Snyder, S.H., eds) Plenum Press, New York, 63–96.

Aghajanian, G.K., Haigler, H.J. and Bloom, F.E. (1972), *Life Sci.,* **11,** 615–622.

Aghajanian, G.K., Kuhar, M.J. and Roth, R.H. (1973), *Brain Res.,* **54,** 85–101.

Aghajanian, G.K., Rosecrans, J.A. and Sheard, M.A. (1967), *Science,* **156,** 402–403.

Aghajanian, G.K. and Wang, R.Y. (1978), *Psychopharmacology: A Generation of Progress* (Pipton, M.A., DiMascio, A. and Killam, K.F., eds), Raven Press, New York, 171–183.

Akil, H. and Mayer, D.J. (1972), *Brain Res.,* **44,** 692–696.

Amin, A.H., Crawford, T.B.B. and Gaddum, J.H. (1954), *J. Physiol.,* **126,** 596–618.

Anden, N.E., Corrodi, H., Fuxe, K. and Hokfelt, T. (1968), *Brit. J. Pharmacol. Chemother.,* **34,** 1–7.

Anderson, K.V., Rosing, H.S. and Pearl, G.S. (1977), in *Pain in the Trigeminal Region,* (Anderson, D.J. and Matthews, B., eds), pp. 149–160, North-Holland Biomedical Press, Amsterdam.

Ashkenazi, R., Holman, R.B. and Vogt, M. (1972), *J. Physiol.,* **223,** 255–259.

Baraban, J.M. and Aghajanian, G.K. (1979), *Neuroscience Abst.,* 1085.

Basbaum, A.I., Clanton, G.H. and Fields, H.L. (1976), *Proc. Natl. Acad. Sci.,* **73,** 4685–4688.

Baumgarten, H.G., Bjorkland, A., Lachenmayer, L., Nobin, A. and Stenevi, U. (1971), *Acta Physiol. Scand. Suppl.,* **373,** 1–15.

Baumgarten, H.G. and Lachenmayer, L. (1972), *Brain Res.,* **38,** 228–232.

Behbehani, M.M. and Fields, H.L. (1979), *Brain Res.,* **170,** 85–93.

Bennett, J.L. and Aghajanian, G.K. (1974), *Life Sci.,* **15,** 1935–1944.

Bennett, J.P. and Snyder, S.H. (1975), *Brain Res.,* **94,** 523–544.

Bennett, J.P. and Snyder, S.H. (1976), *Molec. Pharmacol.,* **12,** 373–389.

Bergstrom, D.A. and Kellar, K.J. (1979), *J. Pharmacol. Expt. Ther.,* **209,** 256–261.

Bertino, J.R., Klee, G.D. and Weintraub, W. (1959), *J. Clin. Exp. Psychopath.,* **20,** 218–222.

Bläsig, J., Reinhold, K. and Herz, A. (1973), *Psychopharmacologia (Berl),* **31,** 111–119.

Bloom, F.E. (1973), *Brain Res.,* **62,** 299–305.

Bloom, F.E., Hoffer, B.J., Siggins, G.R., Barker, J.L. and Nicoll, R.A. (1972), *Fed. Proc.,* **31,** 97–106.

Boakes, R.J., Bradley, P.B., Briggs, I. and Dray, A. (1970), *Brit. J. Pharmacol.,* **40,** 202–248.

Bockaert, J. (1978), in *Molecular Biology and Pharmacology of Cyclic Nucleotides,* (Folco, G. and Puoletti, R., eds), Elsevier/North-Holland, Amsterdam, pp. 189–205.

Bramwell, G.J. and Gonye, T. (1976), *Neuropharmacol.,* **15,** 457–461.

Burt, D.R., Creese, I. and Snyder, S.H. (1976), *Molec. Pharmacol.,* **12,** 631–638.

Buxbaum, D.M., Yarbrough, G.G. and Carter, M.E. (1973), *J. Pharmacol. Exp. Ther.,* **185,** 317–327.

Carlsson, A. (1975), in *Pre- and Postsynaptic Receptors,* (Usdin, E. and Bunney, W.E., eds), Marcell Press, New York, 49–63.

Carlsson, A., Falck, B. and Hillarp, N.A. (1962), *Acta Physiol. Scand.,* **56,** 1–28 (Suppl. 196).

Cerletti, A. and Rothlin, E. (1955), *Nature,* **176,** 785–786.

Chase, T.N., Breese, G.R. and Kopin, I.J. (1967), *Science,* **157,** 1461–1463.

Cristoph, G.R., Kuhn, D.M. and Jacobs, B.L. (1978), *Life Sci.,* **23,** 2099–2110.

Clineschmidt, R.V. and Anderson, E.G. (1970), *Exp. Brain Res.,* **11,** 175–186.

Costa, E. (1956), *Proc. Soc. Exp. Biol.,* **91,** 39–41.

Couch, J.R. (1970), *Brain Res.,* **19,** 136–150.

Couch, J.R. (1976), *Brain Res.,* **110,** 417–424.

Curtis, D.R. and Davis, R. (1962), *Brit. J. Pharmacol.,* **18,** 217–246.

Curtis, D.R. (1964), in *Physiol. Technique in Biological Research. V. Electrophysiological Methods,* (Nastuck, W.L., ed.), Academic Press, New York, 144–190.

Curtis, D.R., Phillis, J.W. and Watkins, J.C. (1961), *J. Physiol. (London),* **158,** 296–323.

Dahlström, A. and Fuxe, K. (1964), *Acta. Physiol. Scand.,* **62,** suppl. 232, 1–55.

Dahlström, A. and Fuxe, K. (1965), *Acta. Physiol. Scand.,* **64,** suppl. 247, 1–35.

Diab, J.M., Freedman, D.X. and Roth, L.J. (1971), *Science,* **173,** 1022–1024.

Dostrovsky, J.O. and Pomeranz, B. (1976), *Exptl. Neurol.,* **52,** 325–329.

Duggan, A.W. and Griersmith, R.T. (1979), *Pain,* **6,** 149–161.

Enjalbert, A., Bourgoin, S., Hamon, M., Adrien, J. and Bockaert, J. (1978), *Mol. Pharmacol.,* **14,** 2–10.

Falck, B., Hillarp, N.A., Thieme, G. and Torp, A. (1962), *J. Histochem. Cytochem.,* **10,** 348–354.

Farrow, J.T. and Van Vunakis, H. (1972), *Nature,* **237,** 164–166.

Farrow, J.T. and Van Vunakis, H. (1973), *Biochem. Pharmacol.,* **22,** 1103–1113.

Fields, H.L., Basbaum, A.I., Clanton, C.H. and Anderson, J.D. (1977), *Brain Res.,* **126,** 441–453.

Fiszer, S. and De Robertis, E. (1969), *J. Neurochem.,* **16,** 1201–1209.

Fredrickson, R.C.A., Jordan, L.M. and Phillis, J.W. (1972), *Comp. Gen. Pharmacol.,* **3**, 443–456.

Freedman, D.X. (1961), *J. Pharmacol. Exp. Ther.,* **134**, 160–166.

Freedman, D.X. and Giarman, N.J. (1962), *Acad. N.Y. of Sci.,* **96**, 98–106.

Freedman, D.X., Gottlieb, R. and Lovell, R.A. (1970), *Biochem. Pharmacol.,* **19**, 1181–1188.

Fox, P.C. and Dray, A. (1979), *Brain Res.,* **161**, 167–172.

Fuxe, K. (1965), *Acta. Physiol. Scand.,* **64**, Suppl. 247, 39–85.

Gaddum, J.H. (1953), *J. Physiol.,* **121**, 15P.

Gallager, D.W. and Pert, A. (1978), *Brain Res.,* **144**, 257–275.

Gorlitz, B.D. and Frey, H.H. (1972), *Eur. J. Pharmacol.,* **20**, 171–180.

Griersmith, B.T. and Duggan, A.W. (1980), *Brain Res.,* **187**, 231–236.

Guilbaud, G., Besson, J.-M., Oliveras, J.L. and Liebeskind, J.C. (1973), *Brain Res.,* **61**, 417–422.

Haigler, H.J. (1976), *Life Sci.,* **19**, 841–858.

Haigler, H.J. (1978a), *European J. Pharmacol.,* **51**, 361–376.

Haigler, H.J. (1978b), in *Iontophoresis and Transmitter Mechanisms in Mammalian Central Nervous System* (Ryall, R.W. and Kelly, J.S., eds), Elsevier/North-Holland Biomedical Press, Amsterdam, 326–328.

Haigler, H.J. and Aghajanian, G.K. (1973), *European J. Pharmacol.,* **21**, 53–60.

Haigler, H.J. and Aghajanian, G.K. (1974a), *J. Pharmacol. Exp. Ther.,* **188**, 688–699.

Haigler, H.J. and Aghajanian, G. K. (1974b), *J. Neural. Trans.,* **35**, 257–273.

Harvey, J.A., Schlosberg, A.J. and Yunger, L.M. (1974), *Adv. Biochem. Psychopharmacol.,* **10**, 233–245.

Hayes, R.L., Price, D.D., Bennett, G.J., Wilcox, G.L. and Mayer, D.J. (1978), *Brain Res.,* **155**, 91–101.

Hebb, C. (1970), *Annual Rev. Physiol.,* **32**, 165–192.

Heller, A., Harvey, J.A. and Moore, R.Y. (1962), *Biochem. Pharmacol.,* **11**, 859–866.

Heller, A. and Moore, R.Y. (1965), *J. Pharmacol. Exp. Ther.,* **150**, 1–9.

Hole, K., Fuxe, K. and Jonsson, G. (1976), *Brain Res.,* **107**, 385–399.

Holman, R.B. and Vogt, M. (1972), *J. Physiol.,* **233**, 243–254.

Horita, A.J. (1963), *J. Neuropsychiat.,* **4**, 270–273.

Isbell, H., Miner, E.J. and Logan, C.R. (1959), *Psychopharmacologia,* **1**, 20–28.

Johns, R. (1976), *Brain Res.,* **101**, 355–361.

Jordan, L.M., Frederickson, R.C.A., Phillis, J.W. and Lake, N. (1972), *Brain Res.,* **40**, 552–558.

Jouvet, M. (1967), *Physiol. Rev.,* **47**, 117–177.

Kang, S.K., Johnson, C.S. and Green, J.P. (1973), *Mol. Pharmacol.,* **9**, 640–648.

König, J.F.R. and Klippel, R.A. (1970), *The Rat Brain: A Stereotoxic Atlas*, R.E. Kreiger Publishing, Co., Huntington, New York, 162 pp.

Koe, B.K. and Weissman, A. (1966), *J. Pharmacol. Exp. Ther.,* **154**, 499–516.

Kostowski, W., Giagalone, E., Garattini, S. and Valzelli, L. (1968), *Eur. J. Pharmacol.,* **4**, 371–376.

Kostowski, W., Giagalone, E., Garattini, S. and Valzelli, L. (1969), *Eur. J. Pharmacol.,* **7**, 170–175.

Kuhar, M.J., Aghajanian, G.K. and Roth, R.H. (1972a), *Brain Res.*, **44**, 165–176.

Kuhar, M.J., Roth, R.H. and Aghajanian, G.K. (1972b), *J. Pharmacol. Exp. Ther.*, **181**, 36–45.

Lee, J. and Fennessey, M.R. (1970), *Eur. J. Pharmacol.*, **12**, 65–71.

Lin, R.C., Ngai, S.H. and Costa, E. (1969); *Science*, **166**, 237–239.

Mansour, T.E. (1957), *Brit. J. Pharmacol.*, **12**, 406–409.

Marchbanks, R.M. (1966), *Biochem. Pharmacol.*, **16**, 1971–1979.

Mayer, D.J. and Price, D.D. (1976), *Pain*, **2**, 379–404.

Mayer, D.J., Wolfe, T.L., Akil, H., Carder, B. and Liebeskind, J.C. (1971), *Science*, **174**, 1351–1353.

McCall, R.D. and Aghajanian, G.K. (1979), *Brain Res.*, **169**, 11–27.

Montigny, C.C. and Aghajanian, G.K. (1978), *Science*, **202**, 1303–1306.

Moran, N.C. (1975), in *Handbook of Physiology-Endocrinology. Section 7*, Volume VI. *Adrenal Medulla*, American Physiological Society, Washington, D.C. pp. 447–472.

Mosko, S.S., Haubrich, D. and Jacobs, B.L. (1977), *Brain Res.*, **119**, 269–290.

Mosko, J.J. and Jacobs, B.L. (1976), *Neurosci. Letters*, **2**, 195–200.

Murfin, R., Bennett, G.J. and Mayer, D.J. (1976), *Proc. Soc. Neurosci.*, **2**, 946.

Nakamura, S. (1975), *Brain Res.*, **93**, 140–144.

Oliveras, J.L., Besson, J.M., Guilbaud, G. and Liebeskind, J.C. (1974), *Exp. Brain Research*, **20**, 32–44.

Oliveras, J.L., Hosobuchi, Y., Redjemi, F., Guilbaud, G. and Besson, J.M. (1977), *Brain Research*, **120**, 221–229.

Oliveras, J.L., Redjemi, F., Guilbaud, G. and Besson, J.M. (1975), *Pain*, **1**, 139–145.

Peacock, M.J. and Wolstencroft, J.H. (1976), *Neurosci. Letters*, **2**, 7–11.

Pert, C.B. and Snyder, S.H. (1973), *Science*, **179**, 1011–1014.

Proudfit, H.K. and Anderson, E.G. (1973), *Brain Research*, **61**, 331–341.

Reynolds, D.V. (1969), *Science*, **164**, 444–445.

Roberts, M.H.T. and Straughan, D.W. (1967), *J. Physiol.*, **193**, 269–294.

Rogawski, M.A. and Aghajanian, G.K. (1979), *Life Sci.*, **24**, 1289–1298.

Rosecrans, J.A., Lovell, R.A. and Freedman, D.X. (1967), *Biochem. Pharmacol.*, **16**, 2011–2012.

Rosecrans, J.A. and Sheard, M.H. (1969), *Eur. J. Pharmacol.*, **6**, 197–199.

Samanin, R. and Bernasconi, S. (1972), *Psychopharmacol.*, **25**, 175–182.

Samanin, R., Ghezzi, D., Mauron, C. and Valzelli, L. (1973), *Psychopharmacologia (Berlin)*, **33**, 365–368.

Samanin, R., Gumulka, W. and Valzelli, L. (1970), *Eur. J. Pharmacol.*, **10**, 339–343.

Samanin, R. and Valzelli, L. (1971), *Eur. J. Pharmacol.*, **16**, 298–302.

Sanders, E. and Bush, M.T. (1967), *J. Pharmacol. Exp. Ther.*, **158**, 340–352.

Sastry, B.S.R. and Phillis, J.W. (1977), *Can. J. Physiol. Pharmacol.*, **55**, 737–741.

Sastry, B.S.R. and Sinclair, J.G. (1976), *Brain Research*, **115**, 427–436.

Satoh, M., Zigelgänsberger, W. and Herz, A. (1976), *Brain Research*, **115**, 99–108.

Sawa, A. and Oka, T. (1976), *Jap. J. Pharmacol.*, **25**, 599–605.

Schneckloth, R., Page, I.H., Del Greco, F. and Corcoran, A.C. (1957), *Circulation*, **16**, 523–532.

Schubert, J., Hyback, H. and Sedvall, G. (1970), *Eur. J. Pharmacol.*, **10**, 215–224.

Segal, M. (1975), *Brain Res.*, **94**, 115–131.

Segal, M. (1976), *Brain Res.*, **103**, 161–166.

Shaw, E. and Woolley, D.W. (1956), *Science*, **124**, 121–122.

Sheard, M.H. and Aghajanian, G.K. (1968), *J. Pharmacol. Exp. Ther.*, **163**, 425–430.

Shields, P.J. and Eccleston, D. (1972), *Neurochem.*, **19**, 265–272.

Shiomi, H., Murakami, H. and Takaji, H. (1978), *Eur. J. Pharmacol.*, **52**, 335–344.

Snyder, S.H. and Richelson, E. (1968), *Proc. Natl. Acad. Sci.*, **60**, 206–213.

Tenen, S.S. (1978), *Psychopharmacologia* (Berl.), **12**, 278–285.

Twarog, B.M. and Page, I.H. (1953), *Am. J. Physiol.*, **175**, 157–161.

Ungerstedt, U. (1971), *Acta Physiol. Scand., Suppl.*, **367**, 1–48.

Vogt, M. (1974), *J. Physiol.*, **236**, 483–498.

von Hungen, K., Roberts, S. and Hill, D.F. (1974), *Nature*, **252**, 588–589.

Wang, R.Y. and Aghajanian, G.K. (1977), *Brain Res.*, **120**, 85–102.

Weiss, B.L. and Aghajanian, G.K. (1971), *Brain Res.*, **26**, 37–42.

Welsh, J.H. (1957), *Ann. N.Y. Acad. Sci.*, **66**, 618–630.

Werman, R. (1966), *Comp. Biochem. Physiol.*, **18**, 745–766.

Whitaker, P.M. and Seeman, P. (1978), *Psychopharmacol.*, **59**, 1–5.

Wolbach, A.B., Jr., Miner, E.J. and Isbell, H. (1962), *Psychopharmacologia*, **3**, 219–223.

Wooley, D.N. and Shaw, E. (1954), *Proc.Natl. Acad. Sci.*, **40**, 228–241.

Yaksh, T.L. (1979), *Brain Res.*, **160**, 180–185.

Yaksh, T.L. and Wilson, P.R. (1979), *J. Pharmacol. Exp. Ther.*, **298**, 446–453.

Yaksh, T.L., DuChateau, J.C. and Rudy, T.A. (1976), *Brain Res.*, **104**, 367–372.

Yaksh, T.L., Plant, R.L. and Rudy, T.A. (1977), *Eur. J. Pharmacol.*, **41**, 399–408.

2 Histamine Receptors

JOHN E. TAYLOR and ELLIOTT RICHELSON

Acknowledgement
Supported by Mayo Foundation and U.S.P.H.S. Grants MH 27692, MH 07925 and DA 1490.

Neurotransmitter Receptors Part 2
(*Receptors and Recognition*, Series B, Volume 10)
Edited by H.I. Yamamura and S.J. Enna
Published in 1981 by Chapman and Hall, 11 New Fetter Lane, London EC4P 4EE
© Chapman and Hall

2.1 INTRODUCTION

Histamine, β-imidazolyethylamine, is ubiquitously distributed in mammalian tissues and has potent and diverse actions on many organ systems. Histamine constricts both vascular and non-vascular smooth muscle, stimulates gastric secretions, increases capillary permeability, and has both inotropic and chronotropic effects on the heart (Beavan, 1976a, b; Douglas, 1975). The principle cellular storage sites for histamine are mast cells and basophils. Other minor sources include the epidermis, intestinal mucosa, and the central nervous system (CNS). The physiological functions of endogenous histamine have been extensively studied and it is currently believed that histamine may be a local mediator of anaphylactic and allergic reactions and may participate in the local inflammatory reactions to tissue injury. Histamine is also thought to be a common local mediator of gastric acid secretion elicited by neuronal and hormonal stimuli. Based on these actions, histamine has been classically described as a local hormone or 'autocoid' (Douglas, 1975). A similar description has also been applied to the localized effects of the prostglandins, kinins and serotonin.

As with the prostaglandins and serotonin, however, there has been within the past 10–15 years a major reorientation of thought concerning the biological role of histamine. This trend has developed as a result of studies which indicate that the endogenous histamine of the CNS has a function distinct from that observed in non-neuronal tissue, namely, that of a neurotransmitter. Although the available evidence in support of this hypothesis is slightly less compelling than that for other putative CNS neurotransmitters, important advances have been made, and several excellent reviews have been published in this regard (Green, 1970; Green et al., 1978a; Schwartz et al., 1976; Schwartz, 1977; Snyder and Taylor, 1972). Some of this evidence is as follows: (i) histamine is synthesized locally within the brain and there is a distinct regional distribution in the CNS with the hypothalamus having the highest concentration (Dismukes and Snyder, 1974; Green, 1970); (ii) subcellular fractionation studies have shown that histamine is located in nerve ending fractions (synaptosomes) with some enrichment in synaptic vesicles (Dismukes and Snyder, 1974; Kuhar et al., 1971); (iii) lesioning studies indicate the presence of specific histaminergic tracts in the medial forebrain bundle (Garbarg et al., 1974, 1976); (iv) in brain slices histamine is released by depolarizing stimuli (Verdiere et al., 1974); (v) the turnover rate of histamine resembles that of other CNS neurotransmitters, but is markedly different from the rate observed in mast cells (Dismukes and Snyder, 1974; Martres et al., 1975).

Furthermore, the induction of anesthesia in rats with thiopental results in a pronounced reduction in the turnover of brain histamine (Pollard *et al.*, 1974).

In addition to the anatomical and biochemical evidence cited above, important progress has been made in understanding the nature of histamine receptors in the CNS and the biochemical events associated with the activation of these receptors. As in non-neural tissues (Douglas, 1975), there appear to be at least two types of recognition sites for histamine in the CNS which have been denoted as H_1 and H_2 receptors; the activation of these receptors results in the formation of cyclic $3',5'$-guanosine monophosphate (cyclic GMP) and cyclic $3',5'$-adenosine monophosphate (cyclic AMP), respectively. Thus, like many neurotransmitters (Phillis, 1977), changes in the intraneuronal levels of cyclic nucleotides may be the initial biochemical event within the cell linked to receptor activation.

In this chapter we will be concerned predominantly with discussing the properties of histamine receptors in mammalian neural tissue. The major emphasis has been placed on the electrophysiological, biochemical, and pharmacological characteristics. However, data in the literature which provide insight into the physiological significance of histamine in the CNS are also reviewed.

2.2 CLASSIFICATION OF HISTAMINE RECEPTORS

Two types of receptors (H_1 and H_2), distinguished by their differential sensitivities to agonists and antagonists, have been identified as mediating the cellular actions of histamine (Ash and Schild, 1966; Black *et al.*, 1972). For example, histamine H_1 receptors are sensitive to the agonists, 2-methylhistamine, 2-(pyridyl)ethylamine, and 2-(2-thiazolyl)ethylamine, whereas H_2 receptors show a greater selectivity towards 4-methylhistamine and dimaprit (S[3-(*N,N*-dimethyl-amino)propyl]isothiourea). The classical antihistamines such as pyrilamine, diphenhydramine, and chlorpheniramine are potent H_1 receptor antagonists and H_2 receptors are sensitive to antagonism by compounds such as burimamide, metiamide, and cimetidine. The structures of some of these compounds are illustrated in Fig. 2.1. Both types of receptors have been identified in the mammalian CNS and in the following two sections we discuss in some detail recent developments concerning histamine H_1 and H_2 receptor-mediated cyclic nucleotide formation in neural tissue.

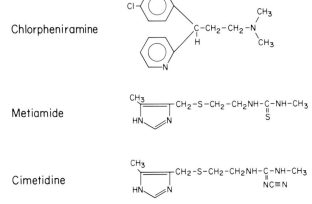

AGONISTS

Histamine

2-Methyl histamine

4-Methyl histamine

Dimaprit

ANTAGONISTS

Pyrilamine

Chlorpheniramine

Metiamide

Cimetidine

Fig. 2.1 Structures of histamine H_1- and H_2-receptor agonists and antagonists.

2.3 BIOCHEMICAL EVENTS COUPLED TO HISTAMINE RECEPTORS

2.3.1 Histamine-stimulated cyclic AMP formation

Histamine may be added to the list of putative neurotransmitters which stimulate cyclic AMP formation in mammalian neural tissue. Using slices of the rat cerebellum, Kakiuchi and Rall (1968) were the first to demonstrate the potent stimulatory effects of histamine. Numerous other studies of this type have confirmed this observation for several mammalian species and for several brain regions (Daly, 1976). The pharmacological characterization of the receptors involved in this response in brain slices has proved difficult and considerable confusion has arisen from these studies. For example, Baudry *et al*. (1975) showed that histamine-stimulated cyclic AMP formation in hippocampal slices of the guinea-pig was partially antagonized by H_1 and H_2 receptor antagonists and that total inhibition occurred in the presence of both. Similar studies by Rogers *et al*. (1975) and Dismukes *et al*. (1976) on guinea-pig cerebral cortical and hippocampal slices also suggested that both H_1 and H_2 receptors could mediate cyclic AMP formation. On the other hand, for cerebral cortical slices of the rat and chicken only H_2 receptor-mediated responses were found (Dismukes and Daly, 1975; Nahorski *et al*., 1974). As discussed by Green *et al*. (1978a, b), the concentrations of H_1 antagonists used in these studies (10^{-6} to 10^{-4} M) were considerably higher than that necessary to block the H_1 receptor (Hill *et al*., 1978; Richelson, 1978a, 1979b; Taylor and Richelson, 1979a; Tran *et al*., 1978). At those high concentrations, H_1 antagonists have significant antagonistic activity at the histamine H_2 receptor (Green *et al*., 1978a, b).

Palacios *et al*. (1978) have suggested that H_1 receptor-mediated cyclic AMP accumulation in brain slices is coupled to the stimulation of H_2-sensitive cyclase. This hypothesis that H_1 receptors mediate cyclic AMP formation has not received support, however, from other neural systems such as the superior cervical ganglion (Study and Greengard, 1978) and cultured mouse neuroblastoma cells (Richelson, 1978a, 1979b; Taylor and Richelson, 1979a) in which H_1 receptor-activation is associated only with cyclic GMP formation. Furthermore, it is clear from studies on the bovine superior cervical ganglion (Study and Greengard, 1978) that histamine-stimulated cyclic AMP formation is linked exclusively to the H_2 receptor.

A histamine-sensitive adenylate cyclase has been identified in homogenates of the guinea-pig hippocampus and has all of the pharmacological properties characteristic of an H_2 receptor-mediated phenomenon (Hegstrand *et al*., 1976; Kanof and Greengard, 1979). The H_2 antagonist metiamide was a competitive inhibitor with an equilibrium dissociation constant (K_B) of 0.87 μM. Pyrilamine, at a concentration of 1 μM (500 × the K_B for the H_1 receptor; Richelson, 1978a), was ineffective. Furthermore, the rank order of potency for histamine agonists was consistent with that expected for an H_2 receptor (Green et al., 1978b; Hegstrand et al., 1976). In non-neural tissues only H_2-sensitive adenylate cyclases have been detected (Verma and McNeill, 1978).

In guinea-pig brain homogenates the specific activity was highest in the hippocampus, neocortex, and corpus striatum, whereas in the rat brain histamine-stimulated adenylate cyclase could be observed only in the neocortex (Hegstrand et al., 1976). Green et al. (1977), however, were able to detect activity in the rat hippocampus.

Kanof et al. (1977) found that histamine-sensitive adenylate cyclase was enriched in the 'nerve ending' fraction of guinea-pig cerebral cortical homogenates, and in subfractions containing primarily synaptic membrane fragments. These findings concerning the non-uniform distribution of histamine-sensitive adenylate cyclase in the mammalian brain have provided some of the strongest evidence that histamine is a neurotransmitter.

Tricyclic antidepressants were competitive antagonists of histamine H_2-stimulated adenylate cyclase activity (Green and Maayani, 1977; Kanof and Greengard, 1978). The values of K_B for this class of psychotherapeutic compounds ranged from 0.55 to 0.05 μM, and those compounds with tertiary side chains (e.g. amitriptyline, doxepin, imipramine and chlorimipramine) were generally more potent than those with secondary amine side chains (Table 2.1). Iprindole and mianserin, neither of which have a measurable effect on the pre-synaptic uptake of norepinephrine or serotonin (Fann et al., 1972; Gluckman and Baum, 1969; Goodlet et al., 1977; Leonard, 1974; Ross et al., 1971), had K_Bs of 0.23 and 0.065 μM, respectively. It was suggested by these investigators that, at least in part, therapeutic effectiveness of the tricyclic antidepressants may be a reflection of their H_2 antagonistic properties. However, many neuroleptics (including the butyrophenone, haloperidol) were more potent than the tricyclic antidepressants at H_2 receptor blockade and there was no correlation between the rank order of potency at H_2 receptor blockade and the therapeutic effectiveness of these compounds.

As discussed in more detail below (Section 2.3.2), most of the tricyclic antidepressants were more potent antagonists at H_1 receptors than at H_2 receptors (Richelson, 1978b, 1979b; Taylor and Richelson, 1979a; Tran et al., 1978). For example, doxepin was approximately several thousand times more potent at H_1 than at H_2 receptors (Table 2.1).

D-Lysergic acid diethylamide (D-LSD) and D-2-bromo-lysergic acid (D-BrLSD) were also potent competitive antagonists of the H_2-stimulated adenylate cyclase of guinea-pig brain homogenates (Green et al., 1977). The K_B for D-LSD was very close to that observed for cimetidine

Table 2.1 Tricyclic antidepressant antagonism of histamine, muscarinic acetylcholine, and α-adrenergic receptors

Compound	K_B (nM)			Muscarinic receptor§ (Mouse neuroblastoma)	K_1 (nM) for α-adrenergic receptor¶ (Rat brain)
	H_1 receptor* (Mouse neuroblastoma)	H_1 receptor[†] (Guinea-pig ileum)	H_2 receptor[‡] (Guinea-pig brain)		
Tertiary amines					
Doxepin	0.03	0.06	160	100	23
Amitriptyline	0.13	0.08	45	24	24
Imipramine	10	1.3	250	140	58
Secondary amines					
Nortriptyline	7	3.2	790	200	71
Protriptyline	35	69	2000	60	280
Desipramine	260	150	1300	420	150

* Richelson, 1978b, 1979b; Taylor and Richelson, 1979a.
† Figge et al., 1979.
‡ Maayani et al., 1978.
§ Richelson and Divinetz-Romero, 1977.
¶ U'Prichard et al., 1978.

($\sim 10^{-6}$ M), whereas D-BrLSD had an affinity ($1/K_B$) which was ten times higher. Based on these observations it was proposed that the antagonism of H_2 receptors may be associated with some of the behavioral effects of D-LSD and D-BrLSD. The hallucinogenic compounds, psilocin and mescaline, however, were inactive as antagonists of histamine-stimulated adenylate cyclase activity and as a group the hallucinogens were less potent antagonists at the H_2 receptor than at the H_1 receptor (Fredrickson and Richelson, 1979).

The structures of D-LSD and H_2 receptor antagonists have obvious similarities (Green *et al.*, 1977) and it has been suggested (Green *et al.*, 1978b) that some of the behavioral reactions associated with the use of H_2 antagonists in therapy (Delaney and Ravey, 1977; McMillen *et al.*, 1978; Menzies-Gow, 1977; Nelson, 1977; Quap, 1978; Robinson and Mulligan, 1977) and those of D-LSD could reflect a common mode of action.

2.3.2 Histamine-stimulated cyclic GMP formation

As discussed above, most of the available evidence would suggest that the initial biochemical event associated with the activation of histamine H_2 receptors in the mammalian nervous system is the activation of adenylate cyclase and the subsequent formation of cyclic AMP. Although the presence of histamine H_1 receptors has been inferred from electrophysiological studies (see Section 2.5) and directly identified with radioligand binding studies (Section 2.4), the biochemical events coupled to the activation of H_1 receptors in the CNS have only been inferred from studies on peripheral sympathetic ganglia and cultured nerve cells.

Study and Greengard (1978) observed that blocks of tissue derived from the bovine superior cervical ganglion responded to histamine exposure with a transient increase in the cyclic GMP levels. The H_1 agonist, 2-(2-aminoethyl)thiazole, was also effective, and the response could be competitively blocked by low concentrations of H_1 receptor antagonists. The ED_{50} for histamine was 6 μM which is comparable to that observed for histamine-stimulated cyclic GMP formation in neuroblastoma cells (see below).

Based on electrophysiological studies of the rabbit superior cervical ganglion (Brimble and Wallis, 1973), it appears that the activation of H_1 receptors is coupled to an excitatory post-ganglionic response. The logical inference is that the postsynaptic, excitatory effects of histamine are mediated by an increase in the intracellular levels of cyclic GMP. It should be emphasized that this conclusion is based on the correlation of information derived from independent test systems. Unequivocal proof would require a more rigorous quantitative and temporal analysis of the biochemical and electrophysiological events.

In spite of these reservations, the above considerations concerning the relationships between cyclic nucleotide formation and electrophysiological events are strikingly similar to data derived for the effects of acetylcholine and dopamine on the superior cervical ganglion by Greengard and co-workers (Kebabian *et al.*, 1975; Greengard and Kebabian, 1974). These investigators demonstrated that dopamine caused an increase in the cyclic AMP content of postsynaptic neurons which was associated with an inhibitory effect on synaptic transmission and that the activation of muscarinic acetylcholine receptors resulted in cyclic GMP formation and excitation of postsynaptic neurons. Thus, both H_2 and dopamine receptors mediated cyclic AMP formation and electrical inhibition, whereas H_1 and muscarinic acetylcholine receptors were linked to cyclic GMP formation and electrical excitation.

As is discussed in Section 2.5, microiontophoretic studies showed that histamine depressed the activity of most neurons in the cortex and hippocampus by action on H_2 receptors (Haas and Wolf, 1977). Interestingly, it was these areas of the brain that were enriched for histamine H_2-sensitive adenylate cyclase (Hegstrand *et al.*, 1976). Histamine excited many single neurons of the hypothalamus (Haas and Wolf, 1977), but it is not certain whether this was an H_1 receptor-mediated phenomenon and there is no evidence in the literature to indicate that histamine stimulates cyclic GMP formation in the intact brain.

Studies on the nature of the histamine H_1 receptor have been greatly facilitated by the use of neuronal cell cultures. Mouse neuroblastoma cells (clone N1E-115), which exhibit many biochemical and electrophysiological properties of differentiated neurons *in vivo* (Richelson, 1979a), responded to histamine exposure with a rapid and transient increase in the intracellular levels of cyclic GMP (Richelson, 1978a). Like that of the superior cervical ganglion (Study and Greengard, 1978), the effect was clearly mediated via H_1 receptors (Fig. 2.2) and dependent on the availability of extracellular calcium ions. The K_A for histamine and the H_1 receptor was 8 μM for mouse neuroblastoma cells (Taylor and Richelson, 1979b), a value similar to that for histamine and its receptor in guinea-pig ileum (Furchgott, 1966).

We have extensively studied the properties of the histamine H_1 receptors of these cells and have found that many psychotropic drugs are potent competitive inhibitors of H_1 receptor-mediated cyclic GMP formation (Richelson, 1978b, 1979b; Taylor and Richelson, 1979a). Equilibrium dissociation constants (K_B) for some of these antagonists are presented in Table 2.1. The tricyclic antidepressant, doxepin, was the most potent H_1 antagonist tested with a $K_B = 3 \times 10^{-11}$ M. Amitriptyline, another tricyclic antidepressant, was nearly as potent as doxepin, and both compounds were considerably more potent than the commonly used antihistamine,

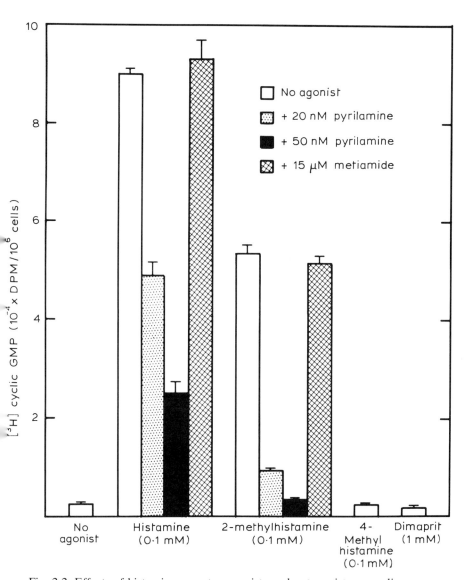

Fig. 2.2 Effects of histamine receptor agonists and antagonists on cyclic [³H]-GMP formation by cultured nerve cells. Mouse neuroblastoma cells (clone N1E-115; subculture 15) were assayed for cyclic [³H]-GMP formation as described by Taylor and Richelson (1979b). The cells were incubated for 30 min with antagonists prior to the addition of agonists for 30 s. There were approximately 2×10^5 cells per assay. Each condition was determined in triplicate and the vertical bars represent the standard error of the mean.

diphenhydramine (K_B = 20 nM). As a group the tertiary amine tricyclics tended to be more potent than the secondary amine drugs and the tertiary amine parent compound was always more potent than its secondary amine derivative. The antipsychotic drug clozapine and the anti-Parkinsonism drug benztropine were also potent antihistamines with K_Bs of 0.4 and 0.3 nM, respectively. For the tricyclic antidepressants, most were more potent as antagonists of H_1 receptor-mediated cyclic GMP formation than as antagonists of the uptake of biogenic amines, histamine H_2 receptors (Green and Maayani, 1977; Kanof and Greengard, 1978), α-adrenergic receptors (U'Prichard *et al.*, 1978) or muscarinic acetylcholine receptors (Richelson, 1977; Richelson and Divinetz-Romero, 1977) (Table 2.1).

In order to validate the potential applicability of these results to H_1 receptors of other systems, we studied the effects of tricyclic antidepressants in a bioassay for H_1 receptors, namely histamine-induced contraction of the isolated guinea-pig ileum (Schild, 1947). The K_B data for the tricyclic antidepressants and the histamine H_1 receptor obtained from the mouse neuroblastoma assay of cyclic GMP formation (Richelson, 1978b, 1979b; Taylor and Richelson, 1979a) and those from the guinea-pig ileum assay (Figge *et al.*, 1979) showed a significant correlation (Table 2.1). These data support our contention that the tricyclic antidepressants are, in general, potent H_1 receptor antagonists. In addition, the correlation also suggests that in at least one sense the H_1 receptors of the mouse neuroblastoma cells are biochemically similar to those of the guinea-pig ileum.

The specific binding of [^{3}H]pyrilamine to brain tissue was reported recently by two laboratories (Hill *et al.*, 1978; Tran *et al.*, 1978). In the studies by Tran *et al.* (1978), the tricyclic antidepressants were found to be very potent inhibitors of specific [^{3}H]pyrilamine binding. Their calculated inhibition constants agree very well with the data described above for the neuroblastoma cells and guinea-pig ileum only for the lower affinity compounds (imipramine, protriptyline, and desipramine). For the higher affinity compounds (doxepin, amitriptyline, and nortriptyline), we obtained affinities ($1/K_B$) at least one order of magnitude greater than those found by Tran *et al.* One possible explanation for these discrepant results may involve the relationship of the K_B to the concentration of receptor (R) and of the radioactively labeled ligand (L) in the binding assay (Chang *et al.*, 1975; Jacobs *et al.*, 1975). Only when $K_B \gg R + L$ will the apparent K_B approximate the true K_B in a binding assay. When these conditions are not met then the apparent K_B becomes a function of R and L and will be overestimated. It is technically difficult because of the limitations on the magnitude of the specific activity of the radioligand to achieve these conditions for high-affinity compounds such as doxepin and amitriptyline.

It is unlikely, however, that the H_1 receptor antagonist properties of the tricyclic antidepressants explains the antidepressant effects of these drugs

(Sigg, 1968). Thus, although amitriptyline is nearly 300 times more potent than protriptyline at blocking H_1 receptors, both are equally effective as antidepressants (Morris and Beck, 1974) and their optimal plasma therapeutic concentrations (in molarity) are nearly identical (Biggs, 1978; Whyte *et al.*, 1976; Ziegler *et al.*, 1977). One of the most prominent CNS effects of antihistamines, however, is sedation, the symptoms of which include drowsiness, inability to concentrate, dizziness, ataxia, and deep sleep (Douglas, 1975; Jick, 1975). Of the six tricyclic antidepressants that we studied, doxepin and amitriptyline are considered the most sedating and desipramine and protriptyline the least (Hollister, 1978; Kessler, 1978). Thus, the apparent sedative properties of these compounds correlated reasonably well with their rank order of potency at the H_1 receptor.

As mentioned above, certain hallucinogens are also competitive antagonists of H_1 receptor-mediated cyclic GMP formation in neuroblastoma cells (Fredrickson and Richelson, 1979). The lysergic acid derivatives were most potent ($K_B = 0.12$ μM for D-LSD), the indolalkylamines occupied an intermediate position, and the phenylalkylamines the least potent. This rank order approximates the order of *in vivo* potencies. The antagonism by hallucinogens at the H_1 receptor of mouse neuroblastoma cells appears to be more potent than that observed at histamine H_2-receptors (Green *et al.*, 1977).

It is quite certain, however, that the hallucinogens have multiple sites of action within the CNS and interact with serotonin, dopamine (Burt *et al.*, 1976), and norepinephrine (Pieri *et al.*, 1978). Yet results do not clearly favor any single receptor as the site of psychotomimetic effects. Such confusion reflects, in part, a lack of information on the structural units and neurotransmitter systems which mediate human behavior.

2.3.3 Regulation of histamine H_1 receptors

The prolonged exposure of a receptor to an agonist (e.g. a neurotransmitter) can cause the development of receptor subsensitivity or desensitization which can be specific (i.e. affecting only one receptor on a cell) or nonspecific (i.e. affecting all receptors on a cell). This ability of receptors to apparently regulate their sensitivity to stimulation may have important consequences in the CNS and may explain in part the phenomenon of cellular tolerance to certain drugs. In addition, the therapeutic effectiveness of some psychotropic drugs may involve long-term changes in receptor sensitivity. Our interest in the effects of psychotropic drugs on histamine H_1 receptors on neuroblastoma cells led us to study the desensitization of these receptors. This section summarizes these results (Taylor and Richelson, 1979b).

Densensitization of the H_1 receptor left largely unaffected the muscarinic

receptor (Richelson, 1978c) and was specific for H_1 agonists whose potencies paralleled their ability to activate H_1 receptors. This specific desensitization was associated with a decrease in the maximum response for cyclic
GMP formation, a result which suggested a loss of agonist binding sites.
The ED_{50} for H_1 receptor-mediated cyclic GMP formation remained
unchanged. In addition, the ED_{50}s for stimulation and desensitization by
histamine closely approximated the equilibrium dissociation constant for
histamine and the H_1 receptor. These results suggest that desensitization
occurred at the level of the H_1 receptor and that receptor occupation by
agonist molecules and receptor 'activation' were required for desensitization.

The rate at which desensitization developed was quite rapid and dependent on the concentration of histamine used to sensitize (at 50 μM,
$t_{1/2}$ = 5 min; at 100 μM, $t_{1/2}$ = 2 min). This observation offered additional
evidence that desensitization of the H_1 receptor required the formation of
an agonist–receptor complex, the concentration of which determined the
rate of receptor inactivation.

$$HA + R \rightleftharpoons HA - R(\text{active}) \rightarrow HA - R'(\text{inactive}) \quad \text{Scheme 1}$$

When the cells were washed free of histamine, there was a return of sensitivity to histamine as determined by H_1 receptor-mediated cyclic GMP
formation. The time course for recovery was prolonged and independent of
the concentration of histamine used to densensitize ($t_{1/2}$ = 8 min). It would
seem from these results that the mechanism is not a simple reversal of the
above model (Scheme 1). The data appear to be most compatible with a
cyclic model for desensitization and recovery (Gosselin, 1977; Katz and
Thesleff, 1957; Rang and Ritter, 1969):

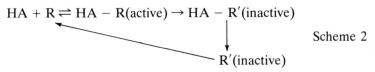

Scheme 2

According to this model (Scheme 2) the rate of recovery of receptor sensitivity is not dependent on the concentration of the agonist–receptor complex.

The nature of R' for the H_1 receptor is not known. For some receptor
systems, R' represents an actual decrease in the population of binding sites
(Mukherjee and Lefkowitz, 1976; Strittmatter *et al.*, 1977). For the H_1
receptor of mouse neuroblastoma cells, however, we have been unable to
detect any change in the specific binding of the H_1 antagonist, [^{3}H]-
pyrilamine, after rapid desensitization of cells to histamine. Whether or not
desensitization results in a decrease in the number of agonist binding sites
is unknown at the present time.

2.4 RECEPTOR BINDING STUDIES

Classically, the properties of drug, hormone, or neurotransmitter receptors have been inferred from an analysis of receptor-mediated biological events (e.g. contraction of muscle, ion fluxes; cyclic nucleotide formation). However, with the recent development of radioligand binding methodology (Hollenberg and Cuatrecasas, 1975; Williams and Lefkowitz, 1978; Yamamura *et al.*, 1978) it has been possible to examine directly the interactions of these compounds with their cellular receptors. When properly used, this technique has provided considerable information about the recognition properties of receptors and how these properties relate to receptor-mediated biological responses.

Progress in the identification and characterization of histamine receptors in the nervous system is in its infancy and at the time of writing this chapter (May 1979) fewer than ten papers have been published on this subject. Nevertheless, much is now known about the kinetics of antagonist binding to the histamine H_1 receptor in mammalian brain tissue. These receptors in the mammalian CNS have been successfully identified with the H_1 antagonist, [^{3}H]pyrilamine (Chang *et al.*, 1978, 1979; Hill and Young, 1978; Hill *et al.*, 1978; Tran *et al.*, 1978). H_1 receptor-specific binding of [^{3}H]pyrilamine to crude membrane fractions of the guinea-pig was reversible and saturable. The equilibrium dissociation constant (K_B) for binding was in the range 2–4 nM which was in accordance with the K_Bs obtained for antagonism of histamine H_1 receptor-mediated cyclic GMP formation by mouse neuroblastoma cells (Richelson, 1978b, 1979b; Taylor and Richelson, 1979a) and by the bovine superior cervical ganglia (Study and Greengard, 1978), and for antagonism of histamine-induced contractions of the guinea-pig ileum (Hill *et al.*, 1977). Estimates of the maximum number of binding sites (B_{max}) were variable and ranged from approximately 100 to 350 pmol/g protein.

The K_Bs determined from the inhibition of [^{3}H]pyrilamine binding by histamine, classical H_1 antagonists (Chang *et al.*, 1978; Tran *et al.*, 1978), and neuroleptics (Chang *et al.*, 1979; Hill and Young, 1978) were generally quite close to those values obtained from biological assay systems such as H_1 receptor-mediated cyclic GMP formation (Richelson, 1978b, 1979b; Taylor and Richelson, 1979a) and histamine-induced contractions of the guinea-pig ileum (Hill *et al.*, 1977; Figge *et al.*, 1979). The (D) isomer of chlorpheniramine was 100 times more potent in inhibiting [^{3}H]-pyrilamine binding than the (L) isomer indicating the stereoselective nature of the H_1 receptor. Similar results have been obtained for the antagonism of H_1 receptor-mediated cyclic GMP formation by mouse neuroblastoma cells (Taylor and Richelson, unpublished observations).

It should be emphasized that one important aspect of radioligand binding studies, namely the comparison of binding kinetics with biological activity in the same tissue (Hollenberg and Cuatrecasas, 1975; Yamamura *et al.*, 1978) has not been realized for brain H_1 receptors. This problem exists because of the current lack of a biological response to H_1 receptor activation in the mammalian brain. Nevertheless, as discussed above, the kinetic constants derived from the binding studies favorably compare (except as noted above in Section 2.3.2) with those derived from H_1 receptor-mediated biological responses in the superior cervical ganglion (Study and Greengard, 1978), cultured nerve cells (Richelson, 1978b, 1979b; Taylor and Richelson, 1979a), and the guinea-pig ileum (Hill *et al.*, 1977; Figge *et al.*, 1979). Thus, the data obtained from these biological models may be applicable to the CNS.

Chang *et al.* (1979) observed a distinct species specificity for the anatomical distribution of [^{3}H]pyrilamine binding sites (Table 2.2). In the bovine and human brain the highest levels of binding were observed in the cerebral cortex, whereas in the rat the highest concentration of binding sites was observed in the hypothalamus. In the guinea-pig the highest levels of binding were in the cerebellum. The binding affinity of [^{3}H]pyrilamine was also species specific. For example, the K_B for [^{3}H]pyrilamine at the H_1 receptor of the guinea-pig whole brain was about 0.5 nM, whereas K_Bs of about 1 and 4 nM were observed for the human and rat brains, respectively. The maximum number of binding sites for the whole brain was similar for all three species and there was no evidence of co-operative interactions. The higher affinity binding of [^{3}H]pyrilamine to the guinea-pig brain was attributed by these investigators to an enhanced rate of association and

Table 2.2 Regional distribution of [^{3}H]pyrilamine binding[*]

Region	% of hypothalamus			
	Rat	Calf	Human	Guinea-pig
Hypothalamus	100	100	100	100
Brain stem	90	30	30–50	80
Midbrain	80	50	100	100
Cerebral cortex	80	120–300	200–480	90
Thalamus	70	100	90	170
Hippocampus	60	90	170	130
Basal ganglia	60	140	90	50
Cerebellum	50	170	40	250

[*] Chang *et al.*, 1978, 1979.

a slower dissociation rate. There was substantial species specific variation in the potencies of some H_1 receptor antagonists whereas for others there was no difference; a result which is difficult to explain. Triprolidine and D-chlorpheniramine were considerably more potent in the guinea-pig brain than in rat brain. Similarly, chlorpromazine, clozapine, and promazine had higher affinities for receptors in the guinea-pig and human brains as compared to those found for these drugs in the rat. It is interesting that the tricyclic antidepressants, which are some of the most potent H_1 antagonists known (Richelson, 1978b; Tran *et al.*, 1978) showed very little species-dependent variation in affinity. The antagonism of [^{3}H]-pyrilamine binding by histamine itself also failed to demonstrate species variation. As stated by Tran *et al.* (1978), these findings suggest the possibility that subtypes of the H_1 receptor exist.

Characterization of the histamine H_2 receptor with the use of radioligand binding studies has been reported only recently (Burkard, 1978). [^{3}H]-cimetidine bound to guinea-pig brain homogenates in a saturable fashion with a K_B of about 40 nM. Although regional variations in specific binding were apparent, the differences were not marked. For example, binding in the three highest regions, the midbrain, cortex and hippocampus, was not more than two-fold greater than that observed in the lowest region, the corpus striatum. These results were only partially compatible with the regional distribution of H_2-stimulated adenylate cyclase of the guinea-pig brain where activity was highest in the hippocampus, followed by the cortex and corpus striatum. An H_2-stimulated adenylate cyclase could not be detected in the midbrain (Hegstrand *et al.*, 1976).

Although the binding of [^{3}H]cimetidine exhibited some of the properties of valid receptor binding (i.e. saturability, tissue specificity), a comparison of the ligand binding data with those from biological assays yielded divergent results. The K_B for cimetidine (40 nM) binding from the above report was much lower than that reported for the inhibition of H_2-stimulated adenylate cyclase ($K_B = 1000$ nM). Furthermore, the tricyclic antidepressant, amitriptyline, was about 100 times more potent as an antagonist of histamine-sensitive adenylate cyclase than was cimetidine (Kanof and Greengard, 1978), but cimetidine was approximately 2000 times more potent in the binding assay. The K_1 ($\sim$80 μM) for histamine as determined from its IC_{50} for antagonism of [^{3}H]cimetidine binding was ten times its K_A for the stimulation of adenylate cyclase. These comparisons underline the need to combine radioligand binding studies with biological studies of a receptor.

In another report, Rehavi and Sokolovsky (1978) observed saturable binding of [^{3}H]amitriptyline to H_2 receptors of the mouse brain. The K_B was 72 mM which was very close to the value obtained from the antagonism of histamine-sensitive adenylate cyclase (Green and Maayani, 1977;

Kanof and Greengard, 1978). Further characterization of the H_2 receptor with this ligand has not been reported.

Palacios *et al.* (1978) recently reported on the binding of [^{3}H]histamine to homogenates of rat brain. A single high-affinity binding site was observed (K_A = 9.4 nM). The regional differences in [^{3}H]histamine binding did not correlate with the distribution of histamine H_1 (Chang *et al.*, 1979) or H_2 receptors (Burkard, 1978). Furthermore, it should be emphasized that the K_A for [^{3}H]histamine binding (9.4 nM) differs significantly (100 to 1000 times lower) from that observed for histamine in binding studies with [^{3}H]pyrilamine (Chang *et al.*, 1979; Tran *et al.*, 1978) and [^{3}H]cimetidine (Burkard, 1978), and in studies of histamine-stimulated cyclic GMP formation (Richelson, 1978a,b, 1979b; Taylor and Richelson, 1979a) and histamine-stimulated cyclic AMP formation (Kanof and Greengard, 1978). The reasons for these discrepant results are not apparent and resolution of this problem awaits further experimentation.

2.5 ELECTROPHYSIOLOGY

As shown in Table 2.3, the microiontophoretic application of histamine depressed neuronal firing in most brain regions. A major exception occurred in the hypothalamus where histamine appeared to function as an excitatory neurotransmitter. Among those cells of the hypothalamus which were excited were those of the supraoptic nucleus and those in the region of the ventromedial nuclei. These latter observations are of interest because of the known effects that histamine has on the secretion of antidiuretic hormone from the supraoptic nucleus and on releasing-hormone secretion from the ventromedial hypothalamus.

In the rabbit superior cervical ganglion (Brimble and Wallis, 1973), histamine had both excitatory and inhibitory actions. The former effect was blocked by relatively high concentrations (2.5 μM) of the H_1 antagonist, pyrilamine, whereas the inhibitory response was antagonized by the H_2 antagonist, burimamide. Similar observations have been made on the cerebral ganglion of the mollusc, *Aplysia californica* (Carpenter and Gaubatz, 1975). These observations suggested that the excitatory and inhibitory actions of histamine are mediated by H_1 and H_2 receptors, respectively.

In mammalian brain, the microiontophoretic application of the H_2 agonists, betazole and 4-methylhistamine resulted in an inhibition of single neurons (Haas and Bucher, 1975; Haas and Wolf, 1977). Moreover, metiamide, an H_2 antagonist, blocked the depressant actions of histamine in the cortex and hippocampus. The H_1 antagonist pyrilamine, however, failed to show any selective antagonism of the excitant or depressant actions of histamine in the mammalian CNS (Haas *et al.*, 1975). This result

Table 2.3 Electrophysiological effects of histamine

Region	Species	Response	Receptor type	Reference
Cerebral cortex	Rat, cat	Inhibition, excitation (minor)	H_2	Haas and Bucher, 1975; Haas and Wolf, 1977
Midbrain central gray	Rat, cat	Inhibition	—	Haas and Wolf, 1977
Thalamus	Rat, cat	Inhibition	—	Haas and Wolf, 1977
Brain stem	Cat	Inhibition		Galindo et al., 1967; Haas and Wolf, 1977; Haas et al., 1973
Hypothalamus	Rat, cat	Excitation, inhibition (minor)	—	Haas et al., 1975; Renaud, 1975
Hippocampus	Rat	Inhibition	H_2	Haas and Wolf, 1977
Spinal cord	Cat	Inhibition	—	Phillis et al., 1968
Cerebellum	Rat	Inhibition		
Superior cervical ganglion	Rabbit	Inhibition, excitation	H_2 H_1	Brimble and Wallis, 1973

was attributed to the local anesthetic properties of the classical H_1 antagonists. It is interesting to note that areas of the brain where histamine had a marked inhibitory action via H_2 receptors, namely, the cerebral cortex and hippocampus (Haas and Wolf, 1977), were also those areas which were enriched for histamine H_2-sensitive adenylate cyclase (Hegstrand *et al.*, 1976).

These data provide considerable support for the existence of specific synaptic receptors for histamine in the mammalian CNS. Nevertheless, the inability to localize those synaptic regions where histamine is thought to have a neurotransmitter function leaves a significant gap in our understanding of the synaptic actions of histamine. When such a synapse is identified, the electrophysiological actions of microiontophoretically applied histamine can be compared with that of endogenous histamine released by stimulation of the presynaptic neuron.

2.6. PHYSIOLOGICAL EFFECTS OF HISTAMINE IN THE CNS

The biochemical, pharmacological, and electrophysiological studies just discussed indicate that histamine receptors are present in the mammalian brain. The physiological significance of these receptors, however, is only partially understood and most of the evidence relating histamine receptors to physiological processes has been restricted to the hypothalamus and the medial forebrain bundle (e.g. arousal reactions). Virtually nothing is known concerning the consequence of histamine-receptor stimulation in other regions of the CNS. In the subsequent sections evidence is presented to show that histamine may play an important role in the homeostatic mechanisms of the hypothalamus, i.e. regulation of the sympathetic nervous system and endocrine system. In this regard, however, it should be emphasized that this function probably involves many other neurotransmitters as well. The interaction of histamine with other neurotransmitter systems, however, has not been explored as yet.

2.6.1 Neuroendocrine regulation

Histamine, caused the secretion of adrenocortical stimulating hormone (ACTH) after systemic injection (Fortier, 1951; Makara *et al.*, 1970; McCann, 1957; Ondo and Kitay, 1972), and stimulated prolactin secretion in rats after systemic or intraventricular administration (Arakelian and Libertun, 1977; Donoso and Bannza, 1976; Goodman *et al.*, 1976; Libertun and McCann, 1976; Rivier and Vale, 1977). The pharmacological specificity of the former effect is not known but in most cases the facilitation of prolactin release appeared to be mediated through H_1 receptors.

Arakelian and Libertun (1977) found that intraventricular administration of the H_2 receptor agonist, 4-methylhistamine, antagonized prolactin secretion in response to sucking. Furthermore, the H_2 antagonist, metiamide, stimulated prolactin release in non-suckling mother rats. It was proposed by these investigators that H_2 receptor activation inhibited prolactin release, whereas H_1 receptor activation was associated with mechanisms facilitating prolactin secretion. This concept has received support from several clinical reports. For example, gynecomastia has been reported to occur in male patients receiving chronic therapy with cimetidine (Delle Fave *et al.*, 1977; Hall, 1976; Sharpe and Hawkins, 1977). In addition, the parenteral administration of large doses of cimetidine stimulated prolactin secretion in man (Burland *et al.*, 1978; Carlson and Ippoliti, 1977; Daubresse, 1978; Delitala *et al.*, 1978).

Histamine has also been reported to facilitate K^+-induced release of thyrotropin releasing hormone from slices of the mediobasal hypothalamus of the rat (Charli *et al.*, 1978). Cimetidine, at a concentration of 1 μM completely antagonized this effect, but the effect of H_1 antagonists was not reported.

Histamine may also be involved in the hypothalamic regulation of gonadal function. Orr and Quay (1975), for example, showed that castration of male rats resulted in an increase in the hypothalamic levels of histamine.

Neurosecretory neurons of the posterior pituitary which release antidiuretic hormone (ADH) into the systemic circulation have their origin in the supraoptic nucleus of the hypothalamus. Histamine, given either intraventricularly or by local application into the supraoptic nucleus, evoked an antidiuretic response which was accompanied by an increase in the blood levels of ADH (Bennett and Pert, 1974; Bhargava *et al.*, 1973; Dogterom *et al.*, 1976; Hoffman and Schmid, 1978; Tuomisto and Eriksson, 1979) indicating that histamine in the hypothalamus may participate in the regulation of ADH release. Histamine-stimulated antidiuresis could be blocked by prior treatment with the H_1 antagonist pyrilamine (Bennett and Pert, 1974; Hoffman and Schmid, 1978). It should also be recalled (Section 2.5) that locally applied histamine increased the rate of action potential discharge of the neurosecretory neurons (Haas *et al.*, 1975).

The activation of thirst mechanisms can also be evoked by the intraventricular injection of histamine (Gerald and Maickel, 1972) or by local application to the anterior-perifornical, lateral, preoptic and anterior-ventral regions of the hypothalamus (Leibowitz, 1973). The pharmacological specificity of this phenomenon also appeared to involve the H_1 receptor.

It is clear on the basis of this evidence and that reviewed in Section 2.6.4 (Cardiovascular regulation) that putative histaminergic systems in the hypothalamus could be involved in generalized homeostatic mechanisms responsible for the regulation of blood pressure. Such mechanisms include participation in the CNS regulation of both the humoral (ADH release) and neural (thirst activation and sympathetic discharge) components of pressor responses.

2.6.2 Ingestive behavior

The injection of histamine into the lateral cerebral ventricle of the cat evoked a profound and long-lasting suppression of ingestive behavior which was blocked by oral pretreatment with H_1 receptor antagonists (Clineschmidt and Lotti, 1973). Histaminergic involvement in ingestive behavior was further documented by the observation that cyproheptadine, a very potent H_1 antagonist (Richelson, 1979b) has appetite-stimulating properties and has been used clinically in this regard (Benady, 1970; Bergen, 1964; Goldberg *et al.*, 1979). Furthermore, the potent H_1 receptor blocking activity of the tricyclic antidepressants and neuroleptics (Richelson, 1979b; Taylor and Richelson, 1979a). may play a role in the appetite-stimulating effects of these compounds (Brown and Brown, 1967; Nakra *et al.*, 1977; Paykel *et al.*, 1973; Robinson *et al.*, 1975; Slettin *et al.*, 1967).

2.6.3 Thermoregulation

Histaminergic neurotransmission may be involved in thermoregulation. The local application of histamine into the rostral area of the hypothalamus elicited a hypothermic response which was blocked by the H_1 antagonist, chlorcyclazine (Brezenoff and Lomax, 1970), whereas a decrease in body temperature subsequent to the intraventricular administration was not sensitive to H_1 receptor antagonism (Shaw, 1971). Hypothermia can also be evoked by the systemic administration of the histamine precursor, histidine (Cox *et al.*, 1976; Green *et al.*, 1975a; Lomax *et al.*, 1975). This response could be blocked by the intraventricular injection of H_2 antagonists, but H_1 antagonists had no effect (Green *et al.*, 1975b).

Based on these observations, the existence of two histaminergic thermoregulatory pathways were proposed (Green *et al.*, 1975b). The first, apparently involving H_1 receptor-mediated mechanisms, is associated with rostral hypothalamic centers, whereas H_2 receptors are associated with another pathway near the third ventricle. It has been further hypothesized that the former pathway is involved in establishing the threshold for heat loss mechanisms, and the latter is involved with pathways mediating heat loss (Cox and Lomas, 1977; Cox *et al.*, 1975).

Indirect evidence for histamine receptors associated with thermoregulation has been derived from the systemic administration of drugs known to have H_2 antagonistic properties. For example, several anecdotal reports of a hyperthermic response to the H_2 antagonist, cimetidine, have been published in the clinical literature (McLoughlin *et al.*, 1978; Ramboer, 1978). In addition, Green *et al.* (1978b) have suggested that the hyperthermic effects occasionally seen in humans (Gorodetzky and Isbell, 1964; Klock *et al.*, 1975) with D-LSD ingestion results from the antagonism of H_2 receptors in the CNS.

2.6.4 Cardiovascular regulation

Given intraventricularly, histamine elicited a transient increase in blood pressure in the anesthetized rat (Delbarre *et al.*, 1974; Finch and Hicks, 1975, 1977) and cat (Trendelenburg, 1957; Delbarre *et al.*, 1974, 1976). This effect was apparently due to a centrally mediated increase in sympathetic nervous system activity (Delbarre *et al.*, 1974; Hoffman and Schmid, 1978). In the unanesthetized cat or rat the intraventricular administration of histamine elicited only a pressor response accompanied by bradycardia (Finch and Hicks, 1976a,b; Hoffman and Schmid, 1978). Pretreatment with the H_1 antagonist, pyrilamine, effectively antagonized the hypertensive response to intraventricular histamine, but the H_2 antagonist metiamide had no effect. Similar results were also obtained by the localized injection of histamine into both the anterior and posterior hypothalamus (Finch and Hicks, 1977). Ventromedial, lateral hypothalamic or anterior preoptic injections failed to evoke a cardiovascular response. As in the cat, this response was antagonized by H_1 receptor blockade, but both 2- and 4-methylhistamine H_1 and H_2 receptor agonists, respectively, were equally effective in eliciting a pressor response.

The studies described above indicate that histaminergic neurotransmission in the CNS involving H_1 receptors could be associated with cardiovascular pressor mechanisms. Recently, data have been reported which would suggest that H_2 receptors in the CNS mediate a decrease in heart rate and blood pressure. This idea has developed indirectly from a series of studies centered around the central effects of the antihypertensive agent, clonidine.

The hypotensive actions of clonidine were thought to result from the stimulation of α-adrenergic receptors in the brain (Kobinger, 1975). Clonidine, however, has been shown to stimulate H_2 receptors in the brain (Audigier *et al.*, 1976) and gastric mucosa (Karppanen and Westermann, 1973), and recently there have been several reports (Finch *et al.*, 1977; Karppanen *et al.*, 1976; Paakkari *et al.*, 1976) which showed that the hypotensive effects of clonidine in rats can be blocked by H_2 receptor antagonists such as metiamide and cimetidine. Finch and Hicks (1976b), however, were unable to confirm this observation for cats. Although these studies imply a role for H_2 receptors in centrally mediating depressor responses, the intraventricular or intrahypothalamic injections of histamine have never been shown to evoke this effect.

2.6.5 Arousal

In therapeutic doses, the most common side effect of H_1 antagonists is sedation (Beavan, 1976a,b; Douglas, 1975). Furthermore, there is a correlation between antagonistic potency at the H_1 receptor and the sedative properties of tricyclic antidepressants (see Section 2.3.2) (Richelson, 1978b, 1979b; Taylor and Richelson, 1978a), suggesting that H_1 receptors may be associated with mechanisms affecting the level of arousal. Consistent with this idea are the observations of Monnier *et al.* (1970), who showed that either intraventricular or systemic histamine administration induced an arousal reaction in rabbits and cats.

2.6.6 Histamine H_1 and muscarinic acetylcholine receptors

Activation of muscarinic acetylcholine or histamine H_1 receptors of various cell types (e.g. smooth muscle, mouse neuroblastoma cells, bovine superior cervical ganglion), causes similar effects (e.g. muscle contraction, cyclic GMP formation). In addition, H_1 receptor antagonists commonly have antimuscarinic properties as well (Bovet, 1950; Van den Brink and Lien, 1977). The time course for the stimulation of cyclic GMP formation is essentially the same after activation of either muscarinic acetylcholine or histamine H_1 receptors of mouse neuroblastoma clone N1E-115 (Richelson, 1977, 1978a) or the bovine superior cervical ganglion (Kebabian *et al.*, 1975; Study and Greengard, 1978); and the dependence of this cyclic GMP synthesis on calcium ions in the external medium is also similar for the two receptors. The characteristics of the specific desensitization of the two receptor-mediated responses in mouse neuroblastoma cells are also very similar (Richelson, 1978c; Taylor and Richelson, 1979a,b). In addition, the time curves for the recovery of sensitivity to histamine and carbamylcholine in neuroblastoma cells that were desensitized to the two agonists were essentially superimposable.

Because of these similarities we tested the possibility that the regional distributions of H_1 and muscarinic receptors in the same preparation of rat brain may be similar (Taylor and Richelson, unpublished observations). In accordance with previously published data derived from different brain preparations (Chang *et al.*, 1979; Yamamura and Snyder, 1974; Yamamura *et al.*, 1974), however, there were some differences in the density of these receptors. For example, the binding of [^{3}H]QNB to muscarinic receptors was highest in the corpus striatum and cerebrum, and lowest in the hypothalamus, medulla, and cerebellum. The thalamus showed intermediate values. On the other hand, the density of histamine H_1 receptors as detected with [^{3}H]pyrilamine, was low in the corpus striatum and the cerebral cortex. The highest H_1 receptor binding was observed for the medulla and hypothalamus. Thus, although the densities of these receptors varied independently from region to region, in all brain regions both receptors were present, in accordance with results for mouse neuroblastoma cells and for the superior cervical ganglion. All these data suggest functional and structural similarities between histamine H_1 and muscarinic acetylcholine receptors.

REFERENCES

Arakelian, M.C. and Libertun, C. (1977), *Endocrin.*, **100**, 890–895.

Ash, A.S.F. and Schild, H.O. (1966), *Brit. J. Pharmacol.*, **27**, 427–439.

Audigier, Y., Virion, A. and Schwartz, J.C. (1976), *Nature (London)*, **262**, 307–308.

Baudry, M., Martres, M.P. and Schwartz, J.C. (1975), *Nature*, **253**, 362–363.

Beaven, M.A. (1976a), *N. Eng. J. Med.*, **294**, 30–36.

Beaven, M.A. (1976b), *N. Eng. J. Med.*, **294**, 320–330.

Benady, D.R. (1970), *Brit. J. Psychiat.*, **117**, 681–682.

Bennett, C.T. and Pert, A. (1974), *Brain Res.*, **78**, 151–156.

Bergen, S.S., Jr. (1964), *Amer. J. Dis. Child.*, **108**, 270–273.

Bhargava, K.P., Kulshrestha, V.K., Santhakumri, G. and Srivastava, Y.P. (1973), *Brit. J. Pharmacol.*, **47**, 700–706.

Biggs, J.T. (1978), *Hospital Practice*, Feb., 79–84.

Black, J.W., Duncan, W.A.M., Durant, C.J., Ganellin, C.R. and Parsons, E.M. (1972), *Nature*, **236**, 385–390.

Bovet, D. (1950), *Ann. N.Y. Acad. Sci.*, **50**, 1089–1126.

Brezenoff, H.E. and Lomax, P. (1970), *Experientia*, **26**, 51–52.

Brimble, M.J. and Wallis, D.I. (1973), *Nature*, **246**, 156–158.

Brown, J.H. and Brown, T.D. (1967), *Canad. Med. Assoc. J.*, **97**, 1361.

Burkard, W.P. (1978), *Eur. J. Pharmacol.*, **50**, 449–450.

Burland, W.L., Gleadle, R.I., Lee, R.M., Rowley-Jones, D. and Groom, G.V. (1978), *Brit. Med. J.*, **1**, 717.

Burt, D.R., Creese, I. and Snyder, S.H. (1976), *Molec. Pharmacol.*, **12**, 800–812.

Carlson, H.E. and Ippoliti, A.F. (1977), *J. Clin. Endocrinol. Metab.*, **45**, 367–370.

Carpenter, D.O. and Gaubatz, G.L. (1975), *Nature*, **254**, 343–344.

Chang, K., Jacobs, S. and Cuatrecasas, P. (1975), *Biochim. Biophys. Acta*, **406**, 294–303.

Chang, R.S.L., Tran, V.T. and Snyder, S.H. (1978), *Eur. J. Pharmacol.*, **48**, 463–464.

Chang, R.S.L., Tran, V.T. and Snyder, S.H. (1979), *J. Neurochem.*, **32**, 1653–1663.

Charli, J.L., Joseph-Bravo, P., Palacios, J.M. and Kordon, C. (1978), *Eur. J. Pharmacol.*, **52**, 401–403.

Clineschmidt, B.V. and Lotti, V.J. (1973), *Arch. Int. Pharmacodyn.*, **206**, 288–298.

Cox, B., Green, M.D. and Lomax, P. (1975), *Pharmacol. Biochem. Behav.*, **3**, 1051–1054.

Cox, B., Green, M.D. and Lomax, P. (1976), *Experientia*, **32**, 498–500.

Cox, B. and Lomax, P. (1977), *Ann. Rev. Pharmacol. Toxicol.*, **17**, 341–353.

Daly, J.W. (1975), *Life Sci.*, **18**, 1349–1358.

Daubresse, J.C., Neunier, J.C. and Ligny, C. (1978), *Lancet*, **1**, 99.

Delaney, J.C. and Ravey, M. (1977), *Lancet*, **1**, 152

Delbarre, B., Schmitt, H. and Senon, D. (1976), *Brit. J. Pharmacol.*, **58**, 443P–444P.

Delbarre, B., Senon, D. and Heyvang, M.H. (1974), *J. Physiol., Paris*, **5**, Suppl., 2, 24.

Delitala, G., Stubbs, W.A., Wass, J.A.H., Yeo, T., Jones, A., Williams, S., Besser, G.M., LaBrody, S.J. and Misiewicz, J.J. (1978), *Lancet*, **2**, 1054–1055.

Delle Fave, G.F., Tamburrano, G., de Magistris, L. Natoli, C., Santoro, M.L., Carratu, R. and Torsoli, A. (1977), *Lancet*, **1**, 1319.

Dismukes, K. and Daly, J.W. (1975), *Life Sci.*, **17**, 199–210.

Dismukes, K., Rogers, M. and Daly, J.W. (1976), *J. Neurochem.*, **26**, 785–790.

Dismukes, K. and Snyder, S.H. (1974), in *Advances in Neurology* (McDowell, F. and Barbeau, A., eds), Vol. 5, pp. 101–109, Raven Press, New York.

Dogterom, J., van Wimersma-Greidanus, Tj. B. and DeWied, D. (1976), *Experientia*, **32**, 659–660.

Donoso, A.O. and Bannza, A.M. (1976), *J. Neural Trans.*, **39**, 95–101.

Douglas, W.W. (1975), in *The Pharmacological Basis of Therapeutics* (Goodman, L.S. and Gilman, A., eds), pp. 590–629, Macmillan, New York.

Fann, W.E., Davis, J.M., Janowsky, D.S., Kaufmann, J.S., Griffith, J.O. and Oates, J.A. (1972), *Arch. Gen. Psychiat.*, **26**, 158–162.

Figge, J., Leonard, P. and Richelson, E. (1979), *Eur. J. Pharmacol.*, **58**, 479–483.

Finch, L. Harvey, C.A., Hicks, P.E. and Owen, D.A.A. (1977), *Brit. J. Pharmacol.*, **59**, 477P.

Finch, L. and Hicks, P.E. (1975), *Brit. J. Pharmacol.*, **55**, 274P–275P.

Finch, L. and Hicks, P.E. (1976a), *Eur. J. Pharmacol.*, **36**, 263–266.

Finch, L. and Hicks, P.E. (1976b), *Eur. J. Pharmacol.*, **40**, 365–368.

Fortier, C. (1951), *Endocrinol.*, **49**, 782–788.

Fredrickson, P. and Richelson, E. (1979), *Eur. J. Pharmacol.*, **56**, 261–264.

Furchgott, R.F. (1966), in *Advances in Drug Research* (Harper, N.J. and Simmonds, A.B., eds), Vol. 3, pp. 21–58, Academic Press, London.

Galindo, A., Krnjevic, K. and Schwartz, S. (1967), *J. Physiol.*, **192**, 359–377.

Garbarg, M., Barbin, G., Bischoff, S., Pollard, H. and Schwartz, J.-C. (1976), *Brain Res.*, **106**, 333–348.

Garbarg, M., Barbin, G., Feger, J. and Schwartz, J.-C. (1974), *Science*, **186**, 833–835.

Gerald, M.C. and Maickel, R.P. (1972), *Brit. J. Pharmacol.*, **44**, 462–471.

Gluckman, M.I. and Baum, T. (1969), *Psychopharmacologia*, **15**, 169–185.

Goldberg, S.E., Halmi, K.A., Eckert, E.D., Casper, R.C. and Davis, J.M. (1979), *Brit. J. Psychiat.*, **134**, 67–70.

Goodlet, I., Mirelylees, S.E. and Sugrue, M.F. (1977), *Brit. J. Pharmacol.*, **611**, 307–313.

Goodman, G., Lawson, D.M. and Gala, R.R. (1976), *Proc. Soc. Exp. Biol. Med.*, **153**, 225–229.

Gorodetzky, C.W. and Isbell, H. (1964), *Psychopharmacologia, 6*, 229–233.

Gosselin, R.E. (1977), in *Kinetics of Drug Action* (van Rossum, J.M., ed.). pp. 323–356, Springer-Verlag, Berlin.

Green, J.P. (1970), in *Handbook of Neurochemistry* (Lajtha, A., ed.). Vol. 4, pp. 221–250, Plenum Press, New York.

Green, J.P., Johnson, C.L. and Weinstein, H. (1978a), in *Psychopharmacology: A Generation of Progress* (Lipton, M.A., DiMascio, A. and Killan, K.F., eds), pp. 319–332, Raven Press, New York.

Green, J.P., Johnson, C.L., Weinstein, H. and Maayani, S. (1977), *Proc. Natl. Acad. Sci. USA, 74*, 5697–5701.

Green, J.P. and Maayani, S. (1977), *Nature, 269*, 163–165.

Green, J.P., Weinstein, H. and Maayani, S. (1978b), in *QuaSAR Research Monograph 22* (Barnett, G., Trsic, M. and Willette, R. E., eds), 38–59, National Institute on Drug Abuse, Rockville, Maryland.

Green, M.D., Cox, B. and Lomax, P. (1975b), *J. Neurosci. Res., 1*, 353–359.

Green, M.D., Simon, M.L. and Lomax, P. (1975a), *Life Sci., 16*, 1292–1299.

Greengard, P. and Kebabian, J.W. (1974), *Fed. Proc., 33*, 1059–1067.

Haas, H.L., Anderson, E.E. and Hosli, L. (1973), *Brain Res., 51*, 269–278.

Haas, H.L. and Bucher, U.M. (1975), *Nature, 255*, 643–645.

Haas, H.L. and Wolf, P. (1977), *Brain Res., 12*, 269–279.

Haas, H.L., Wolf, P. and Nussbaumer, J.-C. (1975), *Brain Res., 88*, 166–170.

Hall, W. (1976), *New Engl. J. Med., 295*, 841.

Hegstrand, L.R., Kanof, P.D. and Greengard, P. (1976), *Nature, 260*, 163–165.

Hill, S.J., Emson, P.C. and Young, J.M. (1978), *J. Neurochem., 31*, 997–1004.

Hill, S.J. and Young, M. (1978), *Eur. J. Pharmacol., 52*, 397–399.

Hill, S.J., Young, J.M. and Marrain, D.H. (1977), *Nature, 270*, 361–363.

Hoffman, W.E. and Schmid, P.G. (1978), *Life Sci., 22*, 1709–1714.

Hollenberg, M.D. and Cuatrecasas, P. (1975), in *Handbook of Psychopharmacology* (Anfinsen, C.B., Edsall, J.T. and Richards, F.M., eds), Vol. 2, pp. 129–177, Plenum Publishing Corp., New York.

Hollister, L.E. (1978), *New Engl. J. Med., 299*, 1106–1109.

Jacobs, S., Chang, K.J. and Cuatrecasas, P. (1975), *Biochem. Biophys. Res. Commun., 66*, 687–692.

Jick, H. (1975), in *Hypnotics* (Kapan, F., Harwood, T., Rickels, K., Rudzik, A.D. and Sorer, H., eds), pp. 145–154, Spectrum, New York.

Kakiuchi, S. and Rall, T.W. (1968), *Mol. Pharmacol., 4*, 379–388.

Kanof, P.D. and Greengard, P. (1978), *Nature, 272*, 329–333.

Kanof, P.D. and Greengard, P. (1979), *J. Pharm. exp. Ther., 209*, 87–95.

Kanof, P.D., Hegstrand, L.R. and Greengard, P. (1977), *Arch. Biochem. Biophys., 182*, 321–334.

Karppanen, H., Paakkari, I., Paakkari, P., Huotari, R. and Orma, A.-L. (1976), *Nature, 259*, 587–588.

Karppanen, H.O. and Westermann, E. (1973), *Naunyn-Schmied. Arch. Pharmacol., 279*, 83–87.

Katz, B. and Thesleff, S. (1957), *J. Physiol. (London), 138*, 63–80.

Kebabian, J.W., Steiner, A.L. and Greengard, P. (1975), *J. Pharmacol. exp. Ther., 193*, 474–488.

Kessler, K.A. (1978), in *Psychopharmacology: A Generation of Progress* (Lipton,

M.A., DiMascio, A. and Killan, K.F., eds), pp. 1289–1302, Raven Press, New York.

Klock, J.C., Boerner, M.S. and Becker, C.H. (1975), *Clin. Toxicol.,* **8**, 191–203.

Kobinger, W. (1975), in *Regulation of Blood Pressure by the Central Nervous System*, pp. 283–292, Grune and Stratton, New York.

Kuhar, N.J., Taylor, K.M. and Snyder, S.H. (1971), *J. Neurochem.,* **18**, 1515–1527.

Leibowitz, S.F. (1973), *Brain Res.,* **63**, 440–444.

Leonard, B.E. (1974), *Psychopharmacologia,* **36**, 221–236.

Libertun, C. and McCann, S.M. (1976), *Neuroendocrinol.,* **20**, 110–120.

Lomax, P., Schonbaum, E. and Jacob, J. (1975), *Temperature Regulation and Drug Action*, Karger, Basel.

Maayani, S., Green, J.P. and Weinstein, H. (1978), *Fed. Proc.,* **37**, 612.

Makara, G.B., Stark, E. and Palkovits, M. (1970), *J. Endocrin.,* **47**, 411–416.

Martres, M.P., Baudry, M. and Schwartz, J.-C. (1975), *Brain Res.,* **83**, 261–275.

McCann, S.M. (1957), *Endocrinol.,* **60**, 664–676.

McLoughlin, J.C., Callander, M.E. and Love, A.H.G. (1978), *Lancet,* **1**, 499–500.

McMillen, M.A., Ambis, D. and Siegel, H. (1978), *New Engl. J. Med.,* **298**, 284–285.

Menzies-Gow, N. (1977), *Lancet,* **1**, 928.

Monnier, M., Sauer, R. and Hatt, A.M. (1970), *Neurobiol.,* **12**, 265–305.

Morris, J.B. and Beck, A.T. (1974), *Arch. Gen. Psychiat.,* **30**, 667–674.

Mukherjee, C. and Lefkowitz, R.J. (1976), *Proc. Natl. Acad. Sci. USA,* **73**, 1494–1498.

Nahorski, S.R., Rogers, K.J. and Smith, B.M. (1974), *Life Sci.,* **15**, 1887–1894.

Nakra, B.R.S., Rutland, P., Verma, S. and Gaind, R. (1977), *Current Medical Research and Opinion,* **4**, 602–606.

Nelson, P.G. (1977), *Lancet,* **1**, 928.

Ondo, J.G. and Kitay, J.E. (1972), *Neuroendocrinol.,* **9**, 72–82.

Orr, E.L. and Quay, W.B. (1975), *Endocrinol.,* **97**, 480–484.

Paakkari, I., Paakkari, P. and Karppanen, H. (1976), *Acta Physiol. Scand. Suppl.,* **440**, 105.

Palacios, J.M., Garbarg, M., Barbin, G. and Schwartz, J.-C. (1978a), *Mol. Pharmacol.,* **14**, 971–982.

Palacios, J.-M., Schwartz, J.-C. and Garbarg, M. (1978b), *Eur. J. Pharmacol.,* **50**, 443–444.

Paykel, E.S., Mueller, P.S. and De La Vergne, P.M. (1973), *Brit. J. Psychiat.,* **123**, 501–507.

Phillis, J.W. (1977), *Le Journal Canadien des Sciences Neurologiques,* **4**, 152–195.

Phillis, J.W., Tebecis, A.K. and York, D.H. (1968), *Eur. J. Pharmacol.,* **4**, 471–475.

Pieri, K., Keller, H.H., Burkard, W. and DaPrada, M. (1978), *Nature,* **272**, 278.

Pollard, H., Bischoff, S. and Schwartz, J.-C. (1974), *J. Pharmacol. exp. Ther.,* **190**, 88–99.

Quap, C.W. (1978), *Drug Intelligence Clin. Pharmacol.,* **12**, 121.

Ramboer, C. (1978), *Lancet,* **1**, 330–331.

Rang, H.P. and Ritter, J.M. (1969), *Mol. Pharmacol.,* **6**, 357–382.

Rehavi, M. and Sokolovsky, M. (1978), *Brain Res.,* **149**, 525–529.

Renaud, L.P. (1975), *Proc. B.P.S.,* **55**, 277p–278p.

Richelson, E. (1977), *Nature,* **266**, 371–373.

Richelson, E. (1978a), *Science*, **201**, 69–71.

Richelson, E. (1978b), *Nature*, **274**, 176–177.

Richelson, E. (1978c), *Nature*, **272**, 366–368.

Richelson, E. (1979a), in *International Review of Biochemistry Series II, Physiological and Pharmacological Biochemistry* (Tipton, K.F., ed.), pp. 81–120, MTP Press, Lancaster.

Richelson, E. (1979b), *Mayo Clin. Proc.*, **54**, 669–674.

Richelson, E. and Divinetz-Romero, S. (1977), *Biol. Psychiat.*, **12**, 771–785.

Rivier, C. and Vale, W. (1977), *Endocrinol.*, **101**, 506–511.

Robinson, R.B., McHugh, P.R. and Bloom, F.E. (1975), *Psychopharmacol. Comm.*, **1**, 37–50.

Robinson, T.J. and Mulligan, T.O. (1977), *Lancet*, **1**, 719.

Rogers, M., Dismukes, K. and Daly, J.W. (1975), *J. Neurochem.*, **25**, 531–534.

Ross, S.B., Renyi, A.L. and Ogren, S.O. (1971), *Life Sci.*, **10**, 1267–1277.

Schild, H.O. (1947), *Brit. J. Pharmacol.*, **2**, 189–206.

Schwartz, J.-C. (1977), *Ann. Rev. Pharmacol. Toxicol.*, **17**, 325–339.

Schwartz, J.-C., Barbin, G., Garbarg, M., Pollard, H., Rose, C. and Verdiere, M. (1976), in *Advances in Biochemical Psychopharmacology*, (Paoletti, R., Costa, E. and Giacobini, E., eds), Vol. 15, pp. 111–126, Raven Press, New York.

Sharpe, P.C. and Hawkins, B.W. (1977), in *Cimetidine: Proceedings of 2nd International Symposium on Histamine H_2-Receptor Antagonists*, Excerpta Medica, Amsterdam, p. 358.

Shaw, G.G. (1971), *Brit. J. Pharmacol.*, **42**, 205–214.

Sigg, E.B. (1968), in *Psychopharmacology: A Review of Progress 1957–1967*, pp. 665–669, US Government Printing Office, Washington, D.C.

Slettin, I., Mou, B., Cazenave, R.N. and Gershon, S. (1976), *Dis. Nerv. Syst.*, August, 519–422.

Snyder, S.H. and Taylor, K.M. (1972), in *Perspectives in Neuropharmacology*, pp. 43–73, Oxford University Press, New York.

Strittmatter, W.J., Davis, J.N. and Lefkowitz, R.J. (1977), *J. biol. Chem.*, **252**, 5478–5482.

Study, R.E. and Greengard, P. (1978), *J. Pharm. exp. Ther.*, **207**, 767–778.

Taylor, J.E. and Richelson, E. (1979a), in *Proceedings 4th International Catecholamine Symposium* (Usdin, E., ed.), Pergamon Press, Oxford, pp. 492–494.

Taylor, J.E. and Richelson, E. (1979b), *Mol. Pharmacol.*, **15**, 462–471.

Tran, B.T., Chang, R.S.L. and Snyder, S.H. (1978), *Proc. Natl. Acad. Sci. USA*, **75**, 6290–6294.

Trendelenburg, U. (1957), *Circ. Res.*, **5**, 105–110.

Tuomisto, L. and Eriksson, L. (1979), *Eur. J. Pharmacol.*, **54**, 191–201.

U'Prichard, D.C., Greenberg, D.A., Sheeha, P.P. and Snyder, S.H. (1978), *Science*, **199**, 197–198.

Van den Brink, F.G. and Lien, E.J. (1977), *Eur. J. Pharmacol.*, **44**, 251–270.

Verdiere, M., Rose, C. and Schwartz, J.-C. (1974), *Agents and Actions*, **4**, 184–185.

Verma, S.C. and McNeill, J.H. (1978), *Can. J. Pharmaceut. Sci.*, **13**, 1–3.

Whyte, S.F., Macdonald, A.J., Naylor, G.J. and Moody, J.P. (1976), *Brit. J. Psychiat.*, **128**, 384–390.

Williams, L.T. and Lefkowitz, R.J. (1978), *Receptor Binding Studies in Adrenergic Pharmacology*, Raven Press, New York.

Yamamura, H.I., Enna, S.J. and Kuhar, M.J. (1978), *Neurotransmitter Receptor Binding*, Raven Press, New York.

Yamamura, H.I., Kuhar, M.J. and Snyder, S.H. (1974), *Brain Res.*, **80**, 170–176.

Yamamura, H.I. and Snyder, S.H. (1974), *Proc. Natl. Acad. Sci. USA*, **71** 1725–1729.

Ziegler, V.E., Clayton, P.J. and Biggs, J.T. (1977), *Arch. Gen. Psychiat.*, **34**, 607–612.

3 Acetylcholine Receptors

GREGORY J. WASTEK and HENRY I.
YAMAMURA

Acknowledgements

Supported in part by USPHS grants. H.I. Yamamura is a recipient of a Research Scientist Development Award (RSDA) from the National Institute of Mental Health (MH 00095).

Neurotransmitter Receptors Part 2
(Receptors and Recognition, Series B, Volume 10)
Edited by H.I. Yamamura and S.J. Enna
Published in 1981 by Chapman and Hall, 11 New Fetter Lane, London
EC4P 4EE
© Chapman and Hall

3.1 INTRODUCTION

The presence of acetylcholine (ACh) in the central nervous system was demonstrated 48 years ago by Chang and Gaddum (1933). Until recently, however, evidence that ACh was functioning as a neurotransmitter in the central nervous system was based mainly on: (1) the distribution of its synthesizing enzyme, choline acetyltransferase (ChAc) and the distribution of its hydrolyzing enzyme, acetylcholinesterase (AChE); (2) changes in the concentration of ACh content of the brain under various conditions; (3) the release of ACh from the central nervous system into the blood or into the cerebroventricular spaces; and (4) the central effects of systemically applied ACh. There was little evidence that ACh altered the function of central neurons by a direct interaction with an ACh receptor.

In this chapter, we review the application of ACh by iontophoretic techniques, the biochemical characterization of central nicotinic and central and peripheral muscarinic receptors, and the involvement of cyclic nucleotides, phospholipids and other agents in cholinergic receptor function.

3.2 ELECTROPHYSIOLOGICAL STUDIES

Since Dale (1914) first described the effects of choline esters on various physiological preparations, it has been customary to classify the responses to ACh as either nicotinic or muscarinic. By definition, nicotinic responses were rapid in onset, of short duration and were blocked by nicotine and D-tubocurarine. Muscarinic responses were slow in onset, of longer duration and were blocked by atropine (Krnjevic, 1974). Initial experiments showed that most central cholinergic responses could be blocked by atropine and were, therefore, mediated by muscarinic receptors (Henderson and Wilson, 1936). Studies, using the microiontophoretic technique of Curtis and Eccles (1958a,b), demonstrated the existence of at least three different types of central responses to ACh: muscarinic excitation (Crawford, 1970; Crawford and Curtis, 1966; Krnjevic and Phillis,1963a,b; Salmoiraghi and Stefanis, 1967; Spehlmann, 1963; Stone, 1972) nicotinic excitation (Curtis and Eccles, 1958a,b; Eccles et al., 1954; Katz and Thesleff, 1957; Curtis and Ryall, 1966a,b; Ueki et al., 1961) and muscarinic inhibition (Crawford and Curtis, 1966; Krnjevic et al., 1971; Jordan and Phillis, 1972; Phillis and York, 1968; Randic et al., 1964; Stone, 1972). The latter response was either fast or slow in onset and prolonged (Jordan and Phillis, 1972; Randic et al., 1964; Stone, 1972). These three responses were mediated by only two types of receptors: muscarinic and nicotinic (Krnjevic, 1974).

Muscarinic inhibition was demonstrated in the cerebral cortex (Legge *et al.*, 1966; Phillis and York, 1968; Randic *et al.*, 1964; Stone, 1972), the olfactory bulb and the caudate nucleus (Bloom *et al.*, 1964, 1965; McLennon and York, 1966), the diencephalon and midbrain (Davis and Vaughan, 1969; Phillis, 1971; Straschill and Perwein, 1971; Tebecis, 1972), the pons-medulla (Salmoiraghi and Steiner, 1963; Bradley *et al.*, 1966; Tebecis, 1973), the cerebellar cortex (Crawford *et al.*, 1966; McCance and Phillis, 1968), and the spinal cord (Curtis *et al.*, 1966a,b; Weight and Salmoiraghi, 1966).

Muscarinic excitation was demonstrated in the cerebral cortex (Crawford and Curtis, 1966; Krnjevic and Phillis, 1963a,b; Stone, 1972), the caudate nucleus (McLennan and York, 1966), the hippocampus (Biscoe and Straughan, 1966), the ventrobasal thalamus (Andersen and Curtis, 1964), the pyriform cortex (Legge *et al.*, 1966), the pons-medulla (Bradley *et al.*, 1966) and the cerebellar cortex (Crawford *et al.*, 1966; McCance and Phillis, 1968).

The hippocampus was shown to have two different types of cholinergic neurons: pyramidal cells, which exhibited atropine-sensitive muscarinic excitation, and interneurons, which exhibited a tubocurarine-sensitive nicotinic inhibition (Segal, 1978).

Renshaw cells of the spinal cord responded to the application of ACh with nicotinic-excitatory responses, muscarinic-excitatory responses and muscarinic-inhibitory responses (Curtis and Ryall, 1966a,b).

Cells of the supraoptic nucleus of the hypothalamus responded to ACh with both nicotinic-excitatory and muscarinic-inhibitory responses (Barker *et al.*, 1971). Most neurons of the mammalian central nervous system were like these cells in that they could not be classified simply as muscarinic-excitatory, muscarinic-inhibitory or nicotinic, but rather showed mixed muscarinic–nicotinic responses as a result of the cell's having variable amounts of both types of receptors (Krnjevic, 1974).

Acetylcholine produced muscarinic excitation in neuroglia (Krnjevic and Schwartz, 1967; Krnjevic *et al.*, 1971) and both nicotinic excitation and muscarinic inhibition in mouse neuroblastoma cells (Harris and Dennis, 1970; Nelson *et al.*, 1971; Peacock and Nelson, 1973).

3.3 BIOCHEMICAL STUDIES

3.3.1 Characterization, isolation and purification of the central nicotinic receptor

Since the introduction of radiolabeled α-neurotoxins by Chang and Lee (1963) and Changeux *et al.* (1970), these toxins have been used to characterize, solubilize and purify nicotinic receptors in fish electric organs and vertebrate skeletal muscle (see reviews by Heidmann and Changeux, 1978; Landau, 1978; Sugiyama, 1978).

Because there are few nicotinic receptors in the brain, it has proved difficult to study them. Moore and Loy (1972) found that $[^{125}I]$-α bungarotoxin ($[^{125}I]$-α-Bgt) bound irreversibly to sodium desoxycholate-extracted protein fractions from eel electroplax and hog cerebral cortex. Gel filtration revealed that the toxin was bound to a single protein fraction (molecular weight 50 000 to 80 000) that resembled the α-Bgt binding component of skeletal muscle. Salvaterra and Moore (1973) found the number of α-Bgt binding sites in rat cerebral cortex to be 3.4 pmol/g tissue.

Eterovic and Bennett (1974) demonstrated $[^{3}H]$-α-Bgt binding in crude mitochondrial fractions of rat cerebral cortex (40–60 fmol of toxin/mg protein). Osmotic lysis of this preparation showed the $[^{3}H]$-α-Bgt binding component to be membrane bound and a variety of cholinergic drugs were able to inhibit the binding.

The P_2B (nerve ending) subfraction of rat cereberal cortex had the highest $[^{125}I]$-α-Bgt binding and its distribution was similar to that of AChE, ChAc and sodium–potassium-ATPase (Salvaterra *et al.*, 1975). $[^{125}I]$-α-Bgt binding, and ChAc and AChE activities were highest in the olfactory lobes, cerebral cortex, thalamus, caudate nucleus and brain stem, with intermediate and low levels in the hippocampus and cerebellum, respectively.

Moore and Brady (1976) reported that $[^{125}I]$-α-Bgt binding to whole rat brain homogenates had a capacity of 2 pmol/g tissue and a dissociation constant of 8 nM. Binding was decreased 90 per cent by 10 μM-tubocurarine and 100 μM-nicotine whereas 100 μM concentrations of choline chloride, atropine sulfate and eserine sulfate had no effect. These results indicated that this binding site was nicotinic. A soluble extract of this tissue (prepared using 1 per cent solution of the detergent Emulphogene) bound $[^{125}I]$-α-Bgt with a dissociation constant (K_D) of 5 nM. 10 μM solutions of nicotine and α-Bgt abolished formation of the toxin–receptor complex. Carbamylcholine and tubocurarine, at similar concentrations, reduced the complex formation by 35 per cent to 40 per cent. 10 μM solutions of atropine, eserine, pilocarpine and decamethionium had no effect on the receptor complex formation.

Lowy *et al.* (1976) solubilized $[^{125}I]$-α-Bgt binding macromolecules from rat brain using 0.1 per cent Triton X-100. Specific toxin binding was limited to a single class of sites and had a dissociation constant of 60 pM. The association and dissociation rate constants of the complex were $7 \times 10^5 \, M^{-1} \, s^{-1}$ and $4 \times 10^{-5} \, s^{-1}$, respectively. The toxin-binding macromolecules resembled peripheral nicotinic receptors in solubility, isoelectric point and binding kinetics.

Salvaterra and Mahler (1976) solubilized the nicotinic receptor of rat cerebral cortex using Triton X-100, partially purified it using affinity chromatography with *Naja naja siamensis* (NNT) toxin (a polypeptide derived from the venom of the cobra *Naja naja kasuthia*) and characterized its binding of $[^{125}I]$-α-Bgt. The binding reaction exhibited second-order kinetics and association and dissociation rate constants of $0.4 \times 10^5 \, M^{-1} \, s^{-1}$ and $1 \times 10^{-5} \, s^{-1}$, respectively. A number of nicotinic cholinergic ligands inhibited toxin binding to the solubilized receptor.

Schmidt (1977) demonstrated that tubocurarine, nicotine, gallamine and dihydro-β-erythroidine inhibited $[^{125}I]$-α-Bgt to rat brain homogenates in the 10 μM range whereas choline and muscarinic compounds inhibited binding only in the millimolar range.

Tindall *et al*. (1978) used $[^{125}I]$-α-NNT toxin to examine nicotinic binding in subcellular fractions of rat brain cortex. Toxin binding was saturable, specific and had a binding capacity of 7 fmol toxin/mg protein. Binding was highest in the hippocampus, corpus striatum and the olfactory-pyriform cortex (i.e. the nucleus accumbens, olfactory tract, olfactory and pyriform cortices and preoptic area). These regional binding data were similar to those obtained by Salvaterra *et al*. (1975). Toxin binding was highest in the brain regions that had the highest dopamine concentrations and suggested that there may be a relationship between these two systems in the olfactory-pyriform cortex similar to that in the caudoputamen of rat brain (Yamamura and Snyder, 1974a,b).

Segal *et al*. (1978) demonstrated that the specific binding of $[^{125}I]$-α-Bgt was highest in the hippocampus and hypothalamus and that the cerebellum was devoid of specific binding. Autoradiographic analysis of the regional distribution of $[^{125}I]$-α-Bgt binding in brain sections of the same tissue showed that binding was highest in the hippocampus, the suprachiasmatic and periventricular nuclei, and in the ventral lateral geniculate and mesoncephalic dorsal tegmental nuclei suggesting that the limbic forebrain, the midbrain and the sensory nuclei are the brain's major nicotinic cholinergic structures.

Although McQuarrie *et al*. (1976) initially reported that crude membrane preparations of rat cerebral cortex contained both high- and low-affinity α-Bgt binding sites, they found that binding to detergent (Triton X-100) extracts of rat brain was saturable and involves a single class of binding sites (0.3 pmol/mg protein). This class of binding sites corresponded to the low-affinity form found in crude homogenates and suggested that either Triton X-100 converted the high-affinity site into a low-affinity site or that Triton X-100 extracted only the low-affinity site. Although it has not been demonstrated conclusively, several studies using the purified nicotinic receptor from fish electric organs favor the first interpretation (Edelstein *et al*., 1975; Gruenhagen and Changeux, 1976; Suarez-Isla and Hucho, 1977; Teichberg and Changeux, 1976).

Hunt and Schmidt (1978) demonstrated α-Bgt binding in the medial septal-hippocampal project (a well-established cholinergic pathway). They also showed that interneurons of the stratum oriens of the hippocampus had nicotinic binding sites. After medial, septal and fimbrial lesions, there was no change in the total number of toxin sites within the hippocampal formation suggesting that the binding sites were located post-synaptically.

Arimatsu *et al.* (1978) demonstrated specific [^{125}I]-α-Bgt binding in mouse brain using light- and electron-microscopic autoradiography. High toxin binding was evident in only a fraction of the regions with high AChE activity (i.e. the interpeduncular nucleus, the nucleus tractus olfactori and the nucleus amygdaloideus medialis posterior) and, at the light microscopic level, toxin binding was evident only in synaptic areas.

3.3.2 Characterization of the peripheral muscarinic receptor

The first radioligand-binding studies of the muscarinic receptor were done using homogenates of the longitudinal smooth muscle of the guinea-pig ileum (Paton and Rang, 1965). Specific [^{3}H]atropine binding in these homogenates had a capacity of 180 pmol/g wet wt and a dissociation constant of 1 nM. [^{3}H]Methylatropine had a specific binding capacity of 90 pmol/g wet wt and a dissociation constant of 0.65 nM. The dissociation constants for both tritiated ligands were similar to their ED_{50} in their ability to antagonize the pharmacological effects of ACh. Nicotinic agonists, at relatively high concentrations, had no effect on [^{3}H]atropine binding whereas muscarinic antagonists, at relatively low concentrations, inhibited the binding. Hydrolysis of atropine abolished its ability to bind the muscarinic receptor and its ability to antagonize the pharmacological effects of ACh in the guinea-pig ileum. The rate constant for atropine's pharmacological antagonism of acetylcholine was relatively high (5×10^{-4} s^{-1}) and it increased with increasing atropine concentrations. This *in vitro* rate constant, however, was lower than that for the pharmacological preparation and was independent of the atropine concentration.

[^{3}H]Dibenamine, an irreversible ligand, was used in an attempt to label the muscarinic receptor. Its non-specific binding, however, was too high for it to be used effectively as a ligand (Takagi and Takahashi, 1968; Takagi *et al.*, 1965).

Gill and Rang (1966) developed an alkylating derivative of the potent muscarinic antagonist benzilylcholine, benzilylcholine mustard (BCM), that proved to be a specific and irreversible muscarinic antagonist when tested in the guinea-pig ileum. The binding of [^{3}H]-BCM to guinea-pig ileum homogenates was saturable and had a specific capacity of 220 pmol/g tissue [^{3}H]-BCM association rate constant (2.3×10^5 M^{-1} s^{-1}) in the binding assay was similar to its association rate constant (2.4×10^5 M^{-1} s^{-1}) for antagonism of the ACh-induced contractions of the guinea-pig ileum (Gill and Rang, 1966; Fewtrell and Rang, 1973). Young *et al.* (1972) developed a derivative of BCM, propyl BCM, and, in all tissues studied, had saturable binding component that was inhibited by 0.1 μM-atropine (Burgen *et al.*, 1974a; Cuthbert and Young, 1973; Taylor *et al.*, 1975). Ward and Young (1977) used various compounds to inhibit the irreversible binding of [³H]-propyl BCM to intact longitudinal muscle strips from the guinea-pig ileum. The Hill coefficients for the muscarinic antagonists tested were consistent with a simple mass-action equilibrium but Hill coefficients for the mus-carinic agonists tested were not. Each compound's IC_{50} in the [³H]propyl BCM assay was higher in the intact muscle strips than in broken-cell preparations suggesting the existence of an 'access-limitation' factor in the intact muscle strips.

Yamamura and Snyder (1974b) used [³H]-3-quinuclidinyl benzilate ([³H]-QNB), a reversible muscarinic antagonist, to study the muscarinic receptor of the longitudinal smooth muscle of the guinea-pig ileum. They found a specific binding component that was saturable at 0.9 nM-[³H]-QNB. The dissociation constant for [³H]-QNB binding was 0.3–0.5 nM as compared with the dissociation constant of 0.5 nM for its ability to inhibit acetylcholine-induced contractions of the longitudinal smooth muscle. [³H]-QNB binding was unaffected by relatively high concentrations of non-muscarinic drugs but was decreased significantly by nanomolar con-centrations of muscarinic antagonists. The affinities of the muscarinic agon-ists and antagonist tested were similar in the binding assay and in intact muscle strips. The specific binding capacity of [³H]-QNB in this prepara-tion was similar to those determined for other tritiated muscarinic ligands in different preparations (Burgen *et al.*, 1974a; Fewtrell and Rang, 1973; Paton and Rang, 1965; Rang, 1967; Taylor *et al.*, 1975; Young *et al.*, 1972).

Roeske and Yamamura (1978) measured [³H]-QNB binding in organ cultures of fetal mouse heart to test the hypothesis that the increasing negative chronotropic effects of ACh with fetal age are mediated by muscarinic receptors. They found a single population of [³H]-QNB binding sites that increased significantly in density during the last trimester of pregnancy. This increase in receptor density was not accompanied by any change in receptor affinity for [³H]-QNB and it paralleled the increase in the heart's responsiveness to ACh (1 μM to 10 mM).

Fields *et al.* (1978) used [³H]-QNB to label the muscarinic receptors of rabbit, rat and guinea-pig hearts. They found a single population of [³H]-QNB binding sites in all three tissues with an apparent dissociation con-stant similar to that found in brain tissue (20 pM). Mathematical analysis of kinetic binding data derived from these tissues gave association and dis-sociation rate constants of 1.03×10^9 M^{-1} min^{-1} and 2.45×10^{-2} min^{-1}, respectively, from which a dissociation constant of 27 pM was calculated.

Muscarinic and nicotinic agonists and antagonists had affinities for these cardiac muscarinic receptors that were similar to those for the brain's muscarinic receptors. Non-cholinergic drugs had little affinity for these binding sites at 100 μM concentration. The inhibition of [^{3}H]-QNB binding by clinically effective cardiotonic and psychotropic drugs suggested that cardiac muscarinic receptors may mediate the clinically relevant effects, and/or the side effects, of these drugs. The distribution of these receptors within the heart was consistent with the relative distributions of ACh and ChAc activity (i.e. receptor densities, in pmol/g protein, were: whole heart 57, left atrium 302, right atrium 200, ventricular septum 58, right ventricle 53, and left ventricle 37).

Sugiyama *et al.* (1977) used [^{3}H]-QNB to characterize the muscarinic receptor in mammalian retina. They found that 6- and 13-day-old chick embryo retina had specific [^{3}H]-QNB binding capacities of 10 and 320 fmol/mg protein, respectively. Autoradiographic studies revealed that the muscarinic receptors of the 13-day embryo were localized in two sharp bands within the inner synaptic layer of the retina. In the adult chicken, muscarinic receptors were limited to three distinct bands in the inner synaptic layer of the retina.

Hruska *et al.* (1978a) characterized [^{3}H]-QNB binding in bovine retina. There was one saturable binding component with a dissociation constant of 27 pM and a binding capacity of 148 fmol/mg protein. The association and dissociation rate constants were $5 \times 10^8 \, \text{M}^{-1} \, \text{min}^{-1}$ and $14 \times 10^{-3} \, \text{min}^{-1}$, respectively, and the kinetic dissociation constant calculated from these two values was 31 pM. The muscarinic antagonists tested had Hill coefficients of 1.0 and the muscarinic agonists had Hill coefficients of 0.5 indicating that, in the retina, muscarinic agonists did not interact with the muscarinic antagonist binding site according to mass-action kinetics. The tricyclic antidepressants and antihistamines tested (imipramine, diphenhydramine and dichlorpheniramine) had Hill coefficients similar to those of the muscarinic antagonists.

3.3.3 Characterization of the central muscarinic receptor

Labeling the brain's muscarinic receptors proved more difficult than labeling peripheral muscarinic receptors because, in the brain, there was no obvious pharmacological responses to measure. Farrow and O'Brien (1973) discovered two [^{3}H]atropine binding sites within subcellular fractions of rat brain and hyosine was able to inhibit the binding to one of these sites.

Bartfai *et al.* (1974) found two [^{3}H]atropine binding sites in rat cerebral cortex but binding to these sites accounted for less than 3 per cent of the total binding indicating that this binding was non-specific.

Hiley *et al.* (1972) and Burgen *et al.* (1974b), using [^{3}H]propyl BCM, found two binding components in homogenates of rat cerebral cortex. One was atropine-sensitive and had a binding capacity of 42 pmol/g tissue and an association rate constant of 2.3×10^6 M^{-1} s^{-1}. The other was insensitive to atropine and increased linearly with increasing substrate concentrations indicating that binding to this component was non-specific.

Hulme *et al.* (1978) measured the binding of several antagonists (*N*-[³H]methylatropine, [³H]-QNB, [³H]-propyl BCM, *N*-[³H]-methylscopolamine and [³H]atropine) to a crude synaptosomal fraction of rat cerebral cortex. Binding of these antagonists adhered to mass-action kinetics giving dissociation constants between 10^5 and 10^{10} M^{-1}. The *in vitro* dissociation constants for these ligands were similar to their affinity constants in longitudinal smooth muscle preparations. Their specific binding capacities were also similar (2 nmol/g protein) and the ratio of non-specific to total binding ranged from 1.7 per cent for *N*-[³H]-methylatropine to 17.2 per cent for [³H]-QNB.

Yamamura and Sndyer (1974a) used [³H]-QNB to characterize the muscarinic receptor in rat brain homogenates. When the specific binding sites were saturated, non-specific binding was only 25 per cent of total binding. Nanomolar concentrations of muscarinic antagonist inhibited 90 per cent of the [³H]-QNB binding whereas muscarinic agonists were required in concentrations 1000-fold higher to inhibit [³H]-QNB binding to the same extent. Non-muscarinic drugs in millimolar concentrations, produced no such decrease in [³H]-QNB binding.

Coyle and Yamamura (1976) found that, in the rat brain, specific [³H]-QNB binding was 10 per cent of adult levels at birth and increased linearly to 90 per cent by 4 weeks postpartum. Specific ChAc activity increased from 1 to 8 per cent of adult levels between 15 days gestation and 7 days postpartum and it then increased linearly to 83 per cent by 4 weeks postpartum. The development of [³H]choline uptake paralleled that of ChAc activity. In all regions of the neonatal rat brain, the level of ACh was higher than that of [³H]-QNB binding which was higher than ChAc activity.

The neonatal parietal cortex and corpus striatum developed more slowly than the pons-medulla, and the hypothalamus and midbrain-thalamus had intermediate developmental rates as compared to the other two.

The *in vitro* regional distribution of muscarinic receptor binding was determined in rat brain (Kobayashi *et al.*, 1978; Yamamura and Snyder, 1974a; Yamamura *et al.*, 1974), dog brain (Hiley and Burgen, 1974) and monkey brain (Yamamura *et al.*, 1974). In all of these studies, muscarinic receptor density was highest in the basal ganglia and cortical areas, intermediate in the olfactory areas, the amygdala, the thalamus and the hypothalamus, and lowest in the pons-medulla and the cerebellum.

There was a good correlation between [³H]-QNB binding and ChAc activity in the basal ganglia, the lateral amygdaloid nucleus, the hypoglossal nucleus, the cerebellum, the substantia nigra and the 'acoustic system' whereas high [^{3}H]-QNB binding, with low CHAc activity was found in cerebrocortical areas, the hippocampus and the nucleus accumbens (Kobayashi *et al.*, 1978). Choline acetyltransferase activity may, therefore, identify cholinergic cell bodies more precisely than cholinergic neurons *per se*. There was also a good correlation between [^{3}H]-QNB binding and AChE-containing terminals as opposed to AChE-containing cell bodies (Kobayashi *et al.*, 1978).

Wastek and Yamamura (1978) used [^{3}H]-QNB to measure the regional distribution of muscarinic receptors in human brain and to characterize muscarinic receptor binding in three regions of the normal human brain. The average association rate constant in these three areas was 7×10^8 M^{-1} min^{-1} the average dissociation rate constant was 14×10^{-3} min^{-1}. The kinetic dissociation rate constant calculated from the ratio of these two values was 20 pM. The three human brain regions had dissociation constants between 60 and 70 pM and specific binding capacities between 600 and 900 fmol/mg protein. Muscarinic antagonists were 1000-fold more potent in inhibiting [^{3}H]-QNB binding in these three brain regions than were muscarinic agonists. The muscarinic antagonists and agonists had Hill coefficients of 1.0 and 0.70–0.85, respectively, indicating once again, that antagonists binding adhered to mass-action kinetics while agonist binding did not. Nicotinic and non-cholinergic drugs were unable to inhibit [^{3}H]-QNB binding at concentrations up to 10 μM. When the apparent dissociation constant for each region was compared to the receptor concentration for that region (Cuatrecasas and Hollenberg, 1976), the regions had 'true' dissociation constants between 20 and 40 pM.

Specific (atropine-displaceable) [^{3}H]-QNB binding was also demonstrated *in vivo* using light microscopy autoradiography (Kuhar and Yamamura, 1975; Yamamura *et al.*, 1974) and the regional distribution and pharmacologic specificity were similar to those determined *in vitro* (Kuhar and Yamamura, 1976; Yamamura *et al.*, 1975).

Kloog and Sokolovsky (1977, 1978a,b) used another potent, reversible muscarinic antagonist. N-[^{3}H]methyl-4-piperidylbenzilate [^{3}H]-4-NMPB), and [^{3}H]atropine to study the muscarinic receptor in mouse brain. They found binding parameters similar to those for [^{3}H]-QNB except that their dissociation studies indicated the existence of two ligand–receptor complexes i.e. the association and dissociation rate constants of binding for atropine, scopolamine, 4-NMPB and QNB appeared to decrease with increasing ligand affinity. The differences between the association rate constants were small whereas those between the dissociation rate constants were relatively large. This kinetic behavior was similar to the time-course of antimuscarinic activity observed in isolated tissues. These investigators concluded that, although there are factors that determine the onset and offset rates of antagonism, other than ligand association and dissociation, the events at the receptor site are dominant. They also proposed that the simplest model that would explain such behavior was a fast-binding step followed by a slow isomerization of the ligand–receptor complex.

Burgermeister *et al*. (1978) used [^{3}H]scopolamine and [^{3}H]-QNB to study the muscarinic receptors of mouse neuroblastoma (clone NIE-115) and neuroblastoma × glioma hybrid (clone NG 108-15) cells. The apparent dissociation constants of [^{3}H]scopolamine and [^{3}H]-QNB binding for each cell type were 0.4 nM (NIE-115), 0.5 nM (NG 108-15), 0.06 nM (NIE-115) and 0.1 nM (NG 108-15), respectively. Receptor densities were 25 fmol mg^{-1} in NIE-115 and 40 fmol mg^{-1} in NG 108-15. The relative potencies of muscarinic and nicotinic compounds in inhibiting the binding of both tritiated ligands in these cells were similar to those obtained by other investigators in rat and human brains. Similarly, antagonists, but not agonists, bound to a single class of receptor sites.

(a) Regulation of muscarinic receptors binding

Aronstam *et al*. (1977, 1978) showed that *p*-chloromecuribenzoate (PCMB) reacts with a group(s) under allosteric control and of the receptor binding site to inhibit both agonist and antagonist binding in rat brain. Muscarinic receptors were protected from PCMB inactivation by pretreatment with muscarinic agonists or antagonists and the inactivation was reversed by treatment with organic sulfhydyl agents. Reductive alkylation of neuronal membranes, using *N*-ethylmaleimide (NEM), could prevent the inhibition of muscarinic antagonist, but not agonist, binding by PCMB treatment indicating that it was the presence of a mercuribenzoate group within the binding site, after PCMB treatment that was antagonistic to muscarinic receptor binding. NEM increased agonist binding by converting the muscarinic receptors from a low- into a high-agonist affinity whereas both conformations appeared to have the same high affinity for muscarinic antagonists. The presence of muscarinic agonist during NEM treatment enhanced NEM's ability to increase the receptor's affinity for agonists. Exposing the receptor to low concentrations of PCMB abolished NEM's ability to increase agonist binding even when saturating concentrations of muscarinic drugs were present during the PCMB treatment. This indicated that NEM affected muscarinic agonist binding by interacting with a group contiguous to the binding site. Transition metal ions, which appeared to interact with all the NEM- and PCMB-reactive moieties, both increased and decreased binding depending on their concentration. These investigators also found a regional distribution of the high- and low-affinity receptor conformations, in terms of the muscarinic receptor's affinity for muscarinic agonists, which was: brainstem, telencephalon, hippocampus.

These data were consistent with the Birdsall-Hulme (1976) model for the muscarinic receptor in that the interactions of muscarinic antagonists with the receptor were independent of the state of the receptor and were unaffected by NEM treatment.

Rosenberger *et al.* (1980) examined the effects of ions and guanyl nucleotides on cardiac muscarinic receptors. They found that sodium ions produced concentration-dependent decreases in the affinity of oxotremorine and atropine for the muscarinic receptor as measured by [^{3}H]-QNB binding. This sodium-effect was much greater in altering agonist affinity than in altering antagonist affinity. The monovalent cations Cs^+, Rb^+ and K^+ had no such effects. Guanyl-5^1-yl imidodiphosphate [Gpp(NH)p], GTP and GDP (in that order of potency) selectively decreased the affinity of oxotremorine for the muscarinic receptor but had no effect on the affinity of atropine. The guanyl nucleotides, in combination with Na^+, decreased the affinity of oxotremorine for the muscarinic receptor more than did either one alone. Such additivity, combined with the difference in Gpp(NH)p's selectivity for agonist and antagonist binding, and the altered Hill value derived in the presence of Na^+, indicated that there may be separate sites of action for Na^+ and the guanyl nucleotides at the cardiac muscarinic receptor.

Ehlert *et al.* (1980) found that 30 μM-Gpp(NH)p decreased oxotremorine's affinity for the [^{3}H]-QNB binding site by a factor of three in the longitudinal smooth muscle of the rat ileum while it had less effect on [^{3}H]-QNB in various rat brain regions. The primary effect of Gpp(NH)p on agonist inhibition of [^{3}H]-QNB binding in both the ileum and the forebrain was a decrease in the affinity of the high-affinity agonist binding site. Gpp(NH)p had no effect on antagonist binding in any of the tissues examined. Sodium (200 mM) also preferentially reduced agonist affinity in homogenates of the forebrain and longitudinal muscle.

(b) Presynaptic muscarinic receptors

The fact that muscarinic agonist inhibited, and atropine stimulated, ACh release from cerebrocortical (Polak and Meeuws, 1966; Szerb and Somogyi, 1973) and hippocampal slices (Hadhazy and Szerb, 1977) suggested that presynaptic muscarinic receptors regulate the release of ACh in the CNS.

Yamamura and Snyder (1974c) tested this hypothesis by lesioning the septal-hippocampal cholinergic afferents of rat brain and measuring [^{3}H]-QNB binding in the hippocampus. After 2 weeks, ChAc and AChE activity in the hippocampus had each decreased approximately 70 per cent with no change in receptor density or affinity. These data suggested the possibilities that: (1) presynaptic muscarinic receptors were different from postsynaptic receptors and were not labeled by QNB; (2) there were no presynaptic receptors on cholinergic nerve terminals in the hippocampus; or (3) presynaptic muscarinic receptors were located on non-cholinergic neurons.

Sharma and Banerjee (1978) destroyed noradrenergic nerve terminals in rat heart ventricles by chemical sympathectomy using 6-hydroxydopamine (6-OHDA)'and reported a decrease in [^{3}H]-QNB binding which they attributed to a loss of muscarinic receptors located on noradrenergic nerve terminals.

Story *et al.* (1979), using the same technique in rat heart, found that, within 2 weeks, there was a decrease in α-adrenergic receptor binding with an increase in [^{3}H]-QNB binding. They concluded that postsynaptic muscarinic receptors in the rat heart ventricle exhibited supersensitivity following sympathetic denervation similar to that seen in the rat salivary gland following postganglionic sympathetic denervation. This latter finding has since been verified by Yamada *et al.* (1980) who found an increase in [^{3}H]-QNB binding in the rat heart 3 weeks after administration of 6-OHDA.

(c) Is there only one population of postsynaptic muscarinic receptors?

It may be concluded from the previous studies that muscarinic antagonist binding sites, in very diverse tissues, have similar dissociation constants and that these dissociation constants are similar to affinity constants derived for the same ligands in whole-tissue preparations. It is this similarity between the binding and pharmacological data that provides the most compelling argument that these tritiated antagonists are labeling the muscarinic receptor. However, the IC_{50} for agonist inhibition of [^{3}H]-antagonist binding cannot be considered indicative of their true affinities because of their substantial deviation from mass-action kinetics (Birdsall *et al.*, 1976; Burgen and Hiley, 1974, 1975; Hulme *et al.*, 1975). Three explanations have been proposed for these results: (1) the receptor is progressively desensitized by increasing agonist concentrations (Young, 1974); (2) there is negative co-operativity between the agonist and antagonist conformations of the receptor (Snyder, 1975); or (3) there is more than one type of muscarinic receptor each having a different affinity for the agonist (Birdsall *et al.*, 1976).

There is no evidence favoring the densensitization theory in lysed synaptosomal preparations of rat brain (Birdsall *et al.*, 1976; Ward and Young, 1977). There is also little indication of negative co-operativity being involved in muscarinic agonist binding, i.e. Birdsall *et al.* (1976, 1978) showed that occluding approximately 90 per cent of the muscarinic receptor sites in cerebrocortical homogenates with propyl BCM did not change the Hill coefficient for the binding of carbachol to the remaining 10 per cent of the receptor sites. Recently, Birdsall *et al.* (1978) used tritiated muscarinic agonist ([³H]oxotremorine, [³H]pilocarpine and [³H]-ACh) to ascertain whether there was more than one agonist binding site. They found that: (1) at sufficiently high concentrations, agonists could completely inhibit specific [³H]-antagonist binding; (2) the occupancy–concentration curves for agonist displacement of [³H]-antagonists were flatter than the mass-action curve and these deviations from mass-action kinetics were marked at low agonist concentrations; and (3) the Hill slopes for agonists was always less than 1.0 and reached a minimum of 0.31 in the region where the per cent inhibition of specific binding was approximately 30 per cent. These data could best be explained by the presence of at least two populations of agonist binding sites that were non-interconvertible and had the same affinity for muscarinic antagonists. Their data showed that there were high-affinity sites ($K_H = 2 \times 10^6$ M^{-1}) and low affinity sites ($K_L = 1 \times 10^4$ M^{-1}) in the ratio of 40 per cent:60 per cent, respectively. [³H]-Oxotremorine binding revealed an additional, minor, super-high-affinity site ($K_{SH} = 4 \times 10^8$ M^{-1}) which, according to these investigators, resolved the discrepancies in dissociation constants as determined by competition with [³H]-agonists and [³H]-antagonists; i.e. at nanomolar concentrations of [³H]-oxotremorine, over half the binding was to the super-high-affinity sites. Agonist-inhibition experiments included competition at both the high- and super-high-affinity sites which explained why the Hill coefficients were less than 1.0. The function of these multiple sites was obscured. These investigators, however, pointed to other evidence indicating that the low-affinity receptors mediated the contractile response in smooth muscle and the activation of quanylate cyclase in neuroblastoma, and that phosphatidylinositol turnover (see Section 3.3.5) in smooth muscle was activated by both the high- and low-affinity receptor.

(d) Isolation and purification of the central muscarinic receptor
In 1974, Beld and Ariens attempted the first isolation of the muscarinic receptor from bovine tracheal smooth muscle and caudate nucleus. They used the stereospecific binding of (+)-[³H]benzetimide and (+)-[³H]-atropine as the primary criteria for the structural integrity of the isolated receptors. (+)-[³H]benzetimide and (+)-[³H]atropine bound to tissue homogenates with dissociation constants of 0.4 and 3 nM, and binding capacites of 12 and 21 pmol/g tissue, respectively. Attempts to solubilize the receptor with a variety of ionic and non-ionic detergents (i.e. 0.1 per cent Triton X-100, 0.1 per cent desoxycholate and 0.1 per cent Lubrol-WX) led to receptor denaturation and/or a loss of stereospecific receptor binding. The use of digitonin, a plant glycoside with mild detergent properties (Tansley, 1931), released bovine tracheal smooth muscle components to which (+) and (−) [³H]benzetimide bound differentially. Binding sites for anticholinergic agents in the caudate nucleus, however, could be

solubilized with digitonin only after hexane extraction of lyophilized homogenates which resulted in a loss of stereoselective binding.

Bartfai *et al*. (1974) tried to isolate the muscarinic receptor from rat
cerebral cortex. Extraction attempts with various concentrations of urea
and detergents failed, but the use of salt extraction and phospholipase A_2
were partially successful. Using salt concentrations greater than 1.5 M
(because AChE is released at low salt concentrations), they isolated two
proteins with[³H]atropine-binding activity. The proteins had molecular
weights of 33 000 and 70 000 and isoelectric points between 4.8 and 5.0.
Phospholipase A_2 treatment released a non-specific [³H]atropine binding
component and shifted the receptor's gel filtration peak to a higher
density.

Alberts and Bartfai (1976) used 2 M salt extraction to isolate a membrane protein from rat brain capable of binding [³H]atropine and [³H]-
PrBCM. Pronase and trypsin decreased the binding capacity of the solubilized receptor. Phospholipase A_2, C and D were ineffective in releasing the
membrane-bound receptor but they did not decrease the atropine binding
capacity of the salt-solubilized receptor. The molecular weight of the salt-
solubilized receptor, as determined by gel filtration in the absence of
detergents, was 30 000. The purified protein had high- and low-affinity
[³H]atropine-binding dissociation constants of 0.3 nM and 0.15 μM, respectively. This binding was both pH-(optimum 7.1) and Ca^{2+}-dependent
(optimum 0.5 mM Ca^{2+}).

Carson *et al*. (1977) measured [³H]-atropine binding to a receptor
extracted with 2 M-NaCl from a crude synaptosomal preparation of ox
cerebral cortex. The binding curve was sigmoidal and had a Hill coefficient
of 1.5. The dissociation constant and [³H]atropine binding capacity of this
preparation were 80 nM and 40 nmol/g protein, respectively. Each muscarinic antagonist tested in the solubilized-receptor binding assay had a
single class of binding sites and a Hill coefficient greater than 1.0. The
agonists tested had a single binding component, Hill coefficients greater
than 1.0 and IC_{50} in the micromolar range. Thus the solubilized receptor
had a single, high-affinity agonist binding site whose binding characteristics
were somewhat different from those in naive synaptosomal preparations.

Gorrissen *et al*. (1978) used gel filtration and a sedimentation gradient
(using [³H]dexetimide and [³H]levetimide as ligands*) to isolate a
digitonin-solubilized complex from rat brain. The receptor protein had a
single sedimentation-gradient peak of 9s (200 000 mol wt) and was similar
to a crude membrane preparation in its [³H]dexetimide binding characteristics. In both preparations, there was a single class of binding sites, with
similar binding capacities, and dissociation constants of 0.5 to 0.7 nM.

---

*Dexetimide = (+)benzetimide; levetimide = (−)benzetimide.

3.3.4 Cyclic nucleotides and the muscarinic receptor

Blume *et al.* (1977) reported that ACh regulated the adenosine $3', 5'$-cyclic phosphoric acid (cAMP) concentration of mouse neuroblastoma (clone NS 20). Acetylcholine did not alter the basal cAMP levels but prevented the increase in cAMP mediated by adenosine or PGE. Pilocarpine and carbamylcholine mimicked ACh in this system but acetate and choline did not. The effect was mediated via the muscarinic receptor, i.e. the action of 10 μM-carbamylcholine was blocked by nanomolar concentration of atropine, isopropamide and QNB but not by nanomolar concentrations of D-tubocurarine or hexamethonium. Of the eight cholinergic analogues tested, only decamethonium and succinylcholine could substitute for ACh postsynaptically and their stimulation of cAMP could be inhibited by nanomolar concentrations of QNB. The ionophores valinomycin, A23187 and X537A also prevented the increase in cAMP leading to the conclusion that ACh inhibited increases in cAMP via a specific membrane depolarization.

Nathanson *et al.* (1978) showed that carbamylcholine (an activator of the muscarinic receptors of NG 108-15 cells) inhibited adenylate cyclase (AC) activity rapidly and reversibly and it evoked a 200–300 per cent increase in AC activity over a period of 24–30 h. These effects were dependent upon the presence of both muscarinic receptors and carbamylcholine (or some muscarinic agonist). Removal of carbamylcholine resulted in a gradual decrease in AC activity, to control levels, over a 6-hour period and indicated that muscarinic receptors mediated both transient and long-lasting effects on AC activity.

Richelson (1978) showed that incubation of mouse neuroblastoma cells (clone N1E-115) with carbamylcholine made cells insensitive to this agonist in terms of its stimulation of guanosine $3', 5'$-cyclic phosphoric acid (cGMP) formation. After the initial incubation, the histamine-mediated stimulation of cGMP (via the H_1 receptor) was decreased drastically whereas the cGMP response to carbamylcholine was only slightly decreased. Therefore, carbamylcholine's ability to decrease muscarinic receptor-mediated cGMP formation represented specific agonist desensitization of one type of receptor. cGMP, *per se*, was not involved in receptor densensitization because the muscarinic receptor-mediated cGMP response in these cells was dependent on external Ca^{2+} and removal of Na^+, K^+, Mg^{2+} and Ca^{2+} had no effect on carbamylcholine-mediated desensitization. Unlike densensitization of the nicotinic or α-adrenergic receptors, this desensitization was associated with a decreased affinity of the muscarinic receptor for carbamylcholine and a decreased number of binding sites. Since there was no change in [^{3}H]-QNB binding to these cells, under conditions which caused desensitization of the cGMP response, the antagonist binding site was most likely not involved in this desensitization.

When carbamylcholine-stimulated N1E-115 cells were incubated with
[^{3}H]guanine, more than 90 per cent of the radioactivity in the eulates was
[^{3}H]cGMP (Richelson *et al.*, 1978). Removal of external Na^+ or Ca^{2+}, in
these cells, reduced the carbamylcholine-stimulated formation of [^{3}H]-
cGMP to 60 per cent and 10 per cent of control, respectively. Ca^{2+}
increased the carbamylcholine-stimulated formation of [^{3}H]-cGMP without
altering carbamylcholine's affinity for the muscarinic receptor. Local
anesthetics functioned as competitive inhibitors of this carbamylcholine
effect and had affinities between 6 and 250 μM.

Richelson and Divenetz-Romero (1977), used the receptor-mediated
formation of [^{3}H]-cGMP from [^{3}H]-guanosine 5'-triphosphate to measure
the ability of antimuscarinics, tricyclic antidepressants and antipsychotics to
block the muscarinic receptor in N1E-115 cells. The tricyclic antidepressants and antipsychotics competitively blocked the muscarinic receptor.
The relative potencies of the antipsychotics tested were similar to those
from receptor-binding studies in rat brain homogenates (Miller and Hiley,
1974; Snyder *et al.*, 1974) supporting the idea that the frequency of
extrapyramidal side effects of antipsychotic drugs may be inversely related
to their ability to block the muscarinic receptor (see Section 3.3.7). These
data also suggested that part of this effect might have been mediated by an
inhibition of muscarinic receptor-stimulated guanylate cyclase (GC)
activity.

Hanley and Iversen (1978) tested cholinergic agonists and antagonists
for their ability to displace [^{3}H]-QNB binding in slices of rat brain striatum
and this response was compared with the effects of those drugs on cGMP
levels in the same preparation.

The muscarinic agonists oxotremorine, arecholine and carbachol
produced transient increase in cGMP reaching maximal levels after 2 h
incubation. There was also a significant increase in cAMP that was
antagonised by muscarinic blocking agents. The ED_{50}s for agonists in
increasing cGMP were similar to their inhibitory constants derived from
the [^{3}H]-QNB binding assay. The cGMP response appeared, therefore, to
be linearly related to muscarinic receptor occupancy. Various muscarinic
antagonists and neuroleptics were able to inhibit the cGMP response
ilicited by oxotremorine with the same relative potencies with which they
inhibited [^{3}H]-QNB binding. The cGMP response to oxotremorine required
Ca^+ and was maximal at Ca^{2+} concentrations greater than 1 mM. These
investigators concluded that occupancy of muscarinic receptors activated a
soluble intracellular GC indirectly with Ca^{2+} acting as an intracellular
mediator. The fact that some neuroleptics decreased the cGMP response to
muscarinic agonists in brain slices supported the claim that these drugs
have significant antimuscarinic actions in the mammalian CNS.

Strange *et al.* (1978) found that [^{3}H]-QNB bound to a single class of muscarinic receptors in plasma membranes from N1E-115 cells with a high affinity (i.e. a dissociation constant of 40 pM) and according to the laws of mass-action. Binding data from this clone corresponded to binding data from whole rat brain, smooth muscle strips and homogenates of the two.

3.3.5 The role of phosphatidylinositol turnover in cholinergic transmission

Evidence gleaned from various tissues indicated a role for phosphatidylinositol (PI) turnover in the stimulus–response coupling of muscarinic cholinergic receptors (see review, Michell *et al.*, 1977). Michell and co-workers (Jafferji and Michell, 1976a,b,c,d; Jones and Michell, 1975, 1976) built a strong case favoring a functional relationship between PI breakdown and the control of cell-surface Ca^{2+} gates; particularly those opened by activation of muscarinic receptors. They proposed that a change in PI breakdown controlled the opening of cell-surface Ca^{2+} gates. This concept seemed reasonable since the removal of the phosphorylinositol headgroup from PI preceded Ca^{2+} influx after activation of the muscarinic receptor.

Several pieces of evidence supported the proposal that PI turnover was integral to stimulus–response coupling at the muscarinic receptor. Increased PI breakdown was a consequence of stimuli that caused an increased influx of Ca^{2+} into the cell after activation of Ca^{2+}-mobilizing receptors (Jafferji and Michell, 1976b,d; Michell, 1975). Enhanced PI turnover occurred in response to muscarinic stimulation in guinea-pig ileum smooth muscle and in isolated sympathetic superior cervical ganglia (Jafferji and Michell, 1976a; Lapetina *et al.*, 1976). PI turnover did not appear to be triggered by an increase in intracellular Ca^{2+} because: (1) muscarinic agonists stimulated PI turnover in cells deprived of Ca^{2+} ions (Jones and Michell, 1975; Oron *et al.*, 1975; Trifaro, 1969); (2) PI turnover was not stimulated by Ca^{2+} ionophores (Jones and Michell, 1975; Oron *et al.*, 1975; Rossignol *et al.*, 1974); and (3) drugs which prevented the receptor-mediated influx of Ca^{2+} ions did not decrease the muscarinic stimulation of PI turnover (Jafferji and Michell, 1976c). Activation of PI turnover gave a dose–response curve for muscarinic agonists that was equivalent to the receptor–occupation curve and indicated a direct coupling between receptor activation and PI breakdown. High K^+ concentrations stimulated PI turnover only in tissues with 'potential-sensitive' Ca^{2+} gates.

On the basis of this evidence, and models suggested by other investigators (Chang and Triggle, 1973a,b; Hurwitz and Suria, 1971; Matthews, 1974; Purves, 1976; Triggle, 1972), Michell *et al.* (1977) proposed that there was a cell-surface-Ca^{2+}-binding site lying in or adjacent to a closed Ca^{2+} gate that released a Ca^{2+} ion into the cell upon receptor activation. The channel remained open to permit passage of a large number of

Ca^{2+} ions and it was then closed by an inactivating mechanism which took a certain period of time to restore responsiveness – hence the phenomenon of desensitization.

With respect to the nicotinic cholinergic receptor, Hawthorne and Kai (1970) proposed that Ca^{2+} bound to two molecules of either 1-phosphatidylinositol-3,4-bisphosphate (TPI) or 1-phosphatidylinositol-4-phosphate (DPI) could obstruct an ion channel and that the dephosphorylation of either to PI would release Ca^{2+} and open the channel. Hendrickson and Reinersten (1971a,b) showed that there was a sufficient difference in the CA^{2+} affinity of TPI and DPI so that just the dephosphorylation of TPI to DPI would decrease membrane-bound CA^{2+} levels. Torda (1972) suggested that the dephosphorylation of TPI to DPI was involved in the generation of action potentials at central nicotinic synapses. This hypothesis, however, was inconsistent with evidence that the nicotinic receptor was an ACh-stimulated ionophoric membrane protein (Hazelbauer and Changeux, 1974; Michaelson *et al.*, 1976; Michell, 1975).

Hitzemann *et al.* (1978) studied the effects of various doses of nicotine on the incorporation of $[^{32}P]$- and $[^{3}H]$-glycerol into TPI and DPI in an attempt to determine the role of TPI and DPI in central nicotinic transmission. The accumulation of $[^{32}P]$- and $[^{3}H]$-labeled TPI was very sensitive to nicotine administration and there were marked changes in phospholipid turnover in response to pharmacologically relevant doses of nicotine. Nicotine preferentially decreased $[^{32}P]$- and $[^{3}H]$-labeled TPI as compared to labeled DPI and it significantly decreased the ratio of $[^{32}P]$-TPI to $[^{32}P]$-DPI. From these data, and previous data showing that a decreased TPI to DPI ratio caused a decrease in membrane lipid-bound Ca^{2+} (Hendrickson and Reinersten, 1971a,b), they concluded that nicotine either enhanced TPI metabolism or blocked the synthesis of TPI from DPI, and that there was a relationship between the interconversion of TPI and DPI and the excitability of the nicotinic receptor.

3.3.6 Muscarinic receptors in the electric organ of *Torpedo*

Pickard and Strange (1978), using $[^{3}H]$-QNB, discovered and partially characterized muscarinic receptor binding in *Torpedo marmorata* membranes. They found muscarinic receptor concentrations of 12 pmol/g protein in crude homogenates and 85 pmol/g protein in partially purified membrane fragments. In these same fragments, they found that muscarinic receptors were far outnumbered by nicotinic receptors (1000 pmol g^{-1}). Atropine and carbamylcholine's IC_{50}s and Hill coefficients were 2.8 nM and 1.07, and 116 nM and 0.7, respectively. These data were similar to those found by other investigators for the same compounds in various mammalian brain preparations. Their observation was even more interesting given the fact that there was an increase in PI turnover in this tissue after electrical stimulation which has characteristically been associated with the muscarinic, rather than the nicotinic receptor (Bleasdale *et al.*, 1976).

Kloog *et al.* (1978) found similar results in the electric organ of *Torpedo ocellata*. There was a nicotinic receptor concentration of 10.6 nmol/g tissue in a homogenate of this organ, and [^{3}H]-QNB and [^{3}H]-4NMPB were bound maximally at 400 fmol/g tissue in a P_2 pellet. This organ, therefore, had approximately 1 muscarinic binding site per 25 000 nicotinic binding sites. [^{3}H]-QNB and [^{3}H]-4NMPB and dissociation constants of 0.3 and 1 nM, respectively. The IC_{50} and Hill coefficients for atropine and oxotremorine were 3.3 nM and 1.0 and 0.1 μM and 0.6, respectively. D-tubocurarine and α-Bgt (at concentration of 10 M) had no effect on the binding of either [^{3}H]-muscarinic ligand. Muscarinic ligands also interfered with Ca^{2+}-induced synaptosomal ACh secretion. Because of this effect, and the finding that muscarinic receptors were enriched in the synaptosomal fraction, it was concluded that these receptors were located presynaptically in the *Torpedo* electric organ and that they modulated the release of ACh.

3.3.7 The muscarinic receptor and neuropsychiatric disorders

Alterations in the brain's muscarinic receptors accompany at least three known neuropsychiatric disorders: Parkinson's Disease (PD), Huntington's Disease (HD) and Alzheimer's Disease (AD) (the symptoms of which are thought to involve primarily a striatal dopaminergic deficiency, a striatal dopaminergic excess and frontal cortical degeneration, respectively). Whether these alterations are the cause or the result of these diseases had never been determined, but the existence of these alterations indicates potential points of pharmacological intervention that may alter the disease processes or alleviate the symptoms of the diseases for a period of time.

Reisine *et al.* (1977) measured ChAc activity and [^{3}H]-QNB binding in the frontal cortex and the basal ganglia of brains taken from patients who had died of PD. There were no changes in either parameter in the frontal cortex but there was enhanced [^{3}H]-QNB binding in the putamen coupled with a decrease in ChAc activity. These data indicated a 'denervation supersensitivity' for ACh in this area, and the decrease in ChAc activity in the basal ganglia, as reported previously by several groups (Hornykiewicz, 1973; Lloyd *et al.*, 1977; Marsden and Parkes, 1977), indicated that a significant amount of the intrastriatal cell loss was cholinergic.

Several investigators found decreases in ChAc activity in the cerebral cortex, hippocampus and corpus striatum of AD brains (Davies and Maloney, 1976; Perry *et al.*, 1977; Reisine *et al.*, 1978; Spillane *et al.*, 1977). Reisine *et al.* (1978) found a reduction of [^{3}H]-QNB binding in the hippocampus of AD brains with no changes in the basal ganglia or the frontal cortex. It was concluded that AD involved primarily a degeneration of the brain's cholinergic system and that muscarinic cortical-hippocampal pathways were involved.

Muscarinic receptor binding (Enna *et al.*, 1976a; Hiley and Bird, 1974; Wastek and Yamamura, 1978; Wastek *et al.*, 1976) and ChAc activity (Bird and Iversen, 1977; Enna *et al.*, 1976a,b; McGeer and McGeer, 1971; McGeer *et al.*, 1973; Stahl and Swanson, 1974; Wastek and Yamamura, 1978; Wastek *et al.*, 1976) were reduced in the corpus striatum of HD brains postmortem. By titrating the amount of tissue protein against the K_D app (Cuatrecasas and Hollenberg, 1976) in the frontal cortex and basal ganglia of HD brains and by using the active stereoisomer of benzetimide to inhibit [^{3}H]-QNB binding in these same regions, Wastek and Yamamura (1978) showed that the decrease in [^{3}H]-QNB binding were due to receptor loss rather than to changes in receptor affinity, i.e. the remaining receptors were 'normal' receptors and treatment with cholinergic drugs might alleviate some of symptoms of HD.

Hruska *et al.* (1978b) examined muscarinic receptor binding in the rat striatum after kainic acid injections because kainic acid, when injected into the striatum, was reported to produce neurochemical alterations similar to those of HD (Coyle and Schwarcz, 1976; Coyle *et al.*, 1977; McGeer and McGeer, 1976). They found a 40 per cent decrease in receptor density in the lesioned caudate nuclei with no alteration in the receptors' affinity for [^{3}H]-QNB. The similarity between these data and those derived from HD brains strengthened the usefulness of kainic acid lesions as an animal model for HD and indicated that this model might prove useful in evaluating various parameters of HD.

(a) Antipsychotics, antidepressants and the muscarinic receptor
The phenothiazines and butyrophenones were known to have comparable antischizophrenic activity. The major criterion in selecting the appropriate neuroleptic, therefore, was the relative frequency of side effects – extrapyramidal side effects in particular. It was hypothesized originally that blockade of dopamine receptors in the brain accounted for both the anti-schizophrenic effects and the extrapyramidal side effects of these drugs. Snyder *et al.* (1974) demonstrated that the extrapyramidal side effects of the neuroleptics were inversely proportional to their affinity for the muscarinic receptor. Neuroleptics exhibiting few extrapyramidal side effects, therefore, had anticholinergic properties that compensated for their intrinsic extrapyramidal side effects.

Similarly, Snyder and Yamamura (1977) showed that the frequency of untoward side effects of the tricyclic antidepressants was directly related to their affinity for the muscarinic receptor, i.e. the greater the affinity, the more intense the anticholinergic side effects. Since atropine-like side effects represent a major hazard in older patients, selecting a drug with minimal anticholinergic properties became essential to effective treatment.

3.4 SUMMARY

Dramatic advances have been made in recent years in the identification and isolation of the peripheral hormonal receptors and of the nicotinic cholinergic receptor of the invertebrates. Relatively few studies, until very recently, have been performed to demonstrate and identify the acetylcholine receptors in the mammalian central nervous system. In the past this was probably due to the lack of a highly stable and specific cholinergic receptor ligand. Recently, however, it has been possible to demonstrate the presence of acetylcholine receptors within the brain by biochemical methods. One of the procedures involves studying the response of cyclic GMP in neuronal tissue to applications of various agonists or antagonists. The other method takes into consideration the specificity of a given ligand for the neurotransmitter receptor. Using the latter procedures, investigators have been able to demonstrate the receptor recognition site in the brain directly by first radiolabeling the ligand to a high specific activity.

The nicotinic cholinergic receptors have been demonstrated in the mammalian brain by the use of a potent, neurotoxin α-bungarotoxin from the snake venom. [^{3}H]-Quinuclidinyl benzilate, propyl benzilylcholine mustards and atropine are just a few of the muscarinic cholinergic ligands which have been used to demonstrate peripheral and central cholinergic receptors.

This chapter reviews the microiontophoretic interactions of acetylcholine with muscarinic and nicotinic receptors in mammalian brain, the biochemical characterization of central nicotinic and central and peripheral muscarinic receptors, and the involvement of cyclic nucleotides, phospholipids and other agents in cholinergic receptor function.

REFERENCES

Alberts, P. and Bartfai, T. (1976), *J. biol. Chem.,* **251**, 1543.
Andersen, P. and Curtis, D.R. (1964), *Acta Physiol. Scand.,* **61**, 100.
Arimatsu, Y., Seto, A. and Amano, T. (1978), *Brain Res.,* **147**, 165.
Aronstam, R.S., Abood, L.G. and Hoss, W. (1978), *Mol. Pharmacol.,* **14**, 575.
Aronstam, R.S., Hoss, W. and Abood, L.G. (1977), *Eur. J. Pharmacol.,* **46**, 279.
Barker, J.L., Crayton, J.W. and Nicoll, R.A. (1971), *J. Physiol.,* **218**, 19.
Bartfai, T., Anner, J., Schultzberg, M. and Montelius, (1974), *Biochem. biophys. Res. Commun.,* **59**, 725.
Beld, A.J. and Ariens, E.J. (1974), *Eur. J. Pharmacol.,* **25**, 203.

Bird, E.D. and Iversen, L.L. (1977), in *Essays in Neurochemistry and Neurophar-macology* (Youdin, M.B.H., Sharmon, O. F., Lovenbert, W. and Lagnado, J.R., eds), Vol. I, p. 177, Wiley, London.

Birdsall, N.J.M., Burgen, A.S.V., Hiley, C.R. and Hulme, E.C. (1976), *J. Sup-ramol. Struct.,* **4**, 367.

Birdsall, N.J.M., Burgen, A.S.V. and Hulme, E.C. (1978), *Mol. Pharmacol.,* **14**, 723.

Birdsall, N.J.M. and Hulme, E.C. (1976), *J. Neurochem.,* **27**, 7.

Biscoe, T.J. and Straughan, D.W. (1966), *J. Physiol.,* **183**, 341.

Bleasdale, J.E., Hawthorne, J.N., Widland, L. and Heilbronn, E. (1976), *Biochem. J.,* **158**, 557.

Bloom, F.E., Costa, E. and Salmoiraghi, G.C. (1964), *J. Pharmacol.,* **146**, 16.

Bloom, F.E., Costa, E. and Salmoiraghi, G.C. (1965), *J. Pharmacol. exp. Ther.,* **150**, 244.

Blume, A.J., Chen, C. and Foster, C.J. (1977), *J. Neurochem.,* **29**, 625.

Bradley, P.B., Dhawan, B.N. and Wolstencroft, J.H. (1966), *J. Physiol.,* **183**, 658.

Burgen, A.S.V. and Hiley, C.R. (1975), in *Cholinergic Mechanisms*, (Waser, P.G., ed), pp. 381–385, Raven Press, New York; *Brit. J. Pharmac.,* **51**, (1974), 127P.

Burgen, A.S.V., Hiley, C.R. and Young, J.M. (1974a), *Brit. J. Pharmacol.,* **50**, 145.

Burgen, A.S.V., Hiley, C.R. and Young, J.M. (1974b), *Brit. J. Pharmacol.,* **51**, 279.

Burgermeister, W., Klein, W.L., Nirenberg, M. and Witkip, B. (1978), *Mol. Pharmacol.,* **14**, 751.

Carson, S., Godwin, S., Masoulie, J. and Kato, G. (1977), *Nature,* **266**, 176.

Chang, C.C. and Lee, C.Y. (1963), *Arch. Int. Pharmaodyn.,* **144**, 241.

Chang, H.C. and Gaddum, J.H. (1933), *J. Physiol.,* **79**, 255.

Chang, K.-J. and Triggle, D.J. (1973a), *J. theor. Biol.,* **40**, 125.

Chang, K.-J. and Triggle, D.J. (1973b), *J. theor. Biol.,* **40**, 155.

Changeux, J.-P., Kasai, M. and Lee, C.Y. (1970), *Proc. natl. Acad. Sci. USA,* **67**, 1241.

Coyle, J.T. and Schwarcz, R. (1976), *Nature,* **263**, 244.

Coyle, J.T. and Yamamura, H.I. (1976), *Brain Res.,* **118**, 429.

Coyle, J.T., Schwarcz, R., Bennett, J.P. and Campochiaro, P. (1977), *Prog. Neuropsychopharm.,* **1**, 13.

Crawford, J.M., Curtis, D.R., Voorhoeve, P.E. and Wilson, V.J. (1966), *J. Physiol.,* **186**, 139.

Crawford, J.M., (1970), *Brain Res.,* **17**, 287.

Crawford, J.M. and Curtis, D.R. (1966), *J. Physiol.,* **186**, 121.

Cuatrecasas, P. and Hollenberg, M.D. (1976), *Adv. Prot. Chem.,* **30**, 251.

Curtis, D.R. and Eccles, R.M. (1958a), *J. Physiol.,* **141**, 435.

Curtis, D.R. and Eccles, R.M. (1958b), *J. Physiol.,* **141**, 446.

Curtis, D.R. and Ryall, R.W. (1966a), *Exp. Brain Res.,* **2**, 49.

Curtis, D.R. and Ryall, R.W. (1966b), *Exp. Brain Res.,* **2**, 66.

Cuthbert, A.W. and Young, J.M. (1973), *Brit. J. Pharmacol.,* **47**, 631P.

Dale, H.H. (1914), *J. Pharmacol. exp. Ther.,* **6**, 147.

Davies, P. and Maloney, A.J.F. (1976), *Lancet,* **II**, 1403.

Davis, R. and Vaughan, P.C. (1969), *J. Neuropharmacol.,* **8**, 475.

Eccles, J.C., Fatt, P. and Koketsu, K. (1954), *J. Physiol.*, **126**, 524.

Edelstein, S.J., Beyer, W.B., Eldefrawi, A.T. and Eldefrawi, M.E. (1975), *J. biol. Chem.*, **250**, 6101.

Ehlert, F.J., Roeske, W.R., Rosenberger, L.B. and Yamamura, H.I. (1980), *Life Sci.*, **26**, 245.

Enna, S.J., Bird, E.D., Bennett, J.P., Bylund, D.B., Yamamura, H.I., Iversen, L.L. and Snyder, S.H. (1976a), *N. Eng. J. Med.*, **294**, 1305.

Enna, S.J., Bennett, J.P., Bylund, D.B., Snyder, S.H., Bird, E.D. and Iversen, L.L. (1976b), *Brain Res.*, **116**, 531.

Eterovic, V.A. and Bennett, E.L. (1974), *Biochim. Biophys. Acta*, **362**, 346.

Fields, J.Z., Roeske, W.R., Morkin, E. and Yamamura, H.I. (1978), *J. biol. Chem.*, **253**, 3251.

Fewtrell, C.M.S. and Rang, H.P. (1973), in *Drug Receptors*, (Rang, H.P., ed.), pp. 211–244, Macmillan, London.

Gill, W. and Rang, H.P. (1966), *Mol. Pharmacol.*, **2**, 284.

Gorrissen, H., Aerts, G. and Laduron, P. (1978), *FEBS Letts.*, **96**, 64.

Gruenhagen, H.H. and Changeux, J.-P. (1976), *J. mol. Biol.*, **106**, 517.

Hadhazy, P. and Szerb, J.C. (1977), *Brain Res.*, **123**, 311.

Hanley, M.R. and Iversen, L.L. (1978), *Mol. Pharmacol.*, **14**, 246.

Harris, A.J. and Dennis, M.J. (1970), *Science*, **167**, 1253.

Hawthorne, J.N. and Kai, M. (1970), in *Handbook of Neurochemistry*, (Lajtha, A., ed.), Vol. 3, p. 491, Plenum Press, New York.

Hazelbauer, G. and Changeux, J.-P. (1974), *Proc. natl. Acad. Sci. USA*, **7**, 14, 83.

Heidmann, T. and Changeux, J.-P. (1978), *Ann. Rev. Biochem.*, **47**, 317.

Henderson, W.R. and Wilson, W.C. (1936), *Q. J. exp. Physiol.*, **26**, 83.

Hendrickson, H.S. and Reinersten, J.L. (1971a), *Biochemistry*, **9**, 4855.

Hendrickson, H.S. and Reinersten, J.L. (1971b), *Biochem. biophys. Res. Commun.*, **44**, 1258.

Hiley, C.R., Young, J.M. and Burgen, A.S.V. (1972), *Biochem. J.*, **127**, 86P.

Hiley, C.R. and Burgen, A.S.V. (1974), *J. Neurochem.*, **22**, 159.

Hiley, C.R. and Bird, E.D. (1974), *Brain Res.*, **80**, 355.

Hitzemann, R.J., Natsuki, J.R. and Loh, H.H. (1978), *Biochem. Pharmacol.*, **27**, 2519.

Hornykiewicz, O. (1973), *Fed. Proc.*, **32**, 183.

Hruska, R.E., White, R., Azari, J. and Yamamura, H.I. (1978a), *Brain Res.*, **148**, 493.

Hruska, R.E., Schwarcz, R., Coyle, J.T. and Yamamura, H.I. (1978b), *Brain Res.*, **152**, 620.

Hulme, E.C., Birdsall, N.J.M., Burgen, A.S.V. and Mehta, P. (1978), *Mol. Pharmacol.*, **14**, 737.

Hulme, E.C., Burgen, A.S.V. and Birdsall, N.J.M. (1975), in *Proc. INSERM Colloquim on the Physiology and Pharmacology of Smooth Muscle*, (Worcel, M. and Vassort, G., eds), INSERM, Paris.

Hunt, S.P. and Schmidt, J. (1978), *Brain Res.*, **142**, 152.

Hurwitz, L. and Suria, A. (1971), *Ann. Rev. Pharmacol.*, **11**, 303.

Jafferji, S.S. and Michell, R.H. (1976a), *Biochem. J.*, **154**, 653.

Jafferji, S.S. and Michell, R.H. (1976b), *Biochem. Pharmacol.*, **25**, 1429.

Jafferji, S.S. and Michell, R.H. (1976c), *Biochem. J.*, **160**, 163.
Jafferji, S.S. and Michell, R.H. (1976d), *Biochem. J.*, **160**, 397.
Jones, L.M. and Michell, R.H. (1975), *Biochem. J.*, **148**, 479.
Jones, L.M. and Michell, R.H. (1976), *Biochem. J.*, **158**, 505.
Jordan, L.M. and Phillis, J.W. (1972), *Brit. J. Pharmacol.*, **45**, 584.
Katz, B. and Thesleff, S. (1957), *J. Physiol.*, **138**, 63.
Kloog, Y., Michaelson, D.M. and Sokolovsky, M. (1978), *FEBS Letts.*, **94**, 331.
Kloog, Y. and Sokolovsky, M. (1977), *Brain Res.*, **134**, 167.
Kloog, Y. and Sokolovksy, M. (1978a), *Biochem. biophys. Res. Commun.*, **81**, 710.
Kloog, Y. and Sokolovsky, M. (1978b), *Brain Res.*, **144**, 31.
Kobayashi, R.M., Palkovits, M., Hruska, R.E., Rothschild, R. and Yamamura, H.I. (1978), *Brain Res.*, **154**.
Krnjevic, K. (1974),*Physiol. Rev.*, **54**, 419.
Krnjevic, K. and Phillis, J.W. (1963a), *J. Physiol.*, **166**, 296.
Krnjevic, K. and Phillis, J.W. (1963b), *J. Physiol.*, **166**, 328.
Krnjevic, K., Pumain, R. and Renaud, L. (1971), *J. Physiol.*, **215**, 247.
Krnjevic, K. and Schwartz, S. (1967), *Exp. Brain Res.*, **3**, 306.
Kuhar, M.J. and Yamamura, H.I. (1975), *Nature,* **253**, 560.
Kuhar, M.J. and Yamamura, H.I. (1976), *Brain Res.*, **110**, 229.
Landau, E.M. (1978), *Prog. Neurobiol.*, **10**, 253.
Lapetina, E.G., Brown, W.E. and Michell, R.H. (1976), *J. Neurochem.*, **26**, 649.
Legge, K., Randic, M. and Straughan, D.W. (1966), *Brit. J. Pharmacol.*, **26**, 87.
Lloyd, K.G., Shemen, L. and Hornykiewicz, O. (1977), *Brain Res.*, **127**, 269.
Lowy, J., McGregor, J., Rosenstone, J. and Schmidt, J. (1976), *Biochemsitry,* **15**, 1522.
Marsden, C.D. and Parkes, J.D. (1977), *Lancet*, **1**, 345.
Matthews, E.K. (1974), in *Secretory Mechanisms of Exocrine Glands*, (Thron, N.A. and Petersen, O.H., eds), pp. 185 195, Munksgaard, Copenhagen.
McCance, I. and Phillis, J.W. (1968), *Int. J. Neuropharmacol.*, **7**, 447.
McGeer, P.L. and McGeer, E.G. (1971), *Arch Neurol.*, **25**, 265.
McGeer, P.L., McGeer, E.G. and Fibiger, H.C. (1973), *Neurol.*, **23**, 912.
McGeer, E.G. and McGeer, P.L. (1976), *Nature,* **263**, 517.
McLennan, H. and York,. D.H. (1966), *J. Physiol.*, **187**, 163.
McQuarrrie, C., Salvaterra, P.M., DeBlas, A., Routes, J. and Mahler, H.R. (1976), *J. biol. Chem.*, **251**, 6225.
Michaelson, D.M., Dugurd, J.R., Miller, D.L. and Raftery, M.A. (1976), *J. Supramolec. Struct.*, **4**, 419.
Michell, R.H. (1975), *Biochim. Biophys. Acta*, **415**, 81.
Michell, R.H., Jones, L.M. and Jafferji, S.S. (1977), *Biochem. Soc. Trans.*, **5**, 77–81.
Miller, R.J. and Hiley, C.R. (1974), *Nature,* **248**, 596.
Moore, W.M. and Brady, R.N. (1976), *Biochim. Biophys. Acta,* **444**, 252.
Moore, W.J. and Loy, N.J. (1972), *Biochem. Biophys, Res. Commun.*, **46**, 2093.
Nathanson, N.M., Klein, W.L. and Nirenberg, M. (1978), *Proc. natl. Acad. Sci. USA,* **75**, 1788.
Nelson, P.G., Peacock, J.H. and Amano, T. (1971), *J. Cell. Physiol.*, **77**, 353.
Oron, Y., Lowe, M. and Selinger, Z. (1975), *Mol. Pharmacol.*, **11**, 79.

Paton, W.D.M. and Rang, H.P. (1965), *Proc. Roy. Soc. B.,* **163**, 1.
Peacock, J.H. and Nelson, P.G. (1973), *J. Neurobiol.,* **4**, 363.
Perry, E.K., Perry, R.H., Blessed, G. and Tomlinson, B. (1977), *Lancet,* **I**, 189.
Phillis, J.W. (1971), *Int. Rev. Neurobiol.,* **14**, 1.
Phillis, J.W. and York, D.H. (1968), *Brain Res.,* **10**, 279.
Pickard, M.R. and Strange, P.G. (1978), *Biochem. Soc. Trans.,* **6**, 129.
Polak, R.L. and Meeuws, M.M. (1966), *Pharmacol.,* **15**, 989.
Purves, R.D. (1976), *Nature,* **261**, 149.
Randic, M., Simonoff, R. and Straughan, D.W. (1964), *Exp. Neurol.,* **9**, 236.
Rang, H.P. (1967), *Ann. N.Y. Acad. Sci. USA,* **144**, 756.
Reisine, T.D., Fields, J.Z. and Yamamura, H.I. (1977), *Life Sci.,* **21**, 335.
Reisine, T.D., Yamamura, H.I., Bird, E.D., Spokes, E. and Enna, S.J. (1978), *Brain Res.,* **159**, 477.
Richelson, E. (1978), *Nature,* **272**, 366.
Richelson, E., Prendergast, F.G. and Divenetz-Romero, S. (1978), *Biochem. Pharmacol.,* **27**, 2039.
Richelson, E. and Divenetz-Romero, S. (1977), *Biol. Psychiatr.,* **12**, 771.
Roeske, W.R. and Yamamura, H.I. (1978), *Life Sci.,* **23**, 127.
Rosenberger, L.B., Yamamura, H.I. and Roeske, W.R. (1980), *J. biol. Chem.,* **255**, 820.
Rossignol, B., Herman, G., Chambaut, A.M. and Keryer, G. (1974), *FEBS Letts.,* **43**, 241.
Salmoiraghi, G.C. and Stefanis, C.N. (1967), *Int. Rev. Neurobiol.,* **10**, 1.
Salmoiraghi, G.C. and Steiner, F.A. (1963), *J. Neurophysiol.,* **26**, 581.
Salvaterra, P.M. and Mahler, H.R. (1976), *J. biol. Chem.,* **251**, 6327.
Salvaterra, P.M., Mahler, H.R. and Moore, W.J. (1975), *J. biol. Chem.,* **250**, 6469.
Salvaterra, P.M. and Moore, W.J. (1973), *Biochem. biophys. Res. Commun.,* **55**, 1311.
Schmidt, J. (1977), *Mol. Pharmacol.,* **13**, 283.
Segal, M. (1978), *Neuropharmacol.,* **17**, 619.
Segal, M., Dudai, Y. and Amsterdam, A. (1978), *Brain Res.,* **148**, 105.
Sharma, V.K. and Banerjee, S.P. (1978), *Nature,* 272, 276.
Snyder, S., Greenberg, D. and Yamamura, H.I. (1974), *Arch. Gen. Psychiatr.,* **31**, 58.
Snyder, S.H. (1975), *Nature,* **257**, 185.
Snyder, S.H. and Yamamura, H.I. (1977), *Arch. Gen. Psychiatr.,* **34**, 236.
Spehlmann, R. (1963), *J. Neurophysiol.,* **26**, 127.
Spillane, J., White, P., Goodhardt, M., Flack, R., Bowen, D.M. and Davison, A. (1977), *Nature,* **266**, 558.
Stahl, W.L. and Swanson, P.D. (1974), *Neurol.,* **24**, 813.
Stone, T.W. (1972), *J. Physiol.,* **225**, 485.
Story, D.F., Briley, M.S. and Langer, S.Z. (1979), In: *Advances in the Biosciences,* Vol. 18, 'Presynaptic Receptors' (Langer, S.Z., Starke, K. and Dubocovich, M.L., eds), pp. 105–109, Pergamon Press, New York.
Strange, P.G., Birdsall, N.J.M. and Burgen, A.S.V. (1978), *Biochem. J.,* **172**, 495.
Straschill, M. and Perwein, J. (1971), *Pfluegers Arch,* **324**, 43.
Suarez-Isla, B.A. and Hucho, F. (1977), *FEBS Letts.,* **75**, 65.

Sugiyama, H. (1978), *Adv. Biophys. (Tokyo)*, **10**, 1.

Sugiyama, H., Daniels, M.P. and Nirenberg, M. (1977), *Proc. natl. Acad. Sci. USA*, **74**, 5524.

Szerb, J.C. and Somogyi, G.T. (1973), *Nature, New Biol.*, **241**, 121.

Takagi, K., Akao, M. and Takahashi, A. (1965), *Life Sci.*, **4**, 2165.

Takagi, K. and Takahashi, A. (1968), *Biochem. Pharmacol.*, **17**, 1609.

Tansley, K. (1931), *J. Phsyiol.*, **71**, 442.

Taylor, I.K., Cuthbert, A.W. and Young, J.M. (1975), *Eur. J. Pharmacol.*, **31**, 319.

Tebecis, A.K. (1972), *J. Physiol.*, **226**, 153.

Tebecis, A.K. (1973), *Exp. Neurol.*, **40**, 297.

Teichberg, V.I. and Changeux, J.-P. (1976), *FEBS Letts.*, **67**, 264.

Tindall, R.S.A., Kent, M., Baskin, F. and Rosenberg, R.N. (1978), *Neurochemistry*, **30**, 859.

Torda, C. (1972), In: *A Depolarization–Hyperpolarization Cycle: A Molecular model*, (Torda, C., ed), pp. 1–100, New York.

Trifaro, J. (1969), *Mol. Pharmacol.*, **5**, 424.

Triggle, D.J. (1972), *Adv. Membr. Surf. Sci.*, **5**, 267.

Ueki, S., Koketsu, K. and Domino, E.F. (1961), *Exp. Neurol.*, **3**, 141.

Ward, D. and Young, J.M. (1977), *Brit. J. Pharmacol.*, **61**, 189.

Wastek, G.J., Stern, L.Z., Johnson, P.C. and Yamamura, H.I. (1976), *Life Sci.*, **19**, 1033.

Wastek, G.J. and Yamamura, H.I. (1978), *Mol. Pharmacol.*, **14**, 768.

Weight, F.F. and Salmoiraghi, G.C. (1966), *J. Pharmacol. exp. Ther.*, **153**, 420.

Yamada, S., Yamamura, H.I. and Roeske, W.R. (1980), *Mol. Pharmacol.*, **18**, 185.

Yamamura, H.I. and Snyder, S.H. (1974a), *Proc. natl. Acad. Sci. USA*, **71**, 1725.

Yamamura, H.I. and Snyder, S.H. (1974b), *Mol. Pharmacol.*, **10**, 861.

Yamamura, H.I. and Snyder, S.H. (1974c), *Brain Res.*, **78**, 320.

Yamamura, H.I., Kuhar, M.J. and Snyder, S.H. (1974), *Brain Res.*, **80**, 170.

Yamamura, H.I., Chang, K.-J., Kuhar, M.J. and Snyder, S.H. (1975), *Croatica Chemica Acta*, **47**, 475.

Young, J.M. (1974), *FEBS Letts.*, **46**, 354.

Young, J.M., Hiley, C.R. and Burgen, A.S.V. (1972), *J. Pharm. Pharmacol.*, **24**, 850.

4 Dopamine Receptors

IAN CREESE

Acknowledgements

David R. Sibley is thanked for his comments on the manuscript and D. Taitano is thanked for manuscript preparation. This research was supported in part by PHS MH32990-01 and a grant from the Pharmaceutical Manufacturer's Association Foundation. I. Creese is an A.P. Sloan Research Fellow and recipient of an NIMH Research Scientist Development award.

Neurotransmitter Receptors Part 2
(*Receptors and Recognition*, Series B, Volume 10)
Edited by H.I. Yamamura and S.J. Enna
Published in 1981 by Chapman and Hall, 11 New Fetter Lane, London
EC4P 4EE
© 1981 Chapman and Hall

4.1 INTRODUCTION

Twenty years ago the only function of dopamine in the brain was thought to be that of a precursor of the then putative CNS neurotransmitter, norepinephrine. It is now apparent that dopamine plays a major role as a CNS neurotransmitter in its own right. A large body of data has accumulated bearing on the metabolism and neuropharmacology of central dopamine systems and at this point, our level of understanding of dopaminergic systems is probably more advanced than that of any other neurotransmitter system in the CNS. It is evident that deficits in dopaminergic function play a central role in a number of clinical diseases: Parkinson's disease, Huntington's chorea, Gilles de la Tourette's syndrome and last, but not least, schizophrenia. Until recently our knowledge of the metabolism and neurochemistry at the presynaptic site of this system far outweighed our appreciation of dopaminergic postsynaptic mechanisms. However, recent biochemical and radioligand binding studies, coupled with iontophoretic drug application and single unit electrical recording have returned the balance. It is clear that functional changes in postsynaptic dopaminergic mechanisms may now be as important as presynaptic alterations in the etiologies of the neurological and psychiatric illnesses previously mentioned.

In the late 1950s, the pharmacological and behavioral effects of reserpine and amphetamine were being investigated. Changes in the metabolism of dopamine were overlooked in preference to the marked effects of these drugs on norepinephrine and serotonin systems. However, in the early 1960s three pivotal studies drew attention to the major role of dopamine in normal and abnormal brain function. On the anatomical side, Falck and Hillarp (Falck, 1962; Falck et al., 1962) developed the fluorescent histochemical technique which allowed visualization of dopamine neuronal pathways in the brain, along with those for norepinephrine and serotonin. This technique was refined by a series of Swedish researchers throughout the 1960s. These studies clearly demonstrated that dopamine neurons were an intimate part of the extrapyramidal motor systems and the limbic forebrain. Secondly, Hornykiewicz (for review, see Hornykiewicz, 1966) discovered that dopamine was markedly depleted from forebrain structures in patients who had died with Parkinson's disease. The subsequent clinical success of therapy with dopamine's immediate precursor, L-DOPA, underlined the pivotal role of dopamine insufficiency in this disorder. Thirdly, biochemical studies by Carlsson and Lindqvist (1963) investigating the effects of antipsychotic drugs on catecholamine systems demonstrated that all active antipsychotic agents had in common the ability to increase brain levels of dopamine metabolites. This finding suggested that the clinical efficacy of antischizophrenic drugs might be mediated through an interaction with dopamine systems. This hypothesis was reinforced by the finding that antipsychotic drugs block the behavioral effects of dopamine agonists in animals. The results of these investigations captured the imagination of many scientists and brought an unprecedented interest in the biochemistry, pharmacology, anatomy and function of dopamine neurons in the brain.

4.2 ANATOMY

Our appreciation of the complexity of the dopamine neuronal systems (Fig. 4.1) has increased immeasurably since the pioneering studies of Dahlstrom and Fuxe in 1964. Because the dopamine pathway which originates in the environs of the substantia nigra and innervates the striatum accounts for about 70 per cent of the total brain content of dopamine, this nigrostriatal pathway became an obvious focus of research. The other major dopamine pathway described at this time originates from a group of cells in the ventrotegmental area surrounding the interpeduncular nucleus and innervates the olfactory tubercle and adjacent limbic and cortical structures. (The substantia nigra and ventrotegmental dopamine cell groups are frequently referred to as the A-9 and A-10 nuclear groups respectively, following the

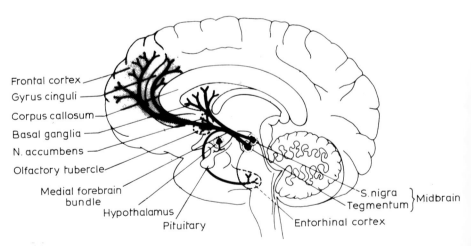

Fig. 4.1 Major CNS dopamine pathways in the human brain.

original designation of Dahlstrom and Fuxe, 1964.) These two dopamine pathways have extensive axonal arborizations in their respective terminal fields, but they can be considered as 'local', distinct systems because of their highly specified, topographically organized, projections. This contrasts with the much more diffuse cortical and subcortical innervation of the noradrenergic systems. With the introduction of the more sensitive glyoxylic acid fluorescence histochemical method (Lindvall and Bjorklund, 1974), combined with information gleaned utilizing immunohistochemical techniques, orthograde and retrograde nerve circuit tracing (Beckstead *et al.*, 1979), it is becoming clear, however, that the dopamine systems are more complex than originally envisaged. The detailed anatomy and histology of the dopamine systems have recently been reviewed in depth (Lindvall and Bjorklund, 1977; Moore and Bloom, 1978) and will be only highlighted here (Fig. 4.1; Table 4.1).

Ontogenetic and mapping studies have now demonstrated that the A-9 and A-10 nuclear groups are more correctly described as a continuum with the more laterally situated cells predominantly innervating the striatum and the more medial cells predominantly innervating the 'mesocortical' areas. The striatal projection includes the caudate nucleus, putamen and globus pallidus, whereas the terminal areas of the mesocortical projection include the mesial frontal, anterior cingulate and entorhinal, perirhinal and piriform cortex. A strong innervation also occurs to the olfactory tubercle, septum, nucleus accumbens and amygdaloid complex. This pathway is frequently referred to as the mesolimbic cortical or limbic dopamine system.

Dopamine cell bodies in the substantia nigra are found only in the pars compacta, although their dendritic trees extend ventrally into the pars reticulata. The cells are of medium size and multi-polar. The pronounced varicosities within the dendritic tree are unusual and as we shall see are indicative of the dendritic release of dopamine. The substantia nigra (A-9) and ventrotegmental (A-10) areas receive multiple afferent inputs from fore-, mid- and hind-brain areas (Dray, 1979; Nauta, 1979). The GABAergic and Substance P pathways from the striatum and globus pallidus, which feed back to the substantia nigra, particularly have received a great deal of interest. The existence of the nigro–striatal pathway was open to doubt for a number of years because the axons are so fine (unmyelinated C fibers with diameters of less than 0.4–0.5 μm) that they were not easily visualized with the then current histological techniques. Their existence was strongly indicated by the observations of Hornykiewicz (1966), who demonstrated that in patients with Parkinson's Disease there was a concomitant loss of dopamine in the striatum along with degeneration of the substantia nigra, pars compacta. Under normal circumstances the nigro–striatal axons contain little dopamine and are not obvious with the Falck–Hillarp fluorescence technique. However, following surgical or

Table 4.1 Dopamine neuron systems in the mammalian brain

System	Nucleus of origin	Site(s) of termination
Nigrostriatal	Substantia nigra, pars compacta; ventral tegmental area	Neostriatum (caudate-putamen), globus pallidus
Mesocortical	Ventral tegmental area; substantia nigra, pars compacta	Isocortex (mesial frontal, anterior cingulate, entorhinal, perirhinal
		Allocortex (olfactory bulb, anterior olfactory nucleus, olfactory tubercle, piriform cortex, septal area, nucleus accumbens, amygdaloid complex)
Tubero-hypophysial	Arcuate and periventricular hypothalamic nuclei	Neuro-intermediate lobe of of pituitary, median eminence
Retinal	Interplexiform cells, of retina	Inner and outer plexiform layers of retina
Incerto-hypothalamic	Zona incerta, posterior hypothalamus	Dorsal hypothalamic area, septum
Periventricular	Medulla in area of dorsal motor vagus, nucleus tractus solitarius, peri-aqueductal and periventricular gray	Periventricular and peri-aqueductal gray, tegmentum, tectum, thalamus, hypo-thalamus
Olfactory bulb	Periglomerular cells	Glomeruli (mitral cells)

Modified from Moore and Bloom (1978).

chemical lesion, there is a rapid build-up of dopamine caudal to the lesion as its transport from the cell body to the terminals is obstructed. The distended axons can then be clearly visualized (Ungerstedt, 1971a). They follow a pathway roughly coincident with the medial forebrain bundle and hence have often been stimulated or lesioned in many classic experiments of physiological psychology. The terminal field of the dopamine neurons is so dense that in fluorescence histochemical sections the striatum is completely fluorescent. When care is taken to restrict diffusion in the preparation of the tissue, it becomes clear that each axon has a massive collateralization in which each branch contains numerous small varicosities estimated at close to half a million (Anden *et al.*, 1966). Although the innervation is diffuse, it does have a distinct topography: the medial rostral striatal areas are innervated from the lateral ventral tegmental area, lateral areas from the lateral pars compacta and the most caudal and ventral portions of the striatum are innervated by the most caudal dopamine neurons. More dorsally placed cells in the mesencephalic dopamine cell groups project ventrally in the striatum while ventrally placed cells project dorsally. In the cortex, it appears that the dopamine innervation is to the deeper layers in contrast to the norepinephrine input which is to the more superficial layers (Berger *et al.*, 1974; Lindvall *et al.*, 1978). A dopamine innervation to the spinal cord, probably originating from the substantia nigra, has recently been described (Commissiong and Neff, 1979; Blessing and Chalmers, 1979; Commisiong *et al.*, 1979).

Of the other dopamine pathways, the tubero-hypophysial system has received most attention. This pathway arises in the arcuate nucleus (A-12) of the hypothalamus and innervates the median eminence (Bjorklund *et al.*, 1973). Some axons terminate here in close approximation to non-aminergic terminals, ependymal cells and the peri-capillary space of the portal system. Other axons continue and innervate the pars intermedia and the neural lobe of the pituitary. Two other dopamine pathways originate in hypothalamic areas – the incerto-hypothalamic and periventricular systems (Bjorklund *et al.*, 1975; Lindvall and Bjorklund, 1977). The periglomerular cells of the olfactory bulb (Hokfelt *et al.*, 1975) and the interplexiform cells of the retina (Ehinger, 1976) both appear to utilize dopamine as a transmitter. In the periphery some small, intensely fluorescent cells in sympathetic ganglia are thought to be dopaminergic (Libet, 1976). Dopaminergic nerves have also been described in the kidney (Bell *et al.*, 1978; Dinerstein *et al.*, 1979). However, although a number of other structures in the periphery such as the stomach, parathyroids and carotid bodies are thought to be responsive to dopamine, no other dopamine neurons have yet been identified.

4.3 ELECTROPHYSIOLOGY

Dopamine appears to be an inhibitory neurotransmitter (Siggins, 1977; York, 1975). However, a concensus of opinion cannot yet be reached as in the striatum, where most studies have been conducted, dopamine has been reported to produce excitatory effects in a small but significant number of experiments (reviewed in Richardson *et al.*, 1977). Iontophoretic studies of dopamine application in the striatum predominantly report inhibition (reviewed in Siggins, 1977). Both spontaneous and glutamate-induced activity is inhibited with extracellular recording. However, in one study (Kitai *et al.*, 1976) with intracellular recording, dopamine has been reported to depolarize cells. Whether this difference is the result of sampling different populations of cells and whether the cells recorded from normally receive a direct dopaminergic input is not clear. Of course it is quite possible that the cells recorded from are being modulated by iontophoretic effects on interneurons, a problem inherent in these studies which cannot easily be resolved. When the very large dendritic network of striatal cells, and the many intertwined axonal collaterals is considered, it is unlikely that most of the iontophoretic studies have recorded from just those cells which have been exposed to drug. Thus, multiple neuronal interactions must always be borne in mind.

Stimulation of the substantia nigra has also led to conflicting results on striatal neuronal activity. Both inhibitory and excitatory effects have been reported in the striatum (Siggins, 1977; Richardson *et al.*, 1977). A problem with these studies is determining whether only a dopaminergic input to the striatum has been activated. Many fibers of other neurotransmitter pathways pass close to the substantia nigra and also innervate the striatum and thus any effects observed may not be specific to dopaminergic activation. The thin, ribbon-shaped structure of the pars compacta of the substantia nigra probably precludes selective stimulation. Consideration of the conduction velocity of nigro–striatal neurons also suggests that many studies have reported the effects of stimulating larger, faster conducting non-dopaminergic neurons. In two studies where stimulation of the substantia nigra has resulted in excitation in the striatum, the excitatory response can be blocked by dopamine antagonists (Norcross and Spehlmann, 1977; Richardson *et al.*, 1977) while the inhibitory responses were not affected. It is possible that antidromic activation of striatal non-dopaminergic interneurons is occurring which gives rise to the non-neuroleptic sensitive inhibition. However, pharmacological studies generally support an inhibitory role for dopamine. Amphetamine, which releases dopamine, and apomorphine, a directly acting dopamine agonist, both depress striatal neurons when iontophoresed. In the cortex the effects of iontophoretic application of dopamine are consistently inhibitory and these effects can be blocked by dopaminergic antagonists (Bunney and Aghajanian, 1976). However, stimulation of the ventrotegmental dopamine area gives rise to excitatory responses in the septum which are sensitive to dopamine antagonists (Assaf and Miller, 1977). In the mammalian sympathetic ganglion dopamine is thought to be responsible for the slow inhibitory postsynaptic potential (Greengard, 1976; but see also Libet, 1979).

4.4 FUNCTION

Because each dopaminergic pathway is so circumscribed, it would be reasonable to expect that it should be fairly easy to allocate functions to each, and this has proved, in part, to be so. In the early 1960s, it became clear that Parkinson's disease was characterized by a depletion of dopamine in the striatum and degeneration of the substantia nigra (Hornykiewicz, 1966). With the success of L-DOPA therapy, which was conclusively demonstrated to raise striatal dopamine levels, the link between dopamine and motor behavior was clear. Animal studies have reinforced this finding and the akinesia and rigidity characteristic of Parksinonism can be produced by lesions of the substantia nigra or the nigro–striatal pathway (Ungerstedt, 1971c). Similar studies have clearly shown that amphetamine and cocaine act as motor stimulants by way of increasing dopaminergic synaptic activity: amphetamine by increasing the release of dopamine and both cocaine and amphetamine inhibiting its re-uptake into presynaptic terminals. Apomorphine increases dopaminergic synaptic activity by a direct agonist action at the postsynaptic dopamine receptor. Lesion experiments and studies with intracerebral micro-injection of dopamine, dopamine agonists or antagonists into various dopamine terminal areas have suggested that the stereotyped gnawing and chewing evoked by amphetamine and apomorphine are mediated in the striatum (Creese and Iversen, 1975a) whereas the increased locomotor activity seen with such stimulants is mediated via the nucleus accumbens (Moore and Kelly, 1978).

'Turning' to other animal studies, the identification of 6-hydroxydopamine as a selective catecholamine toxin enabled functional studies to proceed at a rate unprecedented for any other neurotransmitter. 6-hydroxydopamine is a dopamine analog which is taken up by the selective high-affinity re-uptake system found throughout catecholaminergic neurons. Once concentrated inside catecholaminergic neurons, toxic metabolites are formed which kill the cells within a matter of hours. Since non-catecholamine neurons lack the selective uptake mechanisms, they do not concentrate 6-hydroxydopamine and are thus spared. Selective lesions of dopamine systems are possible either by injecting 6-hydroxydopamine intracerebrally into areas of the brain containing dopamine cell bodies, or into axon or terminal areas following a pre-treatment with desipramine, which inhibits the uptake of 6-hydroxydopamine into noradrenergic neurons. Many early studies focused on the role of the nigro–striatal pathway in motor behavior. Unilateral lesion of the uncrossed nigro–striatal pathway produced animals which, in the first few days following degeneration, rotated in a direction ipsilateral to the lesion (Ungerstedt, 1971c). This rotation indicated an inbalance between the uncrossed nigro–striatal pathways on the two sides of the brain. However, within a few days, the rats' behavior returned to normal. Ungerstedt demonstrated, however, that when challenged with amphetamine, a drug which releases dopamine, the rats once more showed highly exaggerated ipsilateral rotational behavior, as the compensatory mechanisms were overwhelmed by the massive release of dopamine in the intact striatum (Ungerstedt, 1971c). However, if such rats were given the directly acting agonist, apomorphine, they were found to rotate in a direction contralateral to the lesion. At first sight one might have expected the animals to simply demonstrate stimulated forward locomotion since postsynaptic dopaminergic mechanisms should not have been damaged by the 6-hydroxydopamine. However, because the rats turned in the opposite direction to that caused by amphetamine, it indicated that the lesioned striatum was demonstrating greater postsynaptic dopaminergic activity. This was the first experimental suggestion that dopamine receptors can undergo changes following denervation and become supersensitive. This phenomenon is, to some extent, responsible for the success of L-DOPA therapy in Parkinson's disease. It appears that L-DOPA is decarboxylated at a number of sites in the CNS in addition to within catecholamine neurons. The dopamine-denervated striatum still contains a large amount of decarboxylase activity in the serotonin neurons and the pericytes surrounding the capillaries. It is thought the L-DOPA is converted into dopamine at these sites and then diffuses out and makes contact with the denervated and hence supersensitive, postsynaptic receptors.

When bilateral lesions of the nigro–striatal pathway are made, Ungerstedt was surprised to find that the rats died within about 1 week (Ungerstedt, 1971b). They became akinetic and did not eat or drink. Some animals, if tube-fed for a number of weeks, were able to recover from this profound aphagia and adipsia and apparently were then able to maintain homeostasis on their own. The apparent recovery of function that some bilaterally lesioned rats show has been researched in depth and it has been found that it is only the rats with incomplete lesions which can demonstrate recovery. The few remaining dopamine neurons become hyperactive, producing more neurotransmitter, while the postsynaptic receptors become supersensitive and thus respond more efficiently to the reduced amount of dopamine being released. However, close scrutiny indicated that the 'recovered rats' still demonstrated a number of deficits in their food and water intake (Stricker and Zigmond, 1976). It soon became clear that these rats exhibited a syndrome extremely similar to that following the classic lateral hypothalamic lesions which had demonstrated the traditional 'eating centers' of the hypothalamus. It is now agreed that the lateral hypothalamic syndrome results, in part, from the severing of the nigro–striatal pathway which runs through this brain area, although the lateral hypothalamus is still thought to play an important role, in its own right, in food intake regulation. In fact, Leibowitz (1976) has demonstrated that dopamine systems, as well as norepinephrine and epinephrine systems, are involved in the hypothalamic regulation of food and water intake.

Although it is a reasonable hypothesis to suggest that the nigro–striatal lesioned rats do not eat or drink because of motor deficits, it is apparent that they suffer from a motivational deficit as well, which compounds their problems. The rats are capable of movement – if thrown into cold water they will swim rapidly until they reach dry land (Marshall, 1979). Interestingly, a similar phenomenon is seen with Parkinson patients, who although having been immobile for many hours, will jump up and run out of a room in response to someone shouting 'Fire!' A general role for dopamine systems in motivation has also been invoked as the substantia nigra, nigro–striatal pathway, and the striatum are all areas of the brain which will maintain electrical self-stimulation behavior (Fibiger, 1978). By that, I mean rats will work, press bars, in order to receive electrical stimulation in these brain areas through implanted electrodes. Whether the dopamine systems are playing a role in 'drive' mechanisms *per se* or are part of a sensory–motor link is unclear. That the dopamine systems are involved in sensory–motor integration is demonstrated by the syndrome of sensory neglect, which nigro–striatal lesioned animals show (Marshall, 1979). A unilaterally lesioned rat will not respond to sensory stimulation on the contralateral side of its body.

That dopamine is involved in more than just motor behavior is clear from its pivotal role in schizophrenia. Over the past few years it has become clear that deficits in the dopamine systems are, in part, responsible for the psychiatric symptoms of schizophrenia. Evidence to support this hypothesis comes from numerous sources (reviewed in Meltzer and Stahl, 1976). In brief, amphetamine, which is known to release dopamine, will exacerbate schizophrenic symptoms, while in normal adults who abuse this compound a paranoid psychosis can develop which is practically indistinguishable from paranoid schizophrenia (Connell, 1958). On the other hand, decreasing dopamine activity in the brain, either by inhibiting its synthesis with alpha-methyl-*para*-tyrosine or blocking its storage with reserpine, leads to a decrease in schizophrenic symptomatology. As we shall see in later sections, anti-psychotic drugs share in common the ability to block dopaminergic receptors, thus decreasing dopamine synaptic activity in the brain. One of the side effects of treatment with anti-psychotic drugs is, not surprisingly, the development of extrapyramidal side effects such as akinesia and rigidity, which are very similar to the symptoms of Parkinson's Disease. It is thought that these side effects arise from blocking dopamine receptors in the striatum. However, the anti-psychotic activity of the drugs *per se* is thought to be mediated via the mesocortical dopamine system (Snyder *et al.*, 1974). The rationale for this hypothesis is based on the knowledge that the amygdala and cortex are known to be involved in emotional and intellectual behavior, while the striatum is part of the extrapyramidal motor system. In general, this is an attractive hypothesis. Recently, the cortical dopamine systems have been shown to be modulated by stress (Thierry *et al.*, 1976). Furthermore, the cortical system does not develop biochemical tolerance to the neuroleptic-induced increase in dopamine turnover which develops in response to neuroleptic drugs (Bacopoulos *et al.*, 1979). However, the striatum rapidly shows tolerance. This may explain why the antipsychotic effects of neuroleptics are maintained following chronic treatment, while tolerance to the extrapyramidal motor side effects occurs. A general, oversimplified framework in which one might view the function of the dopamine systems is that, in some way, they 'set the scene' for learned and unlearned behavior to occur. With no dopaminergic activity, no sensory motor integration or motor output can occur. When the system is overactive, as occurs when amphetamine is given, multiple stimulus–response pathways are activated leading to flights of thought and disconnected and continuous motor activity. Thus, under normal circumstances, the nigro–striatal and mesocortical dopamine systems can be considered as general facilitators of appropriate behavior.

The functions of the tuberohypothesial system are partially known. The fibers which terminate near the peri-capillary space of the portal system in the median eminence are involved in inhibiting prolactin release from anterior pituitary mammotrophs (Clemens and Meites, 1974). A concensus is forming that dopamine itself, released directly into the portal system, inhibits prolactin release and does not act via a mediating prolactin inhibitory factor (PIF) (MacLeod and Lehmeyer, 1974). Thus, cultures of pituitary mammotrophs, *in vitro*, respond to exogenous dopamine with inhibition of prolactin release (Shaar and Clemens, 1974). The administration of dopamine antagonist drugs, *in vivo*, leads to an increase in blood prolactin levels, suggesting that dopamine is tonically released (Weiner and Ganong, 1978). In the lateral part of the zona externa where almost a third of the terminals present are dopaminergic, it is thought that dopamine might modulate the release of leutinizing hormone-releasing hormone (LH-RH) and growth hormone (Lichtensteiger and Keller, 1974; Weiner and Ganong, 1978). The innervation to the pars intermedia may be involved in the control of α-MSH (Tilders and Smelik, 1977) and endorphin secretion (Vale *et al.*, 1979). Vale has shown that in neuro-intermediate pituitary cell cultures dopamine can inhibit the release of endorphin, and this effect can be blocked by dopamine antagonists. The functional role for the dopamine innervation to the posterior lobe has yet to be identified.

The role of dopamine in the periphery is quite unclear at the moment. Although dopamine has been identified as the sole or major catecholamine in certain peripheral neurons (Bell *et al.*, 1978; Dinerstein *et al.*, 1979), the role of dopamine as a peripheral neurotransmitter has yet to be established. A number of presynaptic effects of dopamine have been identified on peripheral vasculature where dopamine appears to inhibit the release of norepinephrine via presynaptic modulation (Steinsland and Hieble, 1978). The postsynaptic dopamine vascular receptor has been under investigation for more than 15 years (Goldberg *et al.*, 1978). Activation of this receptor results in relaxation of certain blood vessels. The majority of investigations have been concerned with vasodilation produced by dopamine in the renal and mesenteric vascular beds of the intact anaesthetized dog. In the kidney, dopamine is able to increase renal blood flow, while in the heart it can increase cardiac contractility and output. This particular spectrum of peripheral effects on the circulation, in part mediated by β-adrenergic receptors, provides the rationale for dopamine infusion for the treatment of severe shock. Dopamine receptors may be present in parts of the alimentary canal since dopamine antagonists can speed gastric emptying (Van Neuten *et al.*, 1978). The dopaminergic innervation in the spinal cord which has recently been described, has yet to be investigated in any detail. Similarly, the area postrema of the medulla also probably contains a dopamine innervation. Dopamine agonists act at this site to cause emesis which can be blocked by dopamine antagonists.

4.5 DOPAMINE AUTORECEPTORS

4.5.1 Identification of autoreceptors

Although presynaptic adrenergic receptors regulating norepinephrine release have been identified in the peripheral nervous system for a number of years, the inability to study easily dopamine release directly in the brain has obviously hampered the identification of such receptors in the CNS. In 1975 Carlsson provided strong evidence suggesting the presence of presynaptic dopamine receptors on dopamine terminals in the striatum and suggested that 'autoreceptor' was a more appropriate term to describe these receptors functionally (Carlsson, 1975). Although release was not studied directly, he showed that measures of dopamine synthesis and the behavioral consequences of its release were modulated by mechanisms suggestive of presynaptic regulation. Under normal circumstances dopamine synthesis is always positively correlated with nerve impulse flow. Because tyrosine hydroxylase is subject to end-product inhibition by dopamine, it is imagined that following increased impulse flow and release of dopamine, tyrosine hydroxylase is subject to less inhibition and hence neurotransmitter synthesis increases. Carlsson noted, however, that if dopamine neurons were cut, rather than a complete inhibition of neurotransmitter synthesis occurring following the inhibition of dopamine release, there was a marked stimulation of dopamine formation for a period of at least 30 min following axotomy. This increased stimulation of dopamine formation could be inhibited by the peripheral administration of apomorphine, a dopamine agonist, while the effects of apomorphine could be reversed by dopamine antagonists. Since *in vitro* apomorphine has not been shown to be capable of inhibiting tyrosine hydroxylase directly, Carlsson concluded that following the inhibition of impulse flow, a lack of dopamine in the synaptic cleft was somehow responsible for the stimulation of dopamine synthesis and that the presynaptic terminals must possess dopamine receptors on which apomorphine could act. Furthermore he found these effects on dopamine synthesis occurred with low doses of apomorphine – about 1/10th the dose required to stimulate motor activity. When the behavior of animals was observed following administration of these low doses of dopamine agonists it was found that contrary to the expected motor stimulation normally seen following dopamine agonists, the rats appeared sedated. Carlsson concluded that the presynaptic autoreceptors were stimulated by low doses of dopamine agonists resulting in a decrease in dopaminergic synaptic activity, while higher doses of agonists would activate postsynaptic receptors resulting in increased dopaminergic synaptic activity. Thus a dopamine agonist could both decrease and increase synaptic activity in a dose-dependent manner.

That the effects of apomorphine on dopamine synthesis in striatal terminals could occur following axotomy indicated that autoreceptors were present on dopaminergic terminals. Since this initial observation, more recent studies have provided both electrophysiological and biochemical data suggesting that autoreceptors are found on all parts of the dopamine neuron (reviewed in Roth, 1979). In all regions they exert a general inhibitory effect, autoreceptors on the cell soma decreasing the firing rate of the dopamine neuron while those in the terminal areas inhibiting both synthesis and release of dopamine.

Before Carlsson demonstrated the effects of presynaptic modulation of dopamine synthesis, Farnebo and Hamberger (1971) demonstrated that dopamine agonists could inhibit the depolarization-induced release of the neurotransmitter from striatal slices. That this was a receptor-mediated phenomenon was clearly indicated as dopamine's inhibitory effects could be reversed by classic dopamine antagonists. Contradictory effects have been reported by Seeman and Lee (1975) who demonstrated that dopamine antagonists could inhibit the release of dopamine from striatal preparations. They argued that this was the mechanism of action responsible for the clinical efficacy of neuroleptic drugs as antagonists of dopamine synaptic activity. However, these studies have not received general support. Dopamine synthesis can also be studied in slices and synaptosomes, and a number of researchers have demonstrated that dopamine agonists will inhibit dopamine synthesis and that dopamine antagonists can reverse the inhibitory effects of the agonists (Iversen *et al.*, 1976).

In order to overcome the inherent limitations of such *in vitro* studies, Roth and co-workers have developed techniques for studying autoreceptor functioning in *in vivo* preparations (Roth, 1979; Walters and Roth, 1975).

This has allowed examination of the role that autoreceptors play in the modulation of impulse-induced activation of tyrosine hydroxylase and the effects of chronic drug treatments. Dopaminergic agents may potentially influence dopamine synthesis by interacting with dopamine receptors at at least three distinct sites. Interaction with classic postsynaptic dopamine receptors in the striatum indirectly increases dopaminergic impulse flow through a striato–nigral feedback loop (Bunney *et al.*, 1973; Carlsson and Lindqvist, 1963). Activation of dopamine autoreceptors on nigral cell bodies may influence synthesis by decreasing impulse flow (Aghajanian and Bunney, 1974, 1977). Thirdly, these agents may interact with auto-receptors on dopaminergic nerve terminals. In order to study terminal autoreceptors directly, the influence of drug interactions at the other sites must first be eliminated. This can be accomplished, *in vivo*, either by eliminating impulse flow or by holding impulse flow constant. Carlsson's early studies eliminated impulse flow by axotomy. Roth has utilized the administration of γ-butyrolactone which causes a rapid and reversible inhib-ition of firing of the nigro–striatal and mesolimbic dopamine systems. This is accompanied by increases in dopamine levels and tyrosine hydroxylase activity which are similar to those produced by axotomy (Walters *et al.*, 1973). Under these conditions dopamine agonists will prevent the increase in dopamine synthesis caused by γ-butyrolactone. This effect is antagonized by clinically active neuroleptic drugs but not by clinically inactive agents or adrenergic blocking agents. That this effect is the result of interactions with autoreceptors on terminals and not mediated by the striato–nigral feedback loop is demonstrated by the maintenance of this phenomenon following kainic acid lesion of the striatum (Bannon *et al.*, 1980a; Baring *et al.*, 1980). This lesion destroys striatal postsynaptic dopamine receptors and all striatal neurons (*vide infra*) thus removing the possibility that the effects on synthesis are mediated by transynaptic phenomena.

Roth has also utilized another technique to obviate the influence of changes in nigro–striatal firing rate (Roth *et al.*, 1975). The nigro–striatal tract is stimulated electrically by implanted electrodes at supermaximal fre-quencies so that the effects of drugs on postsynaptic dopamine receptors and autoreceptors on the dopamine cell body are unable to affect synthesis via changes in impulse flow. Under these conditions, peripherally adminis-tered dopamine agonists can still decrease tyrosine hydroxylase activity while antagonists can increase tyrosine hydroxylase activity demonstrating that *endogenously* released dopamine is capable of interacting with termi-nal autoreceptors to decrease its own synthesis.

4.5.2 Pharmacological specificity of autoreceptors

The availability of large numbers of structurally distinct adrenergic agonists and antagonists have clearly indicated that peripheral adrenergic autoreceptors have a qualitatively and quantitatively different pharmacology from postsynaptic receptors. Such complete pharmacological analyses have not yet been possible in the study of central dopamine receptors. However, it is quite clear that dopamine autoreceptors are more sensitive to dopamine agonists than are postsynaptic receptors. Recent electrophysiological studies have provided direct evidence for differential sensitivity of dopamine autoreceptors on cell bodies compared to postsynaptic receptors for dopamine agonists in the striatum (Skirboll *et al.*, 1979). The autoreceptors on the dopamine cell bodies were 6–10 times more sensitive to iontophoretically administered dopamine and intravenous apomorphine than the majority of spontaneously active rat striatal cells tested which were inhibited by dopamine. Since the threshold dose of apomorphine for inhibition of firing of substantia nigra dopamine neurons and the dose necessary to inhibit dopamine synthesis in the striatum are almost identical, it would appear that both terminal and somatic autoreceptors are similar (Roth, 1979). However, in investigations of the terminal fields of the mesolimbic dopamine system in the olfactory tubercle, Roth and Nowycky (1977) have found that the presynaptic dopamine receptors in the olfactory tubercle region appear to be about 5–10 fold more sensitive to dopamine agonists than the autoreceptors in the striatum. On the other hand, there appears to be some differential sensitivity as regards antagonists between autoreceptors and postsynaptic dopamine receptors (Walters and Roth, 1975). Whereas common neuroleptics such as haloperidol, fluphenazine, chlorpromazine and thioridazine are equipotent on terminal autoreceptors and postsynaptic receptors, pimozide and clozapine, while effective in blocking postsynaptic receptors, have little or no autoreceptor blocking potency. One study has suggested that metaclopramide might demonstrate differential presynaptic blocking acitivity (Anden, in press).

4.5.3 Functional significance of autoreceptors

Dopamine autoreceptors localized on nerve terminals and neuronal soma influence dopaminergic synaptic activity by modulating the rate of dopamine biosynthesis, impulse-induced release of transmitter and cell firing rate by local negative feedback mechanisms. The preferential sensitivity of pre- versus postsynaptic dopamine receptors is already being ulilized in a number of clinical studies. Although it has not been conclusively demonstrated that the effects of low doses of apomorphine are mediated by preferential dopamine autoreceptor stimulation, its use has resulted in many beneficial effects: reduction of alcohol craving, antimanic effects, antipsychotic effects in schizophrenics, reduction in the symptoms of tardive dyskinesia, induction of drowsiness or sleep, alleviation of the symptoms of Huntington's chorea, alleviation of the symptoms of Tourette's syndrome (reviewed in Meltzer, 1979). The alleviation of psychotic symptoms in schizophrenics by low doses of a dopamine agonist (Corsini *et al.*, 1977; Smith *et al.*, 1977) is obviously of great clinical interest and it would be of devastating significance for the dopamine hypothesis of schizophrenia (*vide supra*) were it not for the conceptual framework of autoreceptors. As of yet there have been no clinical studies suggesting preferential presynaptic activity of dopamine antagonists. Indeed pimozide, which from animal experiments should be a selective postsynaptic antagonist, is able to block the supposedly beneficial presynaptic effects of apomorphine in man. However, it might well be advantageous to develop antipsychotic drugs devoid of presynaptic blocking activity so that the increase in dopamine synthesis and release normally observed following dopamine antagonists (which results from autoreceptor blockade) would not occur to partially offset the competitive drug-induced blockade of postsynaptic receptors.

One might question the functional significance of the dopamine auto-receptors demonstrated electrophysiologically on the soma of dopamine cells within the substantia nigra zona compacta. There is no apparent dopamine innervation to this area from other dopamine cell groups. However, histofluorescence studies have demonstrated large overlapping dendritic trees originating from these cells (Bjorklund and Lindvall, 1975). Biochemical studies have demonstrated dendritic release of dopamine either by the local application *in vivo* of releasing agents such as amphetamine, uptake inhibitors such as benztropine (Cheramy *et al.*, 1978), and depolarization *in vivo* (Nieoullon *et al.*, 1977) and *in vitro* (Geffen *et al.*, 1976) by potassium. Stimulation of structures involved in motor co-ordination such as the ipsilateral motor cortex or the ipsilateral cerebellar dentate nucleus *in vivo* are also effective in modulating dendritic release of dopamine (Leviel *et al.*, 1979). Terminal and dendritic release of dopamine appear to be differentially regulated as demonstrated by the lack of sensitivity of nigral release of dopamine to tetrodotoxin (Nieoullon *et al.*, 1977) and the differential effects of reserpine in the two areas (Tonon *et al.*, 1979). This may be related, in part, to the lack of vesicular storage of dopamine in dendrites and its probable location inside smooth endoplasmic reticulum cisterns of the dendrites (Mercer *et al.*, 1979). That dendritic release of dopamine may be normally of functional significance has been suggested by Wilson *et al.* (1979) who demonstrated that dopaminergic neurons exhibit a prolonged period of decreased firing probability following initiation of an action potential. They hypothesized that this apparent post-firing inhibition might result from a prolonged after-hyperpolarization due to the local release of dopamine. This hypothesis was supported by the finding that systemic haloperidol reduces the strength and duration of post-firing inhibition of nigral dopamine neurons and increases their firing rate.

4.6 BIOCHEMICAL IDENTIFICATION OF POSTSYNAPTIC DOPAMINE RECEPTORS

4.6.1 The dopamine-sensitive adenylate cyclase

Cyclic adenosine monophosphate (cAMP) is a second messenger for a number of neurotransmitters in the periphery. Greengard had found that the inhibitory postsynaptic potential in the bovine superior cervical ganglion was mediated by dopamine and that its effects could be mimicked by exogenous application of cAMP. Biochemical studies soon demonstrated the presence of a dopamine-sensitive adenylate cyclase in this tissue (Greengard, 1976). In comparable studies, Greengard and associates (Kebabian *et al.*, 1972) demonstrated that homogenates of rat corpus striatum would accumulate cAMP when exposed to dopamine. In contrast to the well-studied effects of catecholamines on beta-adrenergic receptors where dopamine is quite weak and isoproterenol is extremely potent, the dopamine-sensitive adenylate cyclase in rat striatum was stimulated greatly by dopamine, less by norepinephrine, and very little by isoproterenol. Dopamine elicited maximal stimulation of cAMP accumulation at 100 μM concentrations with half maximal effects at about 2 μM. The regional distribution of the enzyme in brain tissue also suggested an association with dopamine synapses. Thus high enzymatic activity was observed in the corpus striatum, olfactory tubercle and nucleus accumbens, the three brain regions richest in dopamine innervation, while no enzymatic activity could be demonstrated in other brain areas.

Greengard's group and later Iversen and colleagues (Iversen, 1975) evaluated the effects of neuroleptic drugs (Fig. 4.2) on the dopamine-sensitive adenylate cyclase. The phenothiazines were effective competitive inhibitors of the enzyme (Clement-Cormier *et al.*, 1974; Iversen *et al.*, 1976; Miller *et al.*, 1974). In studies of an extensive series of phenothiazines there was a general parallel between their pharmacological potencies as dopamine antagonists in animals and man and their influences on the cyclase. However, there were marked discrepancies in the case of the butyrophenone neuroleptics (Iversen, 1975; Snyder *et al.*, 1975). For example, haloperidol, which clinically and pharmacologically is about 100 times more potent than chlorpromazine, appeared weaker than, or at best equal to, chlorpromazine in its influences on the cyclase. Furthermore, the most potent butyrophenone, spiroperidol or spiperone, which is about five times more active than haloperidol in intact animals and schizophrenics was weaker than both haloperidol and chlorpromazine on the cyclase.

These discrepancies raised the possibility that butyrophenones might not block dopamine receptors at all, but act in some other system and influence dopaminergic activity indirectly. Such a hypothesis would account for

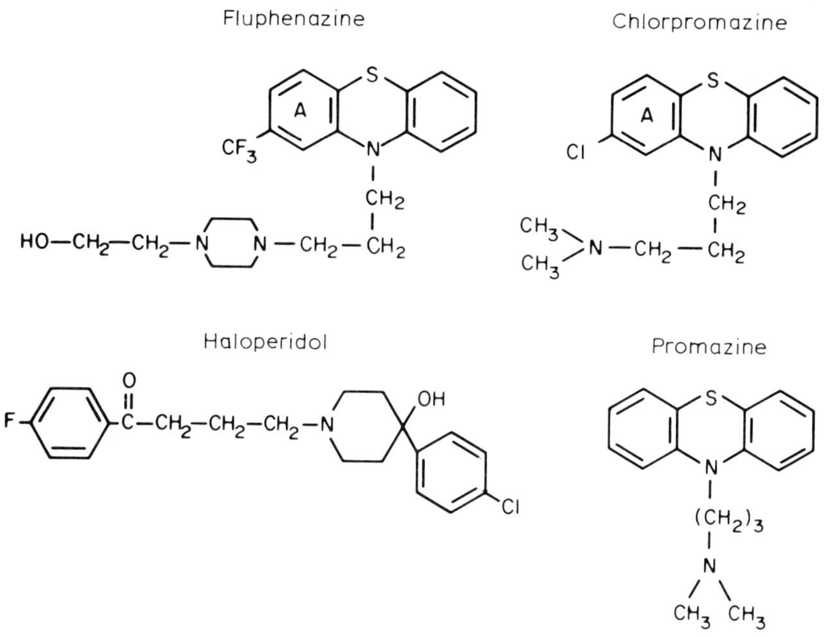

Fig. 4.2 Molecular structures of the phenothiazines fluphenazine, chlorpromazine, and promazine, and the butyrophenone haloperidol.

the marked difference in chemical structure between phenothiazines and butyrophenones despite their pharmacological similarities. This hypothesis was reinforced by computer modeling studies which demonstrated that the phenothiazine molecule could easily take on a conformation which mimicked the extended or trans-conformation of dopamine (Horn and Snyder, 1971). Furthermore, the more potent phenothiazines were more likely, on physicochemical grounds, to take up this particular dopamine mimicking conformation (Feinberg and Snyder, 1975). However, similar calculations for butyrophenones demonstrated that they were no more likely to take up the dopamine mimicking conformation than any other (Tollenaere *et al.*, 1977).

4.6.2 Labeling the 'neuroleptic receptor'

In order to resolve the issue of whether the butyrophenones and phenothiazines produce their pharmacologic and antischizophrenic actions via a common biochemical mechanism, namely blocking dopamine receptors, we investigated the binding sites for labeled butyrophenones in brain membranes. Early studies utilized [³H]-haloperidol (Creese *et al.*, 1975; Seeman *et al.*, 1975) or [³H]-spiroperidol (Fields *et al.*, 1977) labeled to only moderate specific radioactivity (~1 Ci mmol^{-1}) but more recent studies have used [³H]-haloperidol of higher specific radioactivity (~10 Ci mmol^{-1}) (Burt *et al.*, 1977) and [³H]-spiroperidol (23.6 Ci mmol^{-1}) (Creese *et al.*, 1977b; Laduron *et al.*, 1978). Not surprisingly, both drugs bind to membranes from many brain regions. However, in the corpus striatum, the brain region receiving the richest dopamine innervation, the binding was greatly enriched. Micromolar concentrations of dopamine could displace the [³H]-butyrophenones from their binding sites with a maximal effect at about 1 mM suggesting that they might be indeed labeling dopamine receptors. Studies with a large number of catecholamines and other dopamine agonists demonstrated this to be so. Apomorphine, a directly acting dopamine agonist, was more potent than dopamine while dopamine was more potent than norepinephrine and epinephrine by about a factor of 10, while the beta-adrenergic agonist isoproterenol was virtually inactive at millimolar concentrations (Burt *et al.*, 1976).

The amount of [³H]-butyrophenone that could be displaced by dopamine was dependent on both species and [³H]-ligand. For example, in the calf striatum, about 35 per cent of total [³H]-haloperidol binding could be displaced by 1 mM-dopamine. In the rat about 60 per cent of [³H]-haloperidol binding could be displaced by the same concentration of dopamine. However, utilizing [³H]-spiroperidol, about 90 per cent of total [³H]-spiroperidol binding in the rat and calf striatum could be displaced by unlabeled dopamine. [³H]-haloperidol binding in other brain regions could only be displaced by similar concentrations of dopamine in areas which received dopamine innervation. For example, the olfactory tubercle and nucleus accumbens had about half as much dopamine-displaceable [³H]-haloperidol binding as the striatum. In brain regions such as the occipital cortex and cerebellum which do not receive a dopamine innervation, dopamine was ineffective in displacing [³H]-haloperidol binding (Burt *et al.*, 1976). These results suggested that, in part, [³H]-haloperidol and [³H]-spiroperidol were labeling dopamine receptors.

4.6.3 Prediction of clinical and pharmacological potencies of antischizophrenic drugs by dopamine receptor binding

The recently introduced neuroleptic, butaclamol exists as optical isomers of which only the (+)-isomer has pharmacological activity as an antipsychotic agent and dopamine antagonist (Voith and Cummings, 1976). Thioxanthene neuroleptics such as flupenthixol and thiothixene possess geometrical isomers, with the alpha-isomer of flupenthixol and the *cis*-isomer of thiothixene possessing greater pharmacological activity. If [³H]-

haloperidol and [^{3}H]-spiroperidol binding sites are indeed the receptor sites responsible for the pharmacological activity of these drugs, then only their clinically active isomers should be potent in displacing the binding. Indeed (+)-butaclamol, alpha-flupenthixol and *cis*-thiothixene all inhibit [^{3}H]-haloperidol binding with distinct high- and low-affinity components (Burt *et al.*, 1976; see also Seeman *et al.*, 1979). The inactive isomers of these drugs display only low-affinity competition for [^{3}H]-haloperidol binding. The receptor-bound [^{3}H]-haloperidol displaced by the active isomers of these neuroleptics is identical to that displaced by dopamine. This is demonstrated in 'additivity' experiments. Maximal competition by the neuroleptics and by dopamine are not additive showing that both are competing for the same class of [^{3}H]-haloperidol binding sites. Thus [^{3}H]-haloperidol and other neuroleptics appear to bind to the dopamine receptor itself and this dopamine receptor binding can be defined as that portion displaced not only by dopamine but also by the high-affinity, stereospecific component of (+)-butaclamol inhibition.

The affinities of neuroleptics of diverse structures for striatal dopamine receptors labeled with [^{3}H]-haloperidol (and [^{3}H]-spiroperidol) correlate closely with pharmacological actions of these drugs in animals and man (Creese *et al.*, 1976a,b; Seeman *et al.*, 1976). Fig. 4.3 shows that clinical potency as measured by the daily average dose for antipsychotic activity correlates very well ($r = 0.87, p < 0.001$) with affinity for the dopamine receptor. It is quite striking that one can predict clinical potencies from *in vitro* effects of drugs, since average clinical doses vary quite markedly among different patients. Moreover, clinical potencies are determined by variable absorption, metabolism, and penetration of drugs into the brain. Presumably over a wide range of drugs these factors tend to equalize. The close correlation between neuroleptic drugs' clinical potencies and affinities for dopamine receptors is by no means fortuitous. Studies of the potencies of neuroleptics in competing for α-adrenergic (Peroutka *et al.*, 1977), opiate, and muscarinic cholinergic receptors (Enna *et al.*, 1976) do not correlate at all with their clinical potencies as antipsychotic agents.

Because the clinical activity of drugs is difficult to quantify it would be desirable to relate binding properties of neuroleptics with pharmacological actions in animals where *in vivo* activity can be more objectively determined. Apomorphine, a directly acting dopamine agonist, induces a stereotyped motor behavior in rodents consisting of sniffing, licking and gnawing. The ability of neuroleptics to block apomorphine-induced stereotyped behavior also predicts the clinical potencies of these drugs as antipsychotic agents and has been used by the pharmaceutical industry as a screening test (Janssen and Van Bever, 1975). Amphetamine also elicits a similar stereotyped motor behavior, by causing a direct release of dopamine and blockade of dopamine re-uptake in the striatum (Creese and

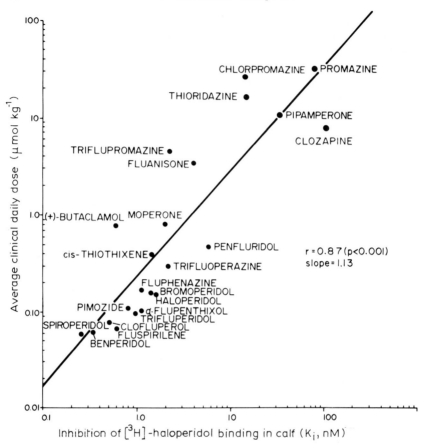

Fig. 4.3 Antischizophrenic drugs: correlation between affinities for [^{3}H]-haloperidol binding and clinical potencies. Clinical data were derived from published results. Mean of each daily dose range listed for each drug was meaned and converted into mol kg^{-1} assuming a human body weight of 70 kg. The correlation coefficient $r = 0.87$ is significant at the $p < 0.001$ level. (From Creese *et al*., 1976b.)

Iversen, 1975a). Blockade of these amphetamine effects also predicts clinical activities of neuroleptics (Janssen and Van Bever, 1975). Interestingly, in higher animals such as cats, monkeys and chimpanzees, the stereotyped behavior provoked by amphetamine tends to resemble such behavior observed in human amphetamine addicts on high doses, close to the time of onset of amphetamine psychosis. Since amphetamine psychosis provides a fairly impressive model of paranoid schizophrenia (Connell, 1958), it has been construed that the stereotyped behavior of rodents may be used as an animal drug model of a human drug model of schizophrenia (Snyder *et al.*, 1974). In any event, potencies of neuroleptics in competing for [³H]-haloperidol binding correlate extremely closely ($r > 0.9$) with their potencies in blocking apomorphine or amphetamine-induced stereotyped behavior (Creese *et al.*, 1976a) (Fig. 4.4).

Neuroleptics are also among the most effective antiemetics known. They are thought to act by blocking dopamine receptors in the chemoreceptive trigger zone situated in the area postrema of the brainstem. The ability of neuroleptics to prevent apomorphine-induced emesis in dogs also correlates

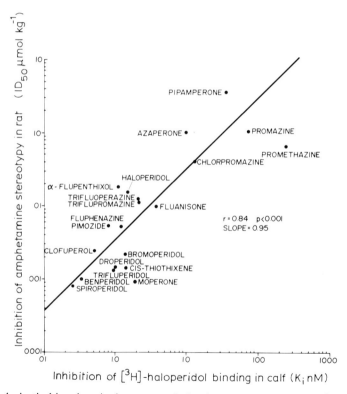

Fig. 4.4 Antischizophrenic drugs: correlation between affinities for [³H]-haloperidol binding sites and antagonism of amphetamine stereotypy in the rat. Animal data were derived from published results and converted into mol kg⁻¹. The correlation coefficient $r = 0.92$ is significant at the $p < 0.001$ level.

well ($r > 0.9$) with their affinity for [³H]-haloperidol binding sites in the striatum (Creese *et al.*, 1976a).

Although these studies have been comparing calf striatal dopamine receptor affinity with drug effects in other animals and man, recent studies have demonstrated that striatal dopamine receptors are quite similar in all species studied including man (Creese *et al.*, 1979a). The impressive correlation between the clinical, antischizophrenic actions of neuroleptics and their blockade of dopamine receptors labeled with [³H]-haloperidol or [³H]-spiroperidol is more striking than has been observed for any other biochemical effect of these drugs. It therefore seems likely that this action is intimately associated with the antischizophrenic effects of the drugs.

4.6.4 Neuroleptic side effects due to receptor interactions

It must be emphasized that few drugs are absolutely specific in their interactions with any one neurotransmitter receptor and at therapeutic dose levels they may interact with many different receptors. In some cases this can lead to undesirable side effects, whereas in other cases an interaction with another neurotransmitter system appears to be able to counteract unwanted side effects that result from interactions with the primary therapeutic site of action of the drug. Chronic drug treatments can also give rise to a spectrum of side effects that do not occur following acute dosage which appear to be mediated via changes in the receptors initially responsible for the therapeutic efficacy of the drug.

(a) Extrapyramidal side effects

One of the most recurrent side effects of neuroleptic therapy is the extrapyramidal motor system side effects of rigidity and akinesia. Since these same motor effects occur in Parkinson's Disease and result from decreased dopaminergic synaptic activity in the striatum following degeneration of the nigro–striatal pathway, it is reasonable to infer that they occur following blockade of striatal dopamine receptors by neuroleptic drugs. This side effect is so common that it was generally supposed that antipsychotic activity and extrapyramidal side effects were inexorably linked. Recently two drugs, clozapine and thioridazine, have attracted a good deal of clinical and biochemical attention. These antipsychotic agents have a much lower incidence of extrapyramidal side effects than are associated with other neuroleptic therapy. The fact that one can obtain effective antischizophrenic activity without extrapyramidal side effects led to the hypothesis that extrapyramidal side effects and antipsychotic activity might be mediated by different dopamine receptors with dissimilar drug specificities in different regions (striatal versus mesolimbic) of the brain (*vide supra*).However, studies to date (both radioreceptor and biochemical) have been conflicting and not provided much evidence to support this hypothesis. The fact that the relative affinities of clozapine and thioridazine for [^{3}H]-haloperidol binding sites in calf striatum in relation to other neuroleptics correspond reasonably well with their clinical potency indicates that these drugs probably exert their antischizophrenic effects by a mechanism similar to that of the other antipsychotic agents (Creese *et al.*, 1976a).

If, then, clozapine and thioridazine produce their antipsychotic effects by the same mechanisms as other neuroleptic agents, why is it that when given in therapeutic antischizophrenic doses these drugs do not produce the same incidence of extrapyramidal side effects? Recent studies of the muscarinic acetylcholine receptor in the brain may provide a resolution of this dilemma (Miller and Hiley, 1974; Snyder *et al.*, 1974). It is well known that concurrent administration of anticholinergic drugs is especially effective in antagonizing the extrapyramidal side effects of neuroleptics without apparently reducing their antipsychotic potency (Snyder *et al.*, 1974). The therapeutic efficacy of the anticholinergics apparently reflects a 'balance' in the corpus striatum between dopamine and acetylcholine neurons involved in motor control (Butcher, 1978). Thus antagonizing the effects of acetycholine is equivalent to enhancing those of dopamine, and vice versa. Hence, if neuroleptics varied in their anticholinergic properties they may well vary in their propensities to induce extrapyramidal side effects.

In studies of the binding of 3-quinuclidinyl benzilate (QNB), a potent antagonist of muscarinic cholinergic receptors, to striatal membrane preparations, this hypothesis was confirmed. Clozapine, which is almost devoid of extrapyramidal side effects, has the greatest affinity for muscarinic receptors, quite close to that of classic anticholinergic agents (Table 4.2). Thioridazine, which, next to clozapine, elicits the fewest extrapyramidal symptoms, is second most potent. The alkylamino phenothiazines, whose moderate incidence of extrapyramidal actions is greater than that of thioridazine, have correspondingly less affinity for the acetylcholine receptor. Piperazine phenothiazines and the butyrophenones, whose frequency of extrapyramidal effects is greatest, have the least affinity for the muscarinic receptors (Miller and Hiley, 1974; Snyder *et al.*, 1974). According to this hypothesis, when given at therapeutic antischizophrenic doses, all neuroleptics produce comparable dopamine receptor blockade and thus all have about the same tendency to elicit extrapyramidal side effects. The simultaneous blockade of acetylcholine receptors by drugs such as clozapine and thioridazine antagonizes their extrapyramidal side effects. However, because of their negligible anticholinergic activity at normal doses, drugs such as haloperidol elicit many more extrapyramidal side effects. Some drugs such as pimozide are relatively weak at cholinergic receptors and their lack of extrapyramidal side effects may be related to

Table 4.2 Relative affinities of phenothiazines and butyrophenones for muscarinic cholinergic receptor binding in brain correlates inversely with extrapyramidal side effects

Drug class	IC_{50} concentration (nM)	Frequency of extrapyramidal side effects
Dibenzodiazepine		
Clozapine	26	+
Piperidine phenothiazine		
Thioridazine	150	+ +
Alkylamino phenothiazine		
Promazine	650	+ + +
Chlorpromazine	1 000	
Triflupromazine	1 000	
Piperazine phenothiazine		
Acetophenazine	10 000	+ + + +
Perphenazine	11 000	
Trifluoperazine	13 000	
Fluphenazine	12 000	+ + + + +
Butyrophenone		
Haloperidol	48 000	

Adapted from Snyder *et al.* (1974).
+ = least side effects.

their slower onset of action (Laduron and Leysen, 1978). However, screening of potentially useful antipsychotic drugs for muscarinic receptor affinity may provide a simple *in vitro* predictor of their propensity to induce extrapyramidal side effects.

(b) Tardive dyskinesia

Tardive dyskinesia is a major complication of the long-term treatment of schizophrenics with neuroleptic drugs (Kobayashi, 1977). It is characterized by abnormal movements of the facial muscles, tongue and extremities that frequently worsen when the dose of neuroleptic is lowered or terminated. Increasing the dose of neuroleptic drug may temporarily alleviate symptoms. However, the dyskinesia soon breaks through this temporary reversal. In a number of patients, tardive dyskinesia has been reported to be irreversible following the termination of neuroleptic therapy. The dyskinesia can be exacerbated by dopamine agonists such as L-DOPA. To provide an animal model of tardive dyskinesia, rats and mice have been treated chronically with neuroleptic drugs (Tarsy and Baldessarini, 1974).

Such treatments may induce abnormal movements in rodents after prolonged treatments. However, after short (1–3 weeks) treatments only an enhanced sensitivity to the motor stimulant effects of apomorphine is apparent. A similar motor supersensitivity to dopamine receptor stimulants is apparent when dopamine synaptic activity is reduced by inhibiting synthesis of dopamine or by depleting dopamine storage sites with reserpine. Lesioning the nigro–striatal dopamine pathway also produces an enhanced sensitivity to dopamine receptor agonists which is hypothesized to result from a dopamine receptor supersensitivity following denervation (Creese and Iversen, 1975b; Ungerstedt *et al.*, 1971b). Thus speculations have linked the development of tardive dyskinesia to supersensitivity of dopamine receptors following prolonged blockade by chronic drug administration (Baldessarini and Tarsy, 1976; Klawans, 1973).

4.6.5 Receptor supersensitivity following denervation

Behavioral changes after specific lesions of the nigro–striatal dopamine pathway suggest that postsynaptic dopamine receptors in the corpus striatum can become supersensitive to dopamine after removal of their normal innervation. After bilateral 6-hydroxydopamine-induced lesions to dopamine cell bodies in the substantia nigra, rats display increased stereotyped behavioral responses to apomorphine, a dopamine-receptor stimulant, and respond to previously subthreshold doses of the drug (Creese and Iversen, 1975a,b; Price and Fibiger, 1974; Ungerstedt, 1971a). After unilateral 6-hydroxydopamine-induced lesions within the nigro–striatal system, behavioral supersensitivity is manifested by rotation following apomorphine treatment in a direction contralateral to the side of the lesion (Thornburg and Moore, 1975; Ungerstedt, 1971b; Von Voigtlander and Moore, 1973). This rotation provides a readily quantified index of behavioral supersensitivity (Ungerstedt and Arbuthnott, 1970).

The enhanced behavioral response to dopamine receptor stimulants after nigro–striatal lesions might result, however, from changes distal to the dopamine receptor or in other neuronal systems. Activity of the striatal dopamine-sensitive adenylate cyclase has been reported to be either unaffected after nigro–striatal lesions (Kreuger *et al.*, 1976; Von Voigtlander *et al.*, 1973) or to show some enhanced activity (Mishra *et al.*, 1974; Prement *et al.*, 1975).

In our study (Creese *et al.*, 1977a) 2–7 months after nigro–striatal lesioning, rats received apomorphine (0.25 mg kg^{-1} subcutaneously) and motor rotation was measured manually 10 min later in a 38-cm diameter opaque plastic hemisphere. The rats showed a variable degree of contralateral rotation after the lesion, presumably reflecting the success of lesioning. Behaviorally supersensitive rats show a 20–120 per cent increase in [^{3}H]-

haloperidol binding on the lesioned side compared to their own contralateral unlesioned striatum (Creese *et al.*, 1977a). Rats which do not turn display essentially no augmentation in binding on the lesioned side. When rats are grouped according to percentage increase in [³H]-haloperidol binding in their lesioned versus control striatum it is apparent that with increasing

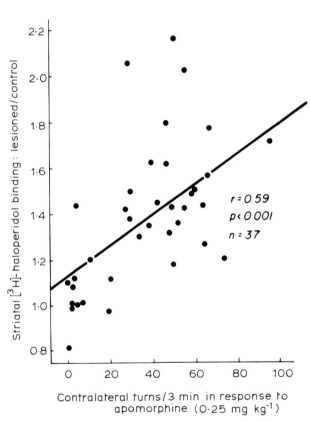

Fig. 4.5 Increased [³H]-haloperidol binding in the lesioned striatum and behavioral supersensitivity to apomorphine following unilateral nigro–striatal 6-hydroxydopamine lesion. Rotational behavior in apomorphine (0.25 mg kg⁻¹ s.c.) was measured between 2 and 7 months after unilateral injection of 6-hydroxydopamine into the substantia nigra. Striatal [³H]-haloperidol binding was assayed in the lesioned and control striatum of each rat separately between 1 and 10 weeks later and is expressed as the percentage increase in specific cpm [³H]-haloperidol bound in the lesioned/control striatum. Each point represents an individual rat.

receptor 'supersensitivity' there is a concomitant increase in behavioral 'supersensitivity'. However, rotational behavior does not increase in direct proportion to the increase in receptor binding although they are significantly correlated (Fig. 4.5). The apparent decrease in behavioral supersensitivity seen in the rats with the most pronounced increase in receptor binding may be more apparent than real. These rats showed greater stereotyped behavior, physically reducing their rotational rate as they stumbled and gnawed their paws.

Increased [^{3}H]-haloperidol binding could be due to a change in the affinity of binding or to a change in the number of binding sites. To discriminate between these two possibilities, each corpus striatum was assayed for [^{3}H]-haloperidol binding at four concentrations of the tritiated ligand (0.4–4.0 nM). Only rats which exhibited at least six contralateral turns per minute (mean 16 ± 1, range 6–31) to 0.25 mg kg^{-1} apomorphine were included in this study. The dissociation constant K_D is unaffected by the lesion, while a highly significant 40 per cent increase in the number of binding sites is apparent in the lesioned striata (16.1 ± 1.1 pmol/g wet wt increasing to 22.7 ± 1.2 pmol/g wet wt, $p < 0.001$). The occurrence of enhanced dopamine receptor binding in association with behavioral supersensitivity indicates that the increased number of receptor sites may, in part, account for the behavioral effects of the lesion.

Supersensitivity of dopamine receptors has considerable clinical implications in both neurology and psychiatry. It is thought that the ability of L-DOPA to alleviate symptoms of Parkinson's Disease derives in part from supersensitivity of the dopamine receptors in the brains of these patients. Recent studies have investigated [^{3}H]-haloperidol binding in post mortem brains from patients who died with Parkinson's Disease (Lee *et al.*, 1978b). Both the putamen and caudate nuclei of the striatum demonstrated about 50 per cent increases in [^{3}H]-haloperidol binding. However, no increase was seen in patients on L-DOPA therapy (see also Quik *et al.*, 1979b; Reisine *et al.*, 1977). In fact, animal studies have also shown that L-DOPA treatment can reverse both behavioral and biochemical manifestations of dopamine receptor supersensitivity (Gudelsky *et al.*, 1975; Seeman, personal communication). This finding may relate to the 'on–off' phenomenon seen with L-DOPA therapy in Parkinson's Disease when refractory periods to L-DOPA's beneficial effects occur.

4.6.6. Receptor supersensitivity following chronic neuroleptic treatment

Since a true receptor supersensitivity appears to accompany the behavioral supersensitivity to dopamine agonists following denervation, it appeared reasonable to test the hypothesis that chronic receptor blockade with neuroleptic drugs which also results in a behavioral supersensitivity might also be related to a receptor supersensitivity.

In order to investigate this hypothesis directly, rats were treated for 3 weeks with the potent butyrophenone neuroleptic haloperidol ($0.5 \text{ mg mg}^{-1} \text{ d}^{-1}$). Five days after terminating the chronic treatment there was a highly significant ($p < 0.001$) 20 per cent increase in specific haloperidol binding (Burt *et al.*, 1977) (Table 4.3). Fluphenazine, one of the most potent phenothiazine neuroleptics, produced a similar increase in binding after administration at the same dose level for 3 weeks. In contrast, treatment for 3 weeks with a five-fold higher dose of the phenothiazine promethazine, which lacks antischizophrenic activity, failed to significantly enhance [^{3}H]-haloperidol binding. Depletion of brain dopamine by chronic administration of reserpine ($0.2 \text{ mg kg}^{-1} \text{ d}^{-1}$) also produced a similar 20 per cent augmentation of [^{3}H]-haloperidol binding. The enhanced receptor binding could be a reflection of either an increased number of binding sites or changes in their affinity. Scatchard analysis of saturation data indicates that it is the result of a 20–25 per cent increase in the total number of binding sites with no change in affinity. A recent study which has utilized a longer treatment period (9 months) has demonstrated a 65 per cent increase in receptor number (Owen *et al.*, 1980).

These data indicate that the motor changes seen after chronic neuroleptic treatment are associated with an increase in the number of dopamine receptor sites (for review, see Muller and Seeman, 1978). This increase in the number of [^{3}H]-haloperidol binding sites is consistent with the behavioral supersensitivity to apomorphine in rats treated with a similar dose schedule of neuroleptics. However, the greater relative enhancement of apomorphine's stimulant effects in such rats compared to the increased dopamine receptor binding described here indicates that other components in the overall system determining the behavioral response may also be changed during chronic neuroleptic treatment, producing additive effects.

Must tardive dyskinesia always be a concomittant of chronic neuroleptic treatment? Some recent animal experiments suggest that it may be con-

Table 4.3 Effect of 21 day chronic drug treatments on [^{3}H]-haloperidol binding in the rat

% increase over control	
Haloperidol	Fluphenazine
$+18.5 \pm 3.9$	$+26.9 \pm 11.8$
$p < 0.0005 (\text{n} = 21)$	$p < 0.05 (\text{n} = 6)$
Reserpine	Promethazine
$+23.3 \pm 6.6$	$+3 \pm 7$
$p < 0.005 (\text{n} = 10)$	NS $(\text{n} = 12)$

trollable by pharmacological means. A current hypothesis for the cause of manic-depressive illness is that there is a cyclical change in adrenergic receptor sensitivity (Bunney and Post, 1977). Lithium is the major pharmacologic treatment for the control of manic symptomatology which has been suggested to involve a supersensitive phase of adrenergic receptors. If this theory were correct, it suggested to Klawans that lithium may in some way modulate supersensitive receptors (Klawans *et al.*, 1977). Thus if tardive dyskinesia were due to a supersensitivity of dopamine receptors, lithium treatment might modulate their sensitivity. Klawans therefore treated rodents concurrently with lithium at the same time as they were receiving chronic neuroleptic treatment. In confirmation of his hypothesis, he observed that the animals did not demonstrate the usual behavioral supersensitivity to dopamine agonists following such drug treatments (Klawans *et al.*, 1977).

In order to test whether the lack of behavior supersensitivity was due to a receptor-mediated phenomenon or some other indirect effect of lithium, Pert and Bunney repeated these experiments but this time investigated dopamine receptor binding in the striatum directly. They clearly demonstrated that concurrent lithium treatment not only blocked the behavioral supersensitivity to chronic neuroleptic treatment but also decreased the receptor supersensitivity that normally would occur (Pert *et al.*, 1978). This did not appear to be due to changes in the distribution of the neuroleptic caused by the lithium treatment, and may thus be a direct effect of lithium on the receptor itself. We have replicated this study and also demonstrated a lithium reversal of the haloperidol-induced increase in dopamine receptor numbers (Creese and Snyder, 1979c). If concurrent lithium treatment along with neuroleptic therapy in schizophrenics does not block the antipsychotic effects of the drugs but inhibits the appearance of tardive dyskinesia it will be highly suggestive that a direct receptor supersensitivity is responsible for this movement disorder in man.

4.6.7 Dopamine receptor changes in schizophrenia

Much evidence suggests that schizophrenia may involve a hyperactivity in dopamine systems (Meltzer and Stahl, 1976; Snyder *et al.*, 1974). All drugs which ameliorate the symptoms of schizophrenia are antagonists of dopamine synaptic activity. Dopamine-releasing agents such as amphetamine or methylphenidate can induce schizophrenia-like psychosis in normal subjects and can exacerbate the symptoms of schizophrenia. However, studies of dopamine metabolites in CSF in acute schizophrenia and in post mortem brain have failed to reveal evidence of increased dopamine turnover, although increased concentrations of dopamine itself have been observed in certain areas of basal ganglia in two post mortem studies (Bird *et al.*, 1977; Crow *et al.*, 1978). It thus remains possible that there may be a disturbance of dopaminergic processes at the level of the postsynaptic receptor.

Recently two studies have reported that there is an increase in the number of neuroleptic receptors in striatum and limbic areas in schizophrenic brain. Lee *et al.* (1978b) report a 50 per cent increase in [^{3}H]-spiroperidol and [^{3}H]-haloperidol binding in schizophrenic caudate nuclei while Owen *et al.* (1978) report up to a doubling in [^{3}H]-spiroperidol binding both in the striatum and nucleus accumbens. Owen's more complete study demonstrated that the increase in binding was due to an increase in the number of neuroleptic binding sites. There was also a significant increase in the dissociation constant in schizophrenic brain probably caused by residual neuroleptic from previous medication. In similar studies (in collaboration with Snyder, Bird, Iversen, and Mackay) we have demonstrated that in ten schizophrenics, who were receiving neuroleptics at time of death, there is a significant increase in the number of receptors for [^{3}H]-spiroperidol in the caudate nucleus (Creese and Snyder, 1979c) (Table 4.4). An increased variability in the K_D for the schizophrenics was also observed and this may result from competition by variable amounts of neuroleptic remaining in the schizophrenic brains.

Of the 15 schizophrenics examined by Own *et al.* (1978), two had no record of receiving any neuroleptic, while three more had no record of receiving medication during the year before death. However, it is notoriously difficult to maintain satisfactory drug histories of schizophrenics. It is

Table 4.4 [^{3}H]-spiroperidol binding to caudate nucleus of control and psychotic patients

	Controls	Psychotic	Schizophrenic	Schizophrenia-like
B_{max} (p mol/g tissue)	5.94 ± 1.62 (8)	11.61 ± 1.2* (10)	12.90 ± 1.8† (6)	9.70 ± 1.85 (4)
K_D (nM)	0.32 ± 0.08 (8)	0.56 ± 0.15 (10)	0.78 ± 0.20‡ (6)	0.22 ± 0.04 (4)

Values are means (±SEM) for numbers of samples in parentheses. Comparisons with controls:
* $p < 0.01$, Student-*t*; $p < 0.05$, Wilcoxon rank,
† $p < 0.02$, Student-*t*; $p = 0.05$, Wilcoxon rank,
‡ $p < 0.05$, Student-*t*; $p = 0.05$, Wilcoxon rank.
The psychotic group was divided into true schizophrenia and schizophrenia-like psychosis post mortem from detailed analysis of each patient's records.

thus, as yet, unclear whether the increase in neuroleptic binding in schizophrenia is the result of chronic neuroleptic treatment which, as we have seen already, can in itself increase receptor binding or whether the increase in receptor number is implicated in the etiology of the disease process itself. These results are both tantalizing and exciting. The demonstration that a psychiatric illness is the result of a biochemical defect in receptor regulation will markedly change current psychiatric concepts and have a major clinical and social impact.

4.7 MULTIPLE DOPAMINE RECEPTORS

When [^{3}H]-butyrophenone binding was identified in the brain it became obvious that the sites labeled by the [^{3}H]-dopamine antagonists and the dopamine receptors studied by the stimulation of adenylate cyclase were different (Creese and Snyder, 1979a; Snyder *et al.*, 1975). Both the qualitative and quantitative pharmacological specificities of the two systems were different. For example, butyrophenones exhibit nanomolar affinities at [^{3}H]-butyrophenone binding sites but micromolar affinities on the dopamine-sensitive adenylate cyclase. Furthermore there is no evidence that a dopamine-stimulated accumulation of cAMP can account for the inhibitory effect of dopamine on prolactin release in the anterior pituitary (Kebabian and Calne, 1979) suggesting that a non-cyclase-linked dopamine receptor controls prolactin release. In addition, these anterior pituitary dopamine receptors also differ from *both* the butyrophenone binding sites and the striatal adenylate cyclase in terms of their pharmacological specificity. Whereas dopamine is active at nanomolar concentrations in inhibiting prolactin release (Caron *et al.*, 1978), it is only active in stimulating adenylate cyclase activity and inhibiting [^{3}H]-butyrophenone binding at micromolar concentrations. Furthermore molindone, metoclopramide and sulpiride are potent antagonists of the pituitary dopamine receptor although they are very weak indeed in antagonizing the dopamine-sensitive adenylate cyclase (reviewed in Kebabian and Calne, 1979). Several ergot derivatives exhibit differential activity between pituitary dopamine receptors and the striatal dopamine-sensitive adenylate cyclase. For example, bromocriptine is a potent agonist of the dopamine receptor in the anterior pituitary but yet exhibits only weak antagonist activity on the dopamine-sensitive adenylate cyclase. Such biochemical data combined with a large behavioral literature (reviewed in Cools and Van Rossum, 1976) clearly indicate the presence of at least two types of dopamine receptor.

Kebabian and Calne (1979) have suggested that dopamine receptors may be divided by such biochemical and pharmacological criteria into two classes. D1 receptors are linked to adenylate cyclase while D2 receptors are not. However, studies of dopamine receptor binding sites with radioligands have indicated that this classification is probably oversimplistic. Since 1975 when the first papers describing radioligand binding to putative dopamine receptors appeared, the number of ligands used in such studies has multiplied and exceeds that for any other neurotransmitter. At present, the following [^{3}H] drugs have all been proposed to label dopamine receptors: haloperidol, spiroperidol, domperidone, pimozide, sulpiride, flupenthixol, LSD, dihydroergocriptine, dopamine, apomorphine, ADTN, and *N-n*-propylnorapomorphine (NPA). It is not surprising that quantitative and qualitative differences in binding properties occur between these structurally diverse ligands. However, all of these ligands demonstrate the crucial attributes necessary (but not sufficient) to support the contention that they label dopamine receptors: (1) a regional distribution paralleling dopamine innervations; (2) dopamine and dopamine agonists are more potent than other neurotransmitters; (3) stereospecificity with respect to dopamine antagonists; and (4) dopamine antagonists are more potent than other neurotransmitter antagonists. The major question is: do differences in radioligand binding parameters represent preferential identification of distinct dopamine receptors, quirks in laboratory technique, or idiosyncratic ligand/receptor interactions? A number of experiments have been conducted which clearly dissociate some dopamine [^{3}H]-ligand binding from the adenylate cyclase, and also dissociate [^{3}H]-antagonist binding from [^{3}H]-agonist binding. Some of these pertinent experiments will now be described.

4.7.1 Dissociation of some dopamine receptor binding from the dopamine-sensitive adenylate cyclase

Kainic acid is a glutamate analog and has been found to be a potentially important new selective lesioning agent (McGeer *et al.*, 1978). Glutamate is known to be an excitatory neurotransmitter. When kainic acid is injected into the striatum it has been found that within a few hours intrinsic neurons within the striatum begin to show signs of damage and die (Coyle and Schwarcz, 1976; McGeer and McGeer, 1976). Within a few days no intrinsic neurons remain in the striatum and there is a complete loss of these cells' neurotransmitters and synthetic enzymes. However, axons in passage and axon terminals within the striatum appear undamaged. At present, the exact mechanism of action of kainic acid is unknown but it is thought that it may result from a potentiated glutaminergic stimulation of the intrinsic neurons. This causes an upset in their ionic balance which leads to rapid cellular death. Nevertheless, these lesions, if done carefully, appear to be selective for the intrinsic neurons in the striatum and do not damage terminals.

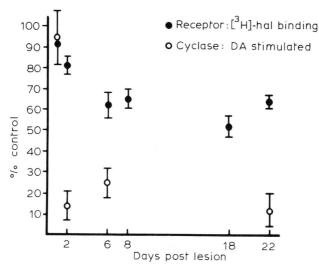

Fig. 4.6 Time course of loss of striatal dopamine-stimulated adenylate cyclase activity and [³H]-haloperidol receptor binding after unilateral striatal kainate injection. Adenylate cyclase activity was stimulated by 50 μM dopamine with basal levels measured in the presence of 5 μM fluphenazine; [³H]-haloperidol binding was assayed with 0.8 nM [³H]-haloperidol in the presence or absence of 0.1 mM dopamine.

Following such kainic lesions in the striatum, we found that there was an almost complete loss of dopamine-sensitive adenylate cyclase (Schwarcz *et al.*, 1978). However there was only a 45 per cent loss of [³H]-haloperidol or [³H]-spiroperidol binding in the striatum (Fig. 4.6) clearly dissociating these [³H]-antagonist binding sites from the cyclase (Govoni *et al.*, 1978; Schwarcz *et al.*, 1978). [³H]-Apomorphine and [³H]-NPA binding, on the

Table 4.5 Localization of striatal dopamine receptors

	% control		
	Kainate	Cortical ablation	Kainate and cortical ablation
[³H]-haloperidol binding	64 ± 3*	68 ± 5*	30 ± 5*
[³H]-NPA binding	22 ± 4*		
[³H]-flupenthixol binding	25 ± 3*		

* $p < 0.001$.

other hand, were decreased about 70 per cent (Table 4.5) (Creese *et al.*, 1979b). This clearly indicates that at least 70 per cent of [³H]-agonist binding and all the dopamine-sensitive adenylate cyclase are postsynaptic on intrinsic striatal neurons.

What is the location of the [³H]-haloperidol binding sites which remain after kainic acid lesion? The only possible locations are on blood vessels within the striatum, glial cells within the striatum or on terminals innervating the striatum. Since there is a massive gliosis following kainic acid lesion but no comparable increase in [³H]-haloperidol binding with time, it seems unlikely that the receptors are predominantly present on glial cells as suggested by Henn *et al.* (1977). A massive terminal innervation in the striatum originates from the cortex. We have found that following cortical ablation there is a 40 per cent loss in striatal [³H]-haloperidol binding sites (Table 4.5). This indicates that [³H]-haloperidol binding sites are present on the axons of cortical neurons terminating in the striatum. If a cortical lesion is combined with a kainic acid lesion of the striatum there is an additive loss of striatal [³H]-haloperidol binding sites indicating there are two distinct populations of [³H]-antagonist binding sites with differing neuronal localizations (Fig. 4.7) (Schwarcz *et al.*, 1978).

It would thus appear that all the dopamine-sensitive adenylate cyclase is

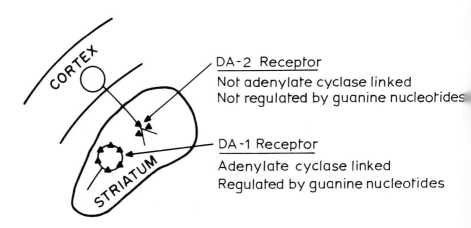

Fig. 4.7 Location of striatal dopamine receptors determined from binding and lesion experiments. The dopamine receptors on intrinsic striatal neurons are linked to adenylate cyclase and are regulated by guanine nucleotides (see Section 4.7.3). The presynaptic dopamine receptors on the cortical afferents are not cyclase linked and not regulated by guanine nucleotides.

located on the postsynaptic intrinsic neurons within the striatum. A majority of [³H]-apomorphine and [³H]-NPA binding is similarly located. About half of the [³H]-antagonist binding sites within the striatum are located on postsynaptic neurons while the remaining 50 per cent is located on the presynaptic terminals of the cortical innervation to the striatum.

These findings are supported· by differential centrifugation experiments which have successfully localized dopamine-sensitive adenylate cyclase activity and [³H]-haloperidol binding to different subcellular fractions (Leysen and Laduron, 1977) on the one hand, and some [³H]-apomorphine binding sites from [³H]-spiroperidol binding sites on the other (Titeler *et al.*, 1978). In the substantia nigra it has also been possible to dissociate some [³H]-butyrophenone binding sites from the dopamine sensitive adneylate cyclase. It appears that the cyclase is present only on the terminals of the striato–nigral pathway (Gale *et al.*, 1977) while [³H]-butyrophenone binding sites are also found on the dopamine cell bodies themselves (Quik *et al.*, 1979a; Reisine *et al.*, 1979).

Seeman and co-workers have also suggested that [³H]-spiroperidol and [³H]-apomorphine binding sites may have a different neuronal localization within the striatum (Nagy *et al.*, 1978). They have found that 6-hydroxydopamine lesions to the substantia nigra, which denervates the striatum, leads to a 50 per cent decrease in [³H]-apomorphine binding while there is a significant increase in [³H]-spiroperidol binding. They interpret their data to indicate that [³H]-spiroperidol binding is postsynaptic and increases as postsynaptic supersensitivity develops, while [³H]-apomorphine labels autoreceptors on dopamine terminals which degenerate following 6-hydroxydopamine lesion. Leysen has repeated these studies but in contrast she has found that neither [³H]-apomorphine nor [³H]-spiroperidol binding was affected by her lesions (Leysen, 1979). Her lesions were not complete, resulting in destruction of between 80 and 90 per cent of striatal dopamine nerve terminals. This is not sufficient to give rise to postsynaptic supersensitivity – measured either biochemically or behaviorally (Creese and Snyder, 1979b). However, if [³H]-apomorphine was labeling presynaptic sites, a large decrease in [³H]-apomorphine binding would have been expected in these studies. We have also conducted similar experiments and obtained almost complete destruction of the nigro–striatal system (Creese and Snyder, 1979b). Under these conditions both [³H]-apomorphine and [³H]-spiroperidol binding increase (Fig. 4.8), with [³H]-apomorphine demonstrating a larger increase than [³H]-antagonist binding. We suggest that, under our conditions, *both* [³H]-apomorphine and [³H]-spiroperidol binding are postsynaptic. This interpretation provides internal consistency with the kainic acid studies which lead to a 70 per cent loss in [³H]-agonist binding sites with postsynaptic neuronal cell loss.

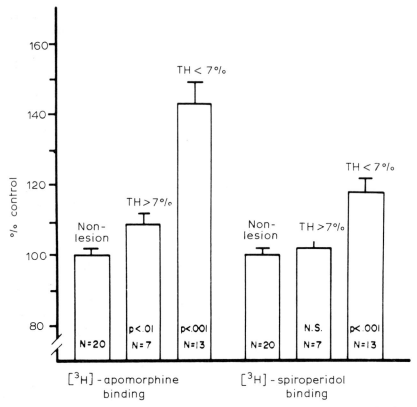

Fig. 4.8 Effect of substantia nigra 6-hydroxydopamine lesion on rat striatal dopamine receptor binding 4 months post-lesion. Only when lesions are almost complete with tyrosine hydroxlyase (TH) activity less than 7 per cent control is [³H]-ligand binding increased. However, with less complete lesions there is no evidence that the binding of either agonist or antagonist is decreased.

4.7.2 Relationship of some [³H]-butyrophenone and [³H]-agonist binding sites to the adenylate cyclase

It should not be surprising that [³H]-butyrophenone and [³H]-agonist binding sites do not exhibit the pharmacological specificity of the dopamine-sensitive adenylate cyclase. Both dopaminergic agonists and the butyrophenones interact with the dopamine-sensitive adenylate cyclase with affinities in the micromolar range (Iversen, 1975). In filtration binding experiments it is almost impossible to label sites with such low affinity. However, [³H]-flupenthixol does appear to label the cyclase as the pharmacological specificity of [³H]-flupenthixol binding sites is much more similar to dopamine-sensitive adenylate cyclase affinities than any other [³H]-dopaminergic ligand (Hyttel, 1978, 1980). This is not unexpected. Flupenthixol and phenothiazines, unlike butyrophenones, have K_is on the dopamine-sensitive adenylate cyclase in the order of 1–10 nM (Iversen, 1975) and thus these sites can be labeled directly. Our recent kainic acid lesion studies support the hypothesis that [³H]-flupenthixol labels the dopamine-sensitive adenylate cyclase-linked receptors directly (Leff *et al.*, in press). Unlike other [³H]-antagonists, [³H]-flupenthixol binding is reduced by 75 per cent, paralleling the loss of dopamine-sensitive cyclase activity (Table 4.5).

Do some of the high-affinity [³H]-agonist and [³H]-butyrophenone binding sites have any relationship to the dopamine-sensitive adenylate cyclase-linked receptor – in spite of their discrepant pharmacologies? For example, are they labeling desensitized forms of the cyclase-linked receptor? Studies of receptor-linked adenylate cyclase in other systems such as the glucagon (Lad *et al.*, 1977; Rodbell *et al.*, 1975) and β-adrenergic receptors (Williams and Lefkowitz, 1978) in the periphery indicate that receptor binding sites and the adenylate cyclase are distinct macromolecules which undergo changes in linkage in the cell membrane. Depending on the linkage between the receptor binding sites and the cyclase, the properties of the binding site can be quite different. This could possibly explain the differences in pharmacological specificities of the agonist binding sites compared with that of the dopamine-sensitive adenylate cyclase. In fact, recent studies of the regulation of the dopamine receptors indicate that some dopamine [³H]-agonist binding sites and some [³H]-butyrophenone binding sites may well be associated with receptors which can become linked to adenylate cyclase.

4.7.3 Regulation of dopamine receptors

Studies of the β-adrenergic receptor in the periphery by Lefkowitz have demonstrated that prolonged exposure to agonists densensitizes the system and further agonist application no longer stimulates cAMP production (Williams and Lefkowitz, 1978). However, the addition of GTP to the incubation restores the ability of agonists to activate the adenylate cyclase. The resensitization is accompanied by a decrease in affinity of agonist binding to the receptor sites. Studies of the glucagon receptor have also demonstrated a regulatory role of GTP in receptor cyclase linkage, again with guanine nucleotides decreasing agonist affinities for receptor binding sites (Rodbell *et al.*, 1975). Although GTP modulates β-adrenergic agonist

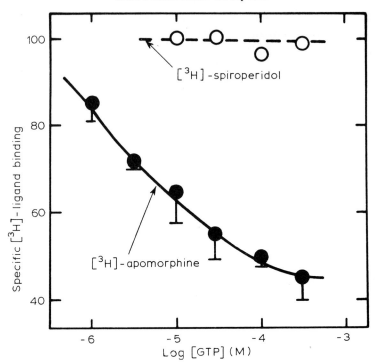

Fig. 4.9 Sensitivity of rat striatal [³H]-apomorphine and [³H]-spiroperidol binding to the inhibitory effects of GTP.

affinity for receptor binding sites it has, however, no effect on β-antagonist drug affinity for receptor sites.

In studying striatal dopamine receptor binding we have demonstrated that guanine nucleotides such as GTP also decrease the binding of dopamine agonists by lowering their affinity (Creese and Snyder, 1978; Creese *et al.*, 1978, 1979b, 1979c). However, the same concentration of guanine nucleotide has no effect on total [³H]-antagonist binding (Fig. 4.9). The studies of Clement-Cormier *et al.* (1975) and Kebabian *et al.* (1979) indicate that GTP, in fact, may be obligatory for dopamine activation of the adenylate cyclase. Such results support the hypothesis that [³H]-agonist binding may be associated with the adenylate cyclase-linked receptors. This is reinforced by the almost parallel loss of [³H]-agonist binding sites and the adenylate cyclase following kainic acid lesion (*vide*

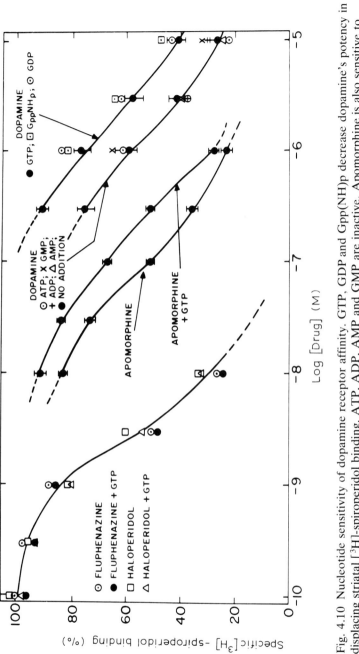

Fig. 4.10 Nucleotide sensitivity of dopamine receptor affinity. GTP, GDP and Gpp(NH)p decrease dopamine's potency in displacing striatal [³H]-spiroperidol binding. ATP, ADP, AMP and GMP are inactive. Apomorphine is also sensitive to modulation by GTP whereas the antagonists fluphenazine and haloperidol are insensitive.

supra). Following kainic acid lesion some [³H]-antagonist binding was also lost and thus may be linked to adenylate cyclase receptors in some way. This is supported by the finding that although guanine nucleotides do not affect directly the binding of [³H]-antagonist themselves, they do decrease the affinity of agonists in displacing [³H]-antagonist binding (Fig. 4.10). Thus addition of 50 μM GTP will decrease the affinity of the agonist dopamine or apomorphine for [³H]-spiroperidol binding sites by three to four fold (Creese *et al.*, 1979b,c). That these guanine nucleotide effects are related to the presence of adenylate cyclase is demonstrated by the fact that following kainic acid lesion which removes all the adenylate cyclase activity in the striatum, the remaining [³H]-spiroperidol binding is no longer affected by guanine nucleotides: dopamine's affinity for [³H]-spiroperidol binding sites becomes insensitive to guanine nucleotides (Fig. 4.11). The remaining [³H]-apomorphine binding is also no longer affected by addition of GTP (Creese and Snyder, 1979a; Creese *et al.*, 1979b). Furthermore bromocriptine, which is an antagonist of the striatal

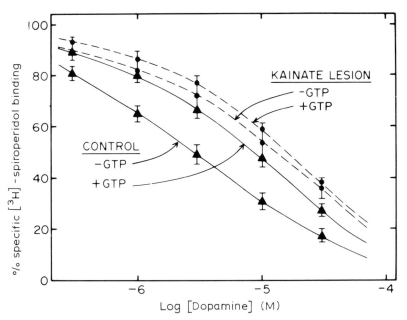

Fig. 4.11 The effect of striatal kainate lesion on GTP alteration of dopamine's potency in competing for striatal [³H]-spiroperidol binding. Following kainic acid lesion, GTP no longer modulates dopamine's ability to displace [³H]-spiroperidol.

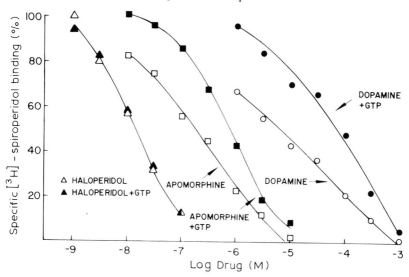

Fig. 4.12 Drug displacements of [³H]-spiroperidol binding in bovine anterior pituitary membranes. Increasing concentrations of each drug, in the presence or absence of 0.1 mM GTP, were added to tubes containing 0.2 nM [³H]-spiroperidol. Specific binding is defined as that displaced by 1 μM (+)-butaclamol.

dopamine-sensitive adenylate cyclase (although it has dopaminergic agonist activity in the pituitary) it not affected by guanine nucleotides with regards to its ability to displace striatal [³H]-butyrophenone binding. This finding again suggests a functional agonist specificity of the guanine nucleotide effect on dopaminergic radioligand binding in the brain.

However, one could argue against an association of [³H]-agonist and [³H]-butyrophenone binding with the dopamine-sensitive adenylate cyclase. Agonist binding in the anterior pituitary is guanine nucleotide sensitive (Sibley and Creese, 1979a,b) (Fig. 4.12). The majority of evidence indicates that there is no dopamine-sensitive adenylate cyclase in the anterior pituitary (Clement-Cormier *et al.*, 1977; Schmidt and Hill, 1977); however, no concensus can yet be reached as a recent paper has identified a dopamine-sensitive adenylate cyclase under very specific conditions (Ahn *et al.*, 1979). Thus, guanine nucleotide sensitivity may *not* be indicative of linkage with an adenylate cyclase. Alternatively, it has been recently reported that neurotransmitter receptor binding, which is guanine nucleotide sensitive, can be linked to a *decrease* in adenylate cyclase activity

(Blume *et al.*, 1980). In this regard, a recent study (DeCamilli *et al.*, 1979) reports that dopamine receptor stimulation might be associated with a *decreased* adenylate cyclase activity in the anterior pituitary.

Some ergot agonists are not affected by guanine nucleotides in the anterior pituitary (Sibley and Creese, 1979a,b) even though they are full agonists in being able to inhibit prolactin release (Caron *et al.*, 1978). This could argue that guanine nucleotide sensitivity bears no relationship to a drug's intrinsic agonist activity. However, our studies have indicated that this is not true for all ergot agonists. Only peptide ergot agonists are guanine nucleotide *in*sensitive, non-peptide ergot agonists are guanine nucleotide sensitive. We suggest that the semi-irreversible nature of peptide ergot binding (Bannon *et al.*, 1980b) results in the ineffectiveness of GTP since guanine nucleotides are generally considered to decrease agonist affinity by speeding up dissociation rates.

The pharmacological specificities of the [^{3}H]-agonist and [^{3}H]-butyrophenone binding sites do not correlate with those of the dopamine-sensitive adenylate cyclase (Snyder *et al.*, 1975). One can partially counter this argument by suggesting that [^{3}H]-agonists label desensitized receptors. In other systems, high-affinity agonist binding does occur to desensitized receptors and GTP is able to resensitize these receptors by decreasing agonist affinity. However, it is unclear what possible relationship high-affinity [^{3}H]-butyrophenone binding affinity has to the dopamine-sensitive adenylate cyclase. It should be reiterated that butyrophenones interact with the dopamine-sensitive adenylate cyclase with micromolar affinities. These discrepancies in pharmacological potencies could result from the use of different buffers, etc., between the two assay systems, but it is unlikely that this could explain the almost 1000-fold difference in affinities. For instance, Watling *et al.* (1979) have recently postulated that in the retina dopamine receptors are exclusively linked to adenylate cyclase (D1 receptors). However, high-affinity (K_D = 1.2 nM) dopaminergic [^{3}H]-spiroperidol binding has recently been found in bovine retina (Magistretti and Schorderet, 1979) which can be completely displaced by domperidone with a K_i = 15 nM (Creese and Sibley, 1979). Since domperidone inhibits the dopamine-sensitive adenylate cyclase with an IC_{50} = 0.2 mM, one has to invoke a 10,000-fold shift in affinity due to a change in assay condition. Alternatively, it must be argued that [^{3}H]-spiroperidol labels other dopamine receptors, distinct from the cyclase-linked dopamine receptors and the retina may not contain D1 dopamine receptors exclusively.

4.7.4 Relationship of [^{3}H]-butyrophenone and [^{3}H]-agonist binding sites

In the bovine striatum we demonstrated that [^{3}H]-agonist binding sites exhibited a different pharmacology from [^{3}H]-antagonist binding sites

Table 4.6 Bovine striatal agonist/antagonist dopamine receptor interactions

Drug	K_i (nM)	
	[³H]-dopamine binding	[³H]-haloperidol binding
Dopamine	20	600
Apomorphine	9	65
Fluphenazine	180	1.2
Haloperidol	650	1.5

(Burt *et al.*, 1976; Creese *et al.*, 1975). Briefly stated, agonists exhibited high affinity in displacing [³H]-agonist binding, but low affinity in displacing [³H]-antagonist binding. The reverse was true, with antagonists exhibiting high affinity for [³H]-antagonist binding sites, but low affinity for [³H]-agonist binding sites (Table 4.6). Moreover, although agonists displacing [³H]-agonists, and antagonists displacing [³H]-antagonists showed displacement curves with Hill coefficients of 1, agonists displacing [³H]-antagonists and antagonists displacing [³H]-agonists exhibited Hill coefficients of less than 1 – often approaching 0.5 (Burt *et al.*, 1976). It must be reiterated that defining binding sites operationally in terms of, for example, [³H]-agonist binding sites, does not imply that antagonists are not active at these sites. Antagonists can displace *all* the [³H]-agonist binding and *vice versa*. Although initially finding a similar pharmacology for both [³H]-agonist and [³H]-antagonist binding sites (Seeman *et al.*, 1975), Seeman also now identifies dissimilar agonist and antagonist binding (Seeman *et al.*, 1978).

In the rat striatum we have also found similar results to those in bovine tissue with [³H]-antagonists (Creese *et al.*, 1979). However, labeling sites with the agonist [³H]-apomorphine, we find that butyrophenones displace with clearly biphasic curves (as opposed to the flat, smooth displacement curves seen in the bovine tissue), clearly demonstrating both a high- (nM) and a low- (µM) affinity phase (Creese *et al.*, 1978). These data suggest that [³H]-apomorphine labels two populations of binding sites which do not interconvert during the binding experiment and which have differential affinity for butyrophenones.

The lesion data previously discussed led us to conclude that striatal, high-affinity [³H]-agonist binding occurs mostly to postsynaptic intrinsic neurons. Some [³H]-antagonist binding also has a similar location (about 50 per cent of striatal [³H]-antagonist binding). However, these lesion studies did not allow us to decide whether these [³H]-agonist and [³H]-antagonist binding sites located on intrinsic striatal neurons are identical receptors or even if they are found on the same cells. Our recent studies of dopamine receptor binding in the anterior pituitary have clarified the relationship of some [³H]-agonist and [³H]-antagonist binding sites.

4.7.5 Radioligand binding to the anterior pituitary

We have identified [³H]-butyrophenone (Creese *et al.*, 1977; Sibley and Creese, 1979; Sibley and Creese, 1979a,b; Creese and Sibley, 1979) and [³H]-agonist ([³H]-apomorphine and [³H]-NPA binding in the bovine anterior pituitary (Sibley and Creese, 1979a,b; Creese and Sibley, 1979)). The identification of high affinity [³H]-agonist binding in a tissue with no direct dopaminergic innervation reinforces our hypothesis that under our assay conditions [³H]-agonists label postsynaptic receptors. The pharmacology of the [³H]-spiroperidol binding sites appears closely similar to striatal [³H]-spiroperidol binding sites (Creese *et al.*, 1977; Creese and Sibley, 1979). Thus, while antagonists displace [³H]-spiroperidol with Hill coefficients of

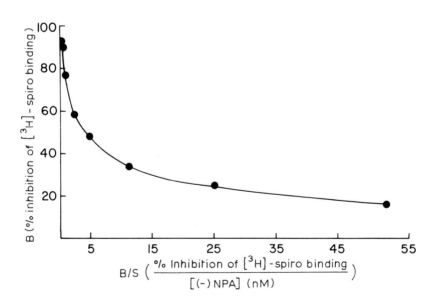

Fig. 4.13 Eadie–Hofstee plot of a (−)*N-n*-propylnorapomorphine displacement curve of [³H]-spiroperidol binding in bovine anterior pituitary. The experiment was performed as in Fig. 4.12. Plotted on the ordinate is per cent inhibition of [³H]-spiroperidol binding, and on the abcissa is this value divided by the concentration of (−)*N-n*-propylnorapomorphine.

1, agonists demonstrate shallow displacement curves (Fig. 4.12). If these data are replotted by the method of Eadie–Hofstee, it is clear that agonists are displacing [³H]-antagonists from two distinct binding sites (Fig. 4.13). Whereas antagonists have equal high affinity for both sites, agonists exhibit high affinity for one population of sites and low affinity for the other (see Fig. 4.14). It would thus be predicted that when labeling pituitary sites with [³H]-agonists, under normal filtration assay conditions utilizing nanomolar concentrations of [³H]-agonists, only the high-affinity sites will be identified. Experimental data support this hypothesis and there are approximately half the number of [³H]-agonist binding sites as [³H]-antagonist sites. Furthermore, since a homogeneous population of sites is labeled by [³H]-agonists, both agonists and antagonists displace [³H]-agonists with high affinity and Hill coefficients equal to 1.

Thus in the pituitary we find a population of binding sites, which do not interconvert during the binding experiment, homogeneous for antagonists but which are heterogeneous for agonists. This is similar to results reported for CNS opiate receptors (Blume *et al.*, 1980) and muscarinic cholinergic receptors (Birdsall *et al.*, 1978). Birdsall *et al.* (1978) have hypothesized that the muscarinic receptor can exist in a number of different conformations – giving rise to the multiplicity of agonist binding sites. It is unclear whether these two dopaminergic binding sites in the pituitary are distinct receptors or different forms of the same receptor. The sites labeled with high affinity by both [³H]-agonists and [³H]-antagonists have similar pharmacological specificity (both qualitatively and quantitatively) to the receptors in the anterior pituitary which regulate prolactin release.

How do these results in the pituitary compare to binding data in the striatum? (Table 4.7). Much of the data is identical; however, in the pituitary, antagonists displace [³H]-agonists with Hill coefficients of 1 (Creese

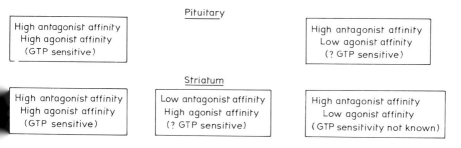

Fig. 4.14 Diagrammatic representation of pituitary and striatal dopamine receptors.

and Sibley, 1979), but in the striatum, antagonist displacement of [³H]-agonist binding is shallow (Burt *et al.*, 1976). This implies, if negative co-operativity is not operational, that [³H]-agonists must also label two populations of binding sites in the striatum – homogeneous for agonists (both high affinity) but which discriminate between antagonists, one having high affinity and one low. This implies at least three populations of striatal binding sites. This extra striatal site has similar pharmacological specificity to Seeman's high-affinity agonist binding site (Titeler *et al.*, 1979), but from our lesion experiments, it is not an autoreceptor.

4.8 FUTURE DIRECTIONS

What is the physiological relevance of this multitude of dopamine receptors? Pharmacologists and biochemists are much happier dealing with an adenylate cyclase as a receptor marker than a simple binding site where a 'response' is not observable. However, the pharmacological specificity of the dopamine-sensitive adenylate cyclase *does not* match the pharmacological specificity of any behavioral, clinical or physiological system or state. Its relevance to what is presently considered 'normal' dopaminergic function is still, therefore, in question. On the other hand, the pharmacological specificity of the [³H]-butyrophenone binding site matches the pharmacological specificity of the receptors mediating classic antidopaminergic behavioral and biochemical effects in animals and man, and thus most certainly labels true dopamine receptors. It is unclear whether the different binding sites identified by [³H]-agonist and [³H]-antagonist ligands represent multiple receptors or multiple states of a single receptor. Such multiple states could have true physiological relevance or could simply represent damaged receptors or receptors in transition from synthesis to degradation. However, the identification of similar multiple binding sites in both the α-adrenergic and cholinergic systems does suggest a more general relevance for this phenomenon. Progress is now being made in the solubilization and purification of dopamine receptor binding sites and the adenylate cyclase (Clement-Cormier, 1980; Gorissen and Laduron, 1979; Hoffman, 1979; Tam and Seeman, 1978). Such studies should throw light on the relationship of these different membrane constituents in the near future.

The identification of different classes of [³H]-butyrophenone binding sites, which may indicate different physiological receptors, as well as the possible receptors identified by the cyclase and [³H]-agonist binding sites, suggests that it may be feasible to produce novel dopamine antagonists which, for example, will be antipsychotic but lack the propensity to produce extrapyramidal side effects or tardive dyskinesia. This will be a major breakthrough in the pharmacological management of schizophrenia. At this time some partially selective agonists and antagonists are already available. For example, molindone and sulpiride are dopamine antagonists at the receptors (non-cyclase linked) in the pituitary regulating prolactin release but yet they do not antagonize the dopamine-sensitive adenylate cyclase. These agents are also antipsychotic and bind with fair avidity to the [^{3}H]-butyrophenone binding sites. Metoclopramide is also active as an antagonist in the pituitary but is inactive on the cyclase. Although it is able to bind to [^{3}H]-butyrophenone binding sites it is not reported to be antipsychotic – although it can produce extrapyramidal side effects. Amongst agonists, we have seen that bromocryptine is a full agonist in the pituitary, yet it is an antagonist of the striatal dopamine-sensitive adenylate cyclase. It is a potent agonist in man in alleviating the symptoms of Parkinson's Disease and can induce a florid psychosis. This again reinforces the association of non-cyclase-linked receptors with the behavioral manifestations of dopaminergic activity. At present there are no selective agonists or antagonists for the cyclase-linked receptors and until these are developed it will be difficult to define their function. However, recent studies suggest that the synthesis of such selective agents is feasible (Setler *et al.*, 1978).

The therapeutic precedents set by the identification of distinct subtypes of adrenoreceptors, histamine and cholinergic receptors portends an exciting future for dopamine receptor studies.

REFERENCES

Aghajanian, G.K. and Bunney, B.S. (1974), in *Frontiers of Neurology and Neuroscience Research* (Seeman, P. and Brown, G.M., eds), University of Toronto Press, Toronto, pp. 4–11.

Aghajanian, G.K. and Bunney, B.S. (1977), *Naunyn-Schmiedeberg's Arch. Pharmacol.*, **297**, 1–7.

Ahn, H.S., Gardner, E. and Makman, M.H. (1979), *Eur. J. Pharmacol.*, **53**, 313–317.

Anden, N.-E. *Advances in Biochem. Psychopharm.*, in press.

Anden, N.-E., Fuxe, K., Hamberger, B. and Hokfelt, T. (1966), *Acta Physiol. Scand.*, **67**, 306–312.

Assaf, S.Y. and Miller, J.J. (1977), *Brain Res.*, **129**, 353–360.

Bacopoulos, N.C., Spokes, E.G., Bird, E.D. and Roth, R.H. (1979), *Science*, **205**, 1405–1407.

Baldessarini, R.J. and Tarsy, D. (1976), in *Mechanisms Underlying Tardive Dyskinesia in the Basal Ganglia* (Yahr, M., ed), Raven Press, New York, pp. 433–446.

Bannon, M.J., Bunney, E.G., Zigun, J.R., Skirboll, L.R. and Roth, R.H. (1980a), *Naunyn-Schmiedeberg's Arch. Pharmacol.*, in press.

Bannon, M.J., Grace, A.A., Bunney, B.S. and Roth, R.H. (1980b), *Naunyn-Schmiedeberg's Arch. Pharmacol.*, in press.

Baring, M.D., Walters, J.R. and Eng, N. (1980), *Brain Res.,* **181**, 214–218.

Beckstead, R.M., Domesick, V.B. and Nauta, W.J.H. (1979), *Brain Res.,* **175**, 191–217.

Bell, C., Lang, W.J. and Laska, F. (1978), *J. Neurochem.,* **31**, 77–83.

Berger, B., Tassin, J.P., Blanc, G., Moyne, M.A. and Thierry, A.M. (1974), *Brain Res.,* **81**, 332–337.

Bird, E.D., Barnes, J., Iversen, L.L., Spokes, E.G., MacKay, A.V. and Shepherd, M. (1977), *Lancet,* **I**, 1157–1159.

Birdsall, N.J.M., Burgen, A.S.V. and Hulme, E.C. (1978), *Mol. Pharmacol.,* **14**, 723–736.

Bjorklund, A. and Lindvall, O. (1975), *Brain Res.,* **83**, 531–537.

Bjorklund, A., Lindvall, O. and Nobin, A. (1975), *Brain Res.,* **89**, 29–42.

Bjorklund, A., Moore, R.Y., Nobin, A. and Stenevi, U. (1973), *Brain Res.,* **51**, 171–191.

Blessing, W.W. and Chalmers, J.P. (1979), *Neuroscience Lett.,* **11**, 35–40.

Blume, A.J., Lichtshtein, D. and Boone, G. (1980), in *Receptors for Neurotransmitters and Peptide Hormones* (Pepeu, G.C., Kuhar, M.J. and Enna, S.J., eds), Raven Press, New York, 339–348.

Butcher, L.L. (1978), *Cholinergic–Monoaminergic Interactions in the Brain*, Academic Press, New York.

Bunney, B.S. and Aghajanian, G.K. (1976), *Life Sci.,* **19**, 1783–1792.

Bunney, W.E. and Post, R.M. (1977), in *Neuroregulators and Psychiatric Disorders* (Usdin, E., Hamburg, D. and Barchas, J.D., eds), Oxford University Press, New York, pp. 151–157.

Bunney, B.S., Walters, J.R., Roth, R.H. and Aghajanian, G.K. (1973). *J. Pharmacol. exp. Ther.,* **185**, 560–571.

Burt, D.R., Creese, I. and Snyder, S.H. (1976), *Mol. Pharmacol.,* **12**, 800–812.

Burt, D.R., Creese, I. and Snyder, S.H. (1977), *Science,* **196**, 326–328.

Carlsson, A. (1975), in *Pre- and Postsynaptic Receptors*. (Usdin, E. and Bunney, W.E., eds), Marcel Dekker, New York, pp. 49–65.

Carlsson, A. and Lindqvist, M. (1963), *Acta Pharmacol. Kobenhavn,* **20**, 140–144.

Caron, M.G., Beaulieu, M., Raymond, V., Gagne, B., Drouin, J., Lefkowitz, R.J. and Labrie, F. (1978), *J. biol. Chem.,* **253**, 2244–2253.

Cheramy, A., Nieoullon, A. and Glowinski, J. (1978), in *Interactions Between Putative Neurotransmitters in the Brain*. (Garattiori, S., Pujol, J.F. and Samarien, R., eds), Raven Press, New York, pp. 175–190.

Clemens, J.A. and Meites, J. (1974), in *Lactogenic Hormones, Fetal Nutrition and Lactation (Problems of Human Production) Vol. 2*. (Josimovich, J.B., ed), John Wiley, New York, pp. 111–151.

Clement-Cormier, Y.C. (1980), in *Receptors for Neurotransmitters and Peptide Hormones*. (Pepeu, G.C., Kuhar, M.J. and Enna, S.J., eds), Raven Press, New York, 159–168.

Clement-Cormier, Y.C., Heindel, J.J. and Robinson, G.A. (1977), *Life Sci.,* **21**, 1357–1363.

Clement-Cormier, Y.C., Kebabian, J.W., Petzold, G.L. and Greengard, P. (1974), *Proc. natl. Acad. Sci. USA,* **71**, 1113–1117.

Clement-Cormier, Y.C., Parrish, R.A., Petzold, G.L., Kebabian, J.W. and Greengard, P. (1975), *J. Neurochem.*, **25**, 143–149.

Commissiong, J.W. and Neff, N.H. (1979), *Biochem. Pharmacol.*, **28**, 1568–1573.

Commissiong, J.W., Gentleman, S. and Neff, N.H. (1979), *Neuropharmacology*, **18**, 565–568.

Connell, P.H. (1958), *Amphetamine Psychosis*, Chapman and Hall, London.

Cools, A.R. and Van Rossum, J.M. (1976), *Psychopharmacologia (Berl.)*, **45**, 243–254.

Corsini, G.U., Del Zompo, M., Marconi, S., Piccardi, M.P., Onali, P.L. and Mangoni, A. (1977), *Life Sci.*, **20**, 1613–1618.

Coyle, J.F. and Schwarcz, R. (1976), *Nature*, **263**, 244–246.

Creese, I. and Iversen, S.D. (1975a), *Brain Res.*, **83**, 419–436.

Creese, I. and Iversen, S.D. (1975b), in *Pre- and Postsynaptic Receptors* (Usdin, E. and Bunney, W.E., eds), Marcel Dekker, New York, pp. 171–190.

Creese, I. and Sibley, D.R. (1979), *Comm. in Psychopharm.*, **3**, 385–396.

Creese, I. and Snyder, S.H. (1978), *Eur. J. Pharmacol.*, **50**, 459–461.

Creese, I. and Snyder, S.H. (1979a), in *Catecholamines: Basic and Clinical Frontiers* (Usdin, E., Kopin, I. and Barchas, J., eds), Pergamon Press, pp. 601–603.

Creese, I. and Snyder, S.H. (1979b), *Eur. J. Pharmacol.*, **56**, 277–281.

Creese, I. and Snyder, S.H. (1979c), *Proceedings of the International Symposium on Long Term Effects of Neuroleptics, Advances in Psychopharmacology*, Raven Press, New York, in press.

Creese, I., Burt, D.R. and Snyder, S.H. (1975), *Life Sci.*, **17**, 993–1002.

Creese, I., Burt, D.R. and Snyder, S.H. (1976a), *Science*, **192**, 481–483.

Creese, I., Burt, D.R. and Snyder, S.H. (1976b), *Science*, **194**, 546.

Creese, I., Burt, D.R. and Snyder, S.H. (1977a), *Science*, **197**, 596–598.

Creese, I., Prosser, T. and Snyder, S.H. (1978), *Life Sci.*, **23**, 495–500.

Creese, I., Schneider, R. and Snyder, S.H. (1977b), *Eur. J. Pharmacol.*, **46**, 377–381.

Creese, I., Stewart, K. and Snyder, S.H. (1979a), *Eur. J. Pharmacol.*, **60**, 55–66.

Creese, I., Usdin, T. and Snyder, S.H. (1979b), *Nature*, **278**, 577–578.

Creese, I., Usdin, T. and Snyder, S.H. (1979c), *Mol. Pharmacol.*, **16**, 69–76.

Crow, T.J., Owen, F., Cross, A.J., Lofthouse, R. and Longden, A. (1978), *Lancet*, i, 36–37.

Dahlstrom, A. and Fuxe, K. (1964), *Acta Physiol. Scand. Suppl.*, **62**, 232, 1–55.

De Camilli, P., Macconi, D. and Spada, A. (1979), *Nature*, **278**, 252–254.

Dinerstein, R.J., Vannice, J., Henderson, R.C., Roth, L.J., Goldberg, L.I. and Hoffmann, P.C. (1979), *Science*, **205**, 497–499.

Dray, A. (1979), *Neuroscience*, **4**, 1407–1439.

Ehinger, B. (1976), in *Transmitters in the Visual Process* (Bonting, S.L., ed), Pergamon Press, Oxford, pp. 145–163.

Enna, S.J., Bennett, J.P., Jr., Burt, D.R., Creese, I. and Snyder, S.H. (1976), *Nature*, **263**, 338–341.

Falck, B. (1962), *Acta Physiol. Scand. Suppl.*, **197**, 56, 1–25.

Falck, B., Hillarp, N.-A., Thieme, G. and Torp, A. (1962), *J. Histochem. Cytochem.*, **10**, 348–354.

Farnebo, L.-O. and Hamberger, B. (1971), *Acta Physiol. Scand. Suppl., 371,* 35–44.

Feinberg, A.P. and Snyder, S.H. (1975), *Proc. natl. Acad. Sci. USA,* **72,** 1899–1903.

Fibiger, H.C. (1978), *Ann. Rev. Pharmacol. Toxicol.,* **18,** 37–56.

Fields, J.Z., Reisine, T.D. and Yamamura, H.I. (1977), *Brain. Res.,* **136,** 578–584.

Gale, K., Guidotti, A. and Costa, E. (1977), *Science,* **195,** 503–505.

Geffen, L.B., Jessell, T.M., Cuello, A.C. and Iversen, L. (1976), *Nature, Lond.,* **260,** 258–260.

Goldberg, L.I., Volkman, R.H. and Kohli, J.D. (1978), *Ann. Rev. Pharmacol. Toxicol.,* **18,** 57–79.

Gorissen, H. and Laduron, P. (1979), *Nature,* **279,** 72–74.

Govoni, S., Olgiati, V.R., Trabucchi, M., Garau, L., Stefanini, E. and Spano, P.F. (1978), *Neurosci. Lett.,* **8,** 207–210.

Greengard, P. (1976), *Nature,* **260,** 101–108.

Gudelsky, G.A., Thornburg, J.E. and Moore, K.E. (1975), *Life Sci.,* **16,** 1331–1338.

Henn, F.A., Anderson, D.J. and Sellstrom, A. (1977), *Nature,* **266,** 637–638.

Hoffmann, F.M. (1979), *J. biol. Chem.,* **254,** 255–258.

Hokfelt, T., Halasz, N., Ljungdahl, A., Johansson, O., Goldstein, M. and Park, D. (1975), *Neurosci. Lett.,* **1,** 85–90.

Horn, A.S. and Snyder, S.H. (1971), *Proc. natl. Acad. Sci. USA,* **68,** 2325–2328.

Hornykiewicz, O. (1966), *Pharmacol. Rev.,* **18,** 925–964.

Hyttel, J. (1978), *Prog. Neuro-Psychopharmac.,* **2,** 329–335.

Hyttel, J. (1980), *Psychopharmacology,* **67,** 107–109.

Iversen, L.L. (1975), *Science,* **188,** 1084–1089.

Iversen, L.L., Rogawski, M. and Miller, R.J. (1976), *Mol. Pharmac.,* **12,** 251–262.

Janssen, P.A.J. and Van Bever, N.F. (1975), in *Current Developments in Psychopharmacology,* Vol. 2, (Essman, W.B. and Valzelli, L., eds), Spectrum, New York, pp. 165–184.

Kebabian, J.W. and Calne, D.B. (1979), *Nature,* **277,** 93–96.

Kebabian, J.W., Chen, T.C. and Cote, T.E. (1979), *Comm. Psychopharm.,* **3,** 421–428.

Kebabian, J.W., Petzold, G.L. and Greengard, P. (1972), *Proc. natl. Acad. Sci. USA,* **79,** 2145–2149.

Kitai, S.T., Sugimori, M. and Kocsis, J.C. (1976), *Exp. Brain. Res.,* **24,** 351–363.

Klawans, H.L. (1973), *Am. J. Psychiatry,* **130,** 82–86.

Klawans, H.L., Weiner, W.J. and Nausieda, P.A. (1977), *Prog. Neuro-Psychopharmac.,* **1,** 53–60.

Kobayashi, R.K. (1977), *N. Engl. J. Med.,* **296,** 257–260.

Kreuger, K., Forn, J., Walters, J.R., Roth, R.H. and Greengard, P. (1976), *Mol. Pharmacol.,* **12,** 639–648.

Lad, P.M., Welton, A.F. and Rodbell, M. (1977), *J. biol. Chem.,* **252,** 5942–5946.

Laduron, P.M. and Leysen, J.E. (1978), *J. Pharm. Pharmac.,* **30,** 120–122.

Laduron, P.M., Janssen, P.F.M. and Leysen, J. (1978), *Biochem. Pharmacol.,* **27,** 307–328.

Lee, T., Seeman, P., Rajput, A., Farley, I. and Hornykiewicz, O. (1978a), *Nature,* **273,** 59–61.

Lee, T., Seeman, P., Tourtellotte, W.W., Farely, I. and Hornykiewicz, O. (1978b), *Nature*, **274**, 897–900.

Leff, S., Adams, L., Hyttel, J. and Creese, I. (1980), *Eur. J. Pharmacol.*, in press.

Leibowitz, S.F. (1976), in *Hunger: Basic Mechanisms and Clinical Implications*, (Novin, D., Wyrwicka, W. and Bray, G., eds), Raven Press, New York, pp. 1–17.

Leviel V., Cheramy, A. and Glowinski, J. (1979), *Nature*, **280**, 236–239.

Leysen, J. (1979), *Comm. Psychopharm.*, in press.

Leysen, J. and Laduron, P. (1977), *Life Sci.*, **20**, 281–288.

Libet, B. (1976), *SIF Cells: Structure and Function of the Small Intensely Fluorescent Sympathetic Cells*, U.S. Government Printing Office, Washington, D.C.

Libet, B. (1979), *Life Sci.*, **24**, 1043–1058.

Lichtensteiger, W. and Keller, P.J. (1974), *Brain Res.*, **74**, 279–303.

Lindvall, O. and Bjorklund, A. (1974), *Histochemistry*, **39**, 97–127.

Lindvall, O. and Bjorklund, A. (1977), in *Handbook of Psychopharmacology*, Vol. 9 (Iversen, L., Iversen, S.D. and Snyder, S., eds), Plenum Press, New York, pp. 139–232.

Lindvall, O., Bjorklund, A. and Divac, I. (1978), *Brain Res.*, **142**, 1–24.

MacLeod, R.M. and Lehmeyer, J.E. (1974), *Endocrinology*, **97**, 1077–1085.

Magistretti, P.J. and Schorderet, M. (1979), *Life Sci.*, **25**, 1675–1686.

Marshall, J.F. (1979), *Brain Res.*, **177**, 311–324.

McGeer, P. and McGeer, E. (1976), *Nature*, **263**, 517–519.

McGeer, E.G., Olney, J.W. and McGeer, P.L. (1978), in *Kainic Acid as a Tool in Neurobiology*, Raven Press, New York.

Meltzer, H.Y. (1979), *Comm. Psychopharm.*, **3**, 457–470.

Meltzer, H.Y. and Stahl, S.M. (1976), *Schizophrenia Bull.*, **2**, 19–76.

Mercer, L., Del Fiacco, M. and Cuello, A.C. (1979), *Experentia*, **35**, 101–103.

Miller, R.J. and Hiley, C.R. (1974), *Nature*, **248**, 596–597.

Miller, R.J., Horn, A.S. and Iversen, L.L. (1974), *Mol. Pharmacol.*, **10**, 759–766.

Mishra, R.K., Gardner, E.L. Katzman, R. and Makman, M.H. (1974), *Proc. natl. Acad. Sci. USA*, **71**, 3883–3887.

Moore, K.E. and Kelly, P.H. (1978), in *Psychopharmacology: A Generation of Progress* (Lipton, M.A., DiMascio, A. and Killam, K.F., eds), Raven Press, New York, pp. 221–234.

Moore, R.Y. and Bloom, F.E. (1978), *Ann. Rev. Neurosci.*, **1**, 129–169.

Muller, P. and Seeman, P. (1978), *Psychopharmacology*, **60**, 1–11.

Nagy, J.I., Lee, T., Seeman, P. and Fibiger, H.C. (1978), *Nature*, **274**, 278–281.

Nauta, H.J.W. (1979), *Neuroscience*, **4**, 1875–1881.

Nieoullon, A., Cheramy, A. and Glowinski, J. (1977), *Nature, Lond.*, **266**, 375–377.

Norcross, K. and Spehlmann, R. (1977), *Neuroscience Lett.*, **6**, 323–328.

Owen, F., Cross, A.J., Waddington, J.L., Poulter, M., Gamble, S.J. and Crow, T.J. (1980), *Life Sci.*, **26**, 55–59.

Owen, F., Crow, T.J., Poulter M., Cross, A.J., Longden, A. and Riley, G.J. (1978), *Lancet*, **1**, 233–236.

Peroutka, S.J., U'Prichard, D.C., Greenberg, D.A. and Snyder, S.H. (1977), *Neuropharmacology*, **16**, 549–556.

Pert, A., Rosenblatt, J., Swit, C., Pert, C. and Bunney, W.E. (1978), *Science,* **201**, 171–173.

Prement, J., Tassin, J.P., Therry, A.M., Glowinski, J. and Bockaert, J. (1975), *Exp. Brain Res.,* **23**, 165.

Price, J.T.C. and Fibiger, H.C. (1974), *Eur. J. Pharmacol.,* **29**, 249–252.

Quik, M., Emson, P.C. and Joyce, E. (1979a), *Brain Res.,* **167**, 355–365.

Quik, M., Spokes, E.G., Mackay, A.V.P. and Bannister, R. (1979b), *J. Neurol. Sci.,* **43**, 429–437.

Reisine, T.D., Fields, J.Z., Yamamura, H.I., Bird, E.D., Spokes, E., Schreiner, P.S. and Enna, S.J. (1977), *Life Sci.,* **21**, 335–344.

Reisine, T.D., Nagy, J.I., Fibiger, H.C. and Yamamura, H.I. (1979), *Brain Res.,* **169**, 209–214.

Richardson, T.L., Miller, J.J. and McLennan, H. (1977), *Brain Res.,* **127**, 219–234.

Rodbell, M., Lin, M.C., Soloman, Y., Landos, C., Harwood, J.P., Moutin, B.R. and Rendall, M. (1975), *Adv. Cyclic. Nucleotide Res.,* **5**, 3–29.

Roth, R.H. (1979), *Comm. Psychopharm.,* **3**, 429–446.

Roth, R.H. and Nowycky, M.C. (1977), *Advances in Biochemical Psychopharmacology*, Vol. 16, Raven Press, New York, 465–470.

Roth, R.H., Morgenroth, V.H., III and Murrin, L.C. (1975), in *Antipsychotic Drugs, Pharmacodynamics and Pharmacokinetics*, (Sedvall, G., ed), Pergamon Press, New York, pp. 133–145.

Schmidt, M.J. and Hill, L.E. (1977), *Life Sci.,* **20**, 789–798.

Schwarcz, R., Creese, I., Coyle, J.T. and Snyder, S.H. (1978), *Nature,* **271**, 766–768.

Seeman, P., Chau-Wong, M., Tedesco, J. and Wong, K. (1975), *Proc. natl. Acad. Sci. USA,* **72**, 4376–4380.

Seeman, P. and Lee, T. (1975), in *Antipsychotic Drugs, Pharmacodynamics and Pharmacokinetics*, (Sedvall, G., ed), Pergamon Press, Oxford, pp. 183–191.

Seeman, P., Lee, T., Chau-Wong, M. and Wong, K. (1976), *Nature,* **261**, 717–719.

Seeman, P., Tedesco, J.L., Lee, T., Chau-Wong, M., Muller, P., Bowles, J., Whitaker, P.M., McManus, C., Tittler, M., Weinreich, P., Friend, W.C. and Brown, G.M. (1978), *Fed. Proc.* **37**, 130–136.

Seeman, P., Westman, K., Protiva, M., Jilek, J., Jain, P.C., Saxena, A.K., Anand, N., Humber, L. and Philipp, A. (1979), *Eur. J. Pharm.,* **56**, 247–251.

Setler, P.E., Sarau, H.M., Zirkle, C.L. and Saunders, H.L. (1978), *Eur. J. Pharm.,* **50**, 419–430.

Shaar, C.J. and Clemens, J.A. (1974), *Endocrinology,* **95**, 1202–1212.

Sibley, D.R. and Creese, I. (1979a), *Eur. J. Pharmacol.,* **55**, 341–343.

Sibley, D.R. and Creese, I. (1979b), *Soc. Neur. Abs.,* **5**, 352.

Sibley, D.R. and Creese, I. (in preparation).

Siggins, G.R. (1977), in *Psychopharmacology – A Generation of Progress*, (Lipton, M.A., DiMascio, A. and Killam, K.F., eds), Raven Press, New York, pp,.143–158.

Skirboll, L.R., Grace, A.A. and Bunney, B.S. (1979), *Science,* **206**,80–82.

Smith, R.C., Tamminga, C.A., Haraszti, J., Pandey, G.N. and Davis, J.M. (1977), *Am. J. Psychi.,* **134**, 763–768.

Snyder, S.H., Banerjee, S.P., Yamamura, H.I. and Greenberg, D. (1974), *Science,* **184**, 1243–1253.

Snyder, S.H., Creese, I. and Burt, D.R. (1975), *Psychopharmacol. Commun.*, **1**, 663–673.

Steinsland, O.S. and Hieble, J.P. (1978), *Science*, **199**, 443–445.

Stricker, E.M. and Zigmond, M.J. (1976), in *Progress in Physiological Psychology and Psychobiology*, (Sprague, J.M. and Epstein, A.N., eds), Academic Press, New York, pp. 121–188.

Tam, S. and Seeman, P. (1978), *Eur. J. Pharm.*, **52**, 151–152.

Tarsy, D. and Baldessarini, R.J. (1974), *Neuropharmacology*, **13**, 927–940.

Thierry, A.M., Tassin, J.P., Blanc, G. and Glowinski, J. (1976), *Nature*, **263**, 242–243.

Thornburg, J.E. and Moore, K.E. (1975), *J. Pharm. exp. Ther.*, **192**, 42–49.

Tilders, R.J.H. and Smelik, P.G. (1977), *Frontiers Hormone Res.*, **4**, 80–93.

Titeler, M., List, S. and Seeman, P. (1979), *Comm. Psychopharm.*, **3**, 411–420.

Titeler, M., Seeman, P. and Henn, F. (1978), *Eur. J. Pharmacol.*, **51**, 459–460.

Tollenaere, J.P., Moereels, H. and Koch, M.H.J. (1977), *Eur. J. Med. Chem.*, **12**, 199–211.

Tonon, G., Saiani, L., Spano, P.F. and Trabucchi, M. (1979), *Brain Res.*, **160**, 553–558.

Ungerstedt, U. (1971a), *Acta Physiol. Scand.*, **367**, 1–48.

Ungerstedt, U. (1971b), *Acta Physiol. Scand. Suppl.*, **367**, 95–122.

Ungerstedt, U. (1971c), *Acta Physiol. Scand. Suppl.*, **367**, 69–93.

Ungerstedt, U. and Arbuthnott, G.W. (1970), *Brain Res.*, **24**, 485–493.

Vale, W., Rivier, J., Guillemin, R. and Rivier, C. (1979), in *Nervous System Effects of Hypothalamic Hormones and Other Peptides*, (Collie, R., ed), Raven Press, New York, pp. 163–176.

Van Neuten, J.M., Ennis, C., Helson, L., Laduron, P.M. and Janssen, P.A.J. (1978), *Life Sci.*, **23**, 453.

Voith, K. and Cummings, J.R. (1976), *Can. J. Physiol.*, **54**, 551–560.

Von Voigtlander, P.F. and Moore, K.E. (1973), *Neuropharmacology*, **12**, 451–462.

Von Voigtlander, P.F., Boukma, S.J. and Johnson, G.A. (1973), *Neuropharmacology*, **12**, 1081–1086.

Walters, J.R. and Roth, R.H. (1975), in *Antipsychotic Drugs, Pharmacodynamics and Pharmacokinetics*, (Sedvall, G., ed), Pergamon Press, Oxford, pp. 147–160.

Walters, J.R., Roth, R.H. and Aghajanian, G.K. (1973), *J. Pharmacol. exp. Ther.*, **186**, 630–639.

Watling, K.J., Dowling, J.E. and Iversen, L.L. (1979), *Nature*, **281**, 578–580.

Weiner, R.I. and Ganong, W.F. (1978), *Physiol. Rev.*, **58**, 905–976.

Westfall, T.C., Besson, M.-J., Giorguieff, M.-F. and Glowinski, J. (1976), *Nauny-Schmiedeberg's Arch. Pharmacol.*, **292**, 279–287.

Williams, L.T. and Lefkowitz, R.J. (1978), *Receptor Binding Studies in Adrenergic Pharmacology*, Raven Press, New York.

Wilson, C.J., Fenster, G.A., Young, S.J. and Groves, P.M. (1979), *Brain Res.*, **179**, 165–170.

York, D.H. (1975), in *Handbook of Psychopharmacology, Vol. 6* (Iversen, L., Iverson, S.D. and Snyder, S.H., eds), Raven Press, New York, pp. 23–61.

5 Adrenergic Receptor Molecules

KENNETH P. MINNEMAN

Neurotransmitter Receptors Part 2
(*Receptors and Recognition*, Series B, Volume 10)
Edited by H.I. Yamamura and S.J. Enna
Published in 1981 by Chapman and Hall, 11 New Fetter Lane, London
EC4P 4EE
© Chapman and Hall

Acknowledgements

I would like to thank Dr Neil C. Moran for helpful discussions and a critical reading of the manuscript, and Ms Marlise Casteel and Teresa Zimmerman for quick and expert preparation of the typescript.

Abbreviations

cyclic AMP	adenosine $3':5'$-cyclic monophosphate
ATP	adenosine $5'$-triphosphate
COMT	catechol O-methyltransferase
[^{3}H]DHA	[^{3}H]dihydroalprenolol
^{125}IHYP	[^{125}I]iodohydroxybenzylpindolol
K_D	equilibrium dissociation constant
IC$_{50}$	concentration of drug causing 50 per cent inhibition
[^{3}H]CLON	[^{3}H]clonidine
[^{3}H]EPI	[^{3}H]epinephrine
[^{3}H]NE	[^{3}H]norepinephrine
[^{3}H]PAC	[^{3}H]para-aminoclonidine
[^{3}H]DHE	[^{3}H]dihydroergokryptine
[^{3}H]PRAZ	[^{3}H]prazosin
k_{+1}	forward rate constant
k_{-1}	backward rate constant
[^{3}H]HBI	[^{3}H]hydroxybenzylisoproterenol
GTP	guanosine $5'$-triphosphate
p$^{[NH]}$ppG	guanosine $5'$-[β,γ-imido]triphosphate
GDP	guanosine $5'$-diphosphate
GMP	guanosine $5'$-monophosphate
cyclic GMP	guanosine $3':5'$-cyclic monophosphate
SNAT	serotonin N-acetyltransferase
RNA	ribonucleic acid
NEM	N-ethylmaleimide
NAD$^+$	oxidized nicotinamide–adenine dinucleotide
ADP	adenosine $5'$-diphosphate

5.1 INTRODUCTION

The physiological effects of epinephrine and norepinephrine are caused by the interaction of these compounds with specific receptor molecules on the external surface of target cells. Since both epinephrine and norepinephrine are found in large quantities in the adrenal gland, these receptors are called adrenergic receptors. Although the existence of these receptor molecules has been suspected for many years, it is only very recently that some information on their molecular and chemical nature has become available.

Historically, the concept of a receptor was introduced to explain the specificity of response of a tissue to added drugs. Until recently therefore, the concept of a receptor encompassed both the specific *recognition* of the drug molecule by the tissue and the *response* of the tissue to the drug molecule. Receptors were measured in terms of the ability of an isolated tissue, such as an intestinal strip, to respond in an appropriate manner, such as contraction or relaxation, to exogenously added drug molecules. Although the existence of discrete receptor molecules was implicit in the theoretical considerations of drug–receptor interactions, there was no experimental evidence to support this concept until about 1975. With the advent of reliable radioligand binding assays over the past five years, this situation has changed dramatically, and much information is now becoming available concerning the properties of adrenergic receptor molecules.

In this chapter I will attempt an overview of our current enormously expanded knowledge of adrenergic receptor molecules. Owing to the practical considerations discussed below, progress in the study of the β-adrenergic receptor has been very rapid, and more is now known about the properties of this receptor than any other, except possibly the nicotinic cholinergic receptor (Heidmann and Changeux, 1978). Since information on α-adrenergic receptors has been slower in coming, I will deal mainly with β-adrenergic receptors. Although the major focus will be on information obtained in the last five years using radioligand-binding assays, a short overview of the historical development of the concept of adrenergic receptors and their function in mammalian tissues is presented to integrate this recent information into its proper functional perspective. For an extended discussion of the history, pharmacology and function of these receptors, the reader is referred to excellent review articles by Furchgott (1972) and Moran (1975).

5.2 HISTORICAL BACKGROUND

5.2.1 The concept of α- and β-adrenergic receptors

The concept of two distinct types of adrenergic receptor grew out of the observation that adrenergic stimuli could produce apparently opposite excitatory and inhibitory responses. Dale (1906) found that excitatory responses of various organs to epinephrine or nerve stimulation were blocked by ergot alkaloids, while inhibitory responses were not blocked. The suggestion by Cannon and Rosenblueth (1937) that these dual adrenergic responses were due to two different endogenous substances was rendered untenable by the work of von Euler (1956), who presented strong evidence toward the concept of a single adrenergic neurotransmitter (norepinephrine). Although Dale (1906) had raised the possibility of different receptors for the excitatory and inhibitory effects of adrenergic stimuli, Ahlquist (1948) first recognized that a more appropriate classification of the receptors would be not with regard to their function, but solely with regard to their pharmacological specificity.

Ahlquist (1948) presented evidence that responses to adrenergic stimuli could be divided into two major categories on the basis of their pharmacological specificity. He showed that the rank order of potency of catecholamines in causing five different excitatory responses and one inhibitory response was epinephrine > norepinephrine > α-methylnorepinephrine > α-methylepinephrine > isoproterenol. He proposed that these receptors be called α-adrenergic receptors. The rank order of potency of catecholamines on responses in other tissues (two excitatory and two inhibitory) was shown to be isoproterenol > epinephrine > α-methylepinephrine > α-methylnorepinephrine > norepinephrine. He proposed that these receptors be called β-adrenergic receptors.

The introduction of dibenamine (Nickerson and Goodman, 1947) and related β-haloalkylamines (Nickerson, 1949) as irreversible (i.e. non-equilibrium) blockers of adrenergic stimuli, in conjunction with the reversibly acting ergot derivatives previously available, supported Ahlquist's classification. All of the responses which he attributed to α-adrenergic receptor stimulation, but none of the responses which he attributed to β-adrenergic receptor stimulation, could be blocked by these drugs (see Furchgott, 1972). Strong support for Ahlquist's α/β subdivision came with the intro-'β-adrenergic-blocking drug'. Soon after this, other selective β-adrenergic-first introduced dichloroisoproterenol as a drug which blocked adrenergic inhibitory responses in several smooth muscles, and Moran and Perkins (1958) showed that this drug also blocked adrenergic excitatory responses in mammalian heart. The fact that dichloroisoproterenol selectively blocked those responses which Ahlquist had classified as β-adrenergic led Moran and Perkins (1958) to suggest that this drug be called a 'β-adrenergic-blocking drug'. Soon after this, other selective β-adrenergic-blocking drugs were introduced, the most notable being propranolol (Black *et al.*, 1964). The availability of selective blocking drugs for both α- and β-adrenergic receptors greatly strengthened Ahlquist's proposed classification scheme.

5.2.2 The concept of β_1- and β_2-adrenergic receptors

Upon further experimentation, it became apparent that all β-adrenergic receptors might not have identical properties. Examination of the effects of the α-methyl congeners of methoxamine, including isopropylmethoxamine (Burns *et al.*, 1964) and butoxamine (Levy, 1966), showed that these drugs blocked the β-adrenergic receptors mediating the metabolic and vascular effects of catecholamines at concentrations where they did not block the β-adrenergic receptors mediating the cardiac-stimulatory effects. Strong evidence for the existence of more than one type of β-adrenergic receptor was first presented by Lands and co-workers (1967a,b). These authors compared the rank order of potency of a series of catecholamines on a number of β-adrenergic-receptor-mediated responses and showed that these responses could be subdivided into two major groups, which they proposed reflected the existence of two distinct types of β-adrenergic receptor. The β-adrenergic receptors controlling cardiac stimulation, fatty acid mobilization from adipose tissue and inhibition of contraction of rabbit small intestine were stimulated by catecholamines with the rank order of potency isoproterenol > epinephrine = norepinephrine. They proposed that these receptors be called β_1. The β-adrenergic receptors controlling bronchodilation, vasodilation, inhibition of uterine contraction and increased contraction of the diaphragm were stimulated by catecholamines with the rank order of potency isoproterenol > epinephrine > norepinephrine. They proposed that these receptors be called β_2.

The development of new synthetic drugs with increasing selectivity supported the β_1/β_2 subclassification proposed by Lands *et al.* (1967a,b). Dunlop and Shanks (1968) reported that practolol selectively blocked the cardiac β-adrenergic receptors mediating inotropic and chronotropic stimulation (β_1), but had no effect on the vascular β-adrenergic receptors mediating vasodilation (β_2), suggesting that this drug was a β_1-selective antagonist. The development of selective β_2 agonists was also reported, as salbutamol (Brittain *et al.*, 1968) and soterenol (Dungan *et al.*, 1968) were shown to stimulate bronchial β-adrenergic receptors (β_2) without affecting cardiac β-adrenergic receptors (β_1). As discussed above, the α-methyl congeners of methoxamine appeared to be selective β_2 antagonists. Further compounds in all of these classes have become available and have greatly strengthened the subdivision of β-adrenergic receptors into two subtypes, β_1 and β_2 (see Minneman *et al.*, 1981).

Table 5.1 Adrenergic receptor subtypes.

Name	Potency order of catecholamines	Examples of selective agonists	Examples of selective antagonists
α-Adrenergic	EPI $\geq$ NE $\gg$ ISO	clonidine*, phenylephrine*	phentolamine, dihydroergotamine
α_1	NE $\geq$ EPI $\gg$ ISO	methoxamine, phenylephrine	prazosin, WB 4101
α_2	EPI $\geq$ NE $\gg$ ISO	clonidine, α-methylnorepinephrine	yohimbine, phentolamine
β-Adrenergic	ISO $>$ EPI $\geq$ NE	isoproterenol	propranolol, sotalol
β_1	ISO $>$ EPI $=$ NE	norepinephrine	practolol, metoprolol
β_2	ISO $>$ EPI $>$ NE	salbutamol, soterenol	butoxamine, IPS 339

The potency order of catecholamines and the selectivity of various drugs were derived from the various literature sources referenced in the text. See particularly reviews by Furchgott (1972), Moran (1975), Berthelsen and Pettinger (1977) and Minneman et al. (1981). ISO = isoproterenol; EPI = epinephrine; NE = norepinephrine.
* There are no agonists presently available which stimulate α-receptors more potently than β-receptors but which do not discriminate between α_1- and α_2-receptors.

5.2.3 The concept of α_1- and α_2-adrenergic receptors

More recently it has also been suggested that all α-adrenergic receptors are not pharmacologically identical. On the basis of differences observed in the potency of phenoxybenzamine in inhibiting presynaptic increases in transmitter release and postsynaptic changes in contractility in cat spleen (Cubeddu *et al.*, 1974), Langer (1974) proposed that postsynaptic α-adrenergic receptors be referred to as 'α_1'-receptors and presynaptic α-adrenergic receptors be referred to as 'α_2'-receptors. Berthelsen and Pettinger (1977) suggested that α_2-receptors may also have several non-neuronal effects, such as inhibiting renin release from the kidney and subserving a centrally mediated fall in blood pressure, and proposed that these receptors also be classified by pharmacological specificity rather than by pre- or post-synaptic localization. Agonists such as methoxamine and phenylephrine are relatively selective for stimulation of α_1-receptors, while α-methylnorepinephrine and clonidine (Starke *et al.*, 1974) are relatively selective for stimulation of α_2-receptors. α_1- and α_2-receptors, like β_1- and β_2-receptors, can be distinguished either by comparing the rank order of potency of agonists (Wikberg, 1978) or by blockade with selective antagonists (Miach *et al.*, 1978). Prazosin (α_1-selective; Cambridge *et al.*, 1977) and yohimbine (α_2-selective; Starke *et al.*, 1975) are examples of selective antagonists.

The availability of antagonists with a very high degree of selectivity between α_1- and α_2-receptors (100–1000-fold) has resulted in substantial progress in the differentiation of these two receptor subtypes in the past few years. In contrast, the limited selectivity of the drugs available for distinguishing β_1- and β_2-receptors (10–50-fold) has made that task much more difficult. However, overwhelming evidence now supports the hypothesis that both the α and β classes of adrenergic receptors contain at least two subclasses of receptor with different pharmacological properties.

5.2.4 Classification of receptors on the basis of function

There is at present no basis for a functional or anatomical classification of discrete types of adrenergic receptors. All such generalizations that have been proposed (i.e. excitatory/inhibitory for α/β; post-/pre-synaptic for α_1/α_2) have proved to have exceptions. An α-adrenergic receptor can mediate excitation in some tissues (contraction of uterus and nictitating membrane) and inhibition in others (inhibition of intestinal smooth muscle), and similarly a β-adrenergic receptor can mediate excitation in some tissues (stimulation of heart rate and contractility) and inhibition (vasodilation and relaxation of the uterus) in others. In a like manner, α_2-receptors have been shown to be presynaptic in some cases (on cholinergic neurons in guinea pig ileum) and postsynaptic in others (inhibiting renin release in the kidney).

The only type of functional classification of these receptors that has not yet been experimentally disproved is the proposal by Ariens and Simonis (1976) and Carlsson and Hedberg (1977) and that β_1- and β_2-receptors represent the neuronally innervated and hormonally stimulated receptors respectively. Since norepinephrine is the major adrenergic neurotransmitter and has a much lower affinity for β_2-receptors than it does for β_1-receptors, it seems unlikely that the effects of norepinephrine would be mediated through β_2-receptors. It has in fact recently been demonstrated that β_2-receptors in dog gracilis muscle do not respond to sympathetic nerve stimulation (Russell and Moran, 1980). Although such a neuronal/hormonal functional classification for β_1- and β_2-receptors has yet to be disproved, this teleological hypothesis does not take into account the fact that β_1-receptors can be stimulated with equal potency by both epinephrine and norepinephrine and therefore might serve as either neuronal or hormonal receptors. In addition, epinephrine may also act as a neurotransmitter in some areas of the central nervous system (Hokfelt *et al.*, 1974), and in some mammals such as cats, norepinephrine makes up a substantial amount of total adrenal catecholamines (von Euler, 1956).

The evidence therefore suggests that the classification of adrenergic receptors should be viewed in strictly pharmacological, rather than functional or anatomical, terms and that the differences between these receptors rest solely on the relative potency of agonists and antagonists in the stimulation and inhibition of these receptors. The differences between these receptors are probably due to physical differences in the recognition sites on the receptor molecules, a conclusion which is supported by the data from radioligand-binding assays discussed below.

5.3 FUNCTION OF ADRENERGIC RECEPTORS

Adrenergic receptors are involved in a wide spectrum of physiological processes, and are instrumental in controlling respiration, circulation, digestion, body temperature and metabolism and exocrine gland function. These receptors are also found in the central nervous system and have been implicated in behavioral phenomena ranging from feeding to aggression. Although the functions subserved by adrenergic receptors are summarized below, an exhaustive discussion is beyond the scope of this article, and a more complete discussion is presented by Moran (1975) and Mayer (1980).

5.3.1 Cardiovascular system

The function of adrenergic receptors in the control of the cardiovascular system is fairly well understood. α-Adrenergic receptors mediate catecholamine-induced vasoconstriction and β-adrenergic receptors mediate vasodilation and increases in heart rate and contractility (Ahlquist, 1948). β-Adrenergic receptors also increase glycogen breakdown (Mayer and Moran, 1960) and have other metabolic effects in the heart as in other tissues (see below). In general, the β-adrenergic receptors in the heart appear to be of the β_1-subtype (Lands *et al.*, 1967a,b), although there seems to also be a significant β_2-receptor population involved in increasing heart rate (Carlsson *et al.*, 1977) but not contractility. Some α-adrenergic receptors may also exist in the heart and stimulation of these receptors may also increase cardiac contractility (Govier, 1968; Schumann *et al.*, 1974). The non-cardiac β-adrenergic receptors mediating vasodilation in the periphery are generally of the β_2-subtype (Lands *et al.*, 1967), while in the brain they are of the β_1-subtype (Edvinsson and Olson, 1974; Sercombe *et al.*, 1977). The α-adrenergic receptors mediating vasoconstriction are generally of the α_1-subtype (Berthelsen and Pettinger, 1977).

5.3.2 Non-vascular smooth muscle

Adrenergic receptors play a major role in controlling the contractile state of a number of non-vascular smooth muscles. Stimulation of α-adrenergic receptors causes contraction of the spleen (Bickerton, 1963), nictitating membrane, radial muscle of the iris, and the uterus (Ahlquist, 1948). α-Adrenergic receptor stimulation of the gastrointestinal tract is more complicated and can lead to either contraction or relaxation, depending on the particular segments studied. Interestingly, β-adrenergic receptor stimulation of the gastrointestinal tract causes similar effects to α-receptor stimulation (see Moran, 1975). Stimulation of β-adrenergic receptors causes relaxation of the spleen (Ignarro and Titus, 1968), nictitating membrane (Smith, 1963), uterus (Ahlquist, 1948), and bronchial and tracheal smooth muscle (Powell and Slater, 1958). Thus, with the possible exception of the gastrointestinal tract, stimulation of α-adrenergic receptors generally causes contraction of non-vascular smooth muscle, while stimulation of β-adrenergic receptors causes relaxation. When these tissues have been studied with regard to the α- or β-subtype involved, they are generally found to be α_1 and β_2 (Berthelsen and Pettinger, 1977; Lands *et al.*, 1967a,b).

5.3.3 Skeletal muscle

The effects of catecholamines on skeletal muscles are generally mediated through β-adrenergic receptors. Fast skeletal muscle responds to β-adrenergic receptor stimulation by increased contraction, while slow skeletal muscle responds to β-adrenergic receptor stimulation by decreased contraction (see Bowman and Nott, 1969).

5.3.4 Metabolic responses

Catecholamines exert three major metabolic effects: glycogenolysis, lipolysis and calorigenesis. These effects are generally caused by interaction with β-adrenergic receptors (see Robison *et al.*, 1971), although glycogenolysis in the liver of some species appears to be stimulated by both α- and β-adrenergic receptors (Exton, 1979). The β-adrenergic receptors in the liver are of the β_2-subtype (Minneman *et al.*, 1979c), while the α-adrenergic receptors are α_1 (Exton, 1979). Similarly glycogenolysis in skeletal muscle is controlled by β_2-receptors (Arnold *et al.*, 1968), while lipolysis and calorigenesis (Arnold and McAuliff, 1969) are controlled by β_1-receptors.

5.3.5 Central nervous system

The effects of adrenergic agonists and antagonists have also been examined in mammalian brain with microiontophoretic techniques. There is substantial evidence for the existence of β-adrenergic receptors inhibiting neuronal firing on identified cell populations in several brain regions, including cerebellar Purkinje cells (Hoffer *et al.*, 1971), hippocampal pyramidal cells (Segal and Bloom, 1974), identified pyramidal tract neurons (Stone, 1976) and unidentified neurons in the cerebral cortex (Dillier *et al.*, 1978). More recently, the capacity of norepinephrine to amplify inhibition of the spontaneous spiking activity of cerebellar Purkinje cells by γ-aminobutyric acid (GABA) has also been shown to be a β-adrenergic-receptor-mediated effect (Moises *et al.*, 1979). The uncertain nature of drug concentrations when applied by microiontophoresis has made it difficult to determine whether these are β_1- or β_2-receptors. Stimulation of α-adrenergic receptors also inhibits the spontaneous firing of neurons in the locus coeruleus (Cedarbaum and Aghajanian, 1977), and it has been suggested that this response may involve an α_2-receptor. α-Adrenergic receptors have also been identified affecting the firing rate of individual neurons in the cerebral cortex (Bevan *et al.*, 1977) and raphe (Baraban and Aghajanian, 1980), although they have not yet been classified with regard to subtype.

5.4 SECOND MESSENGERS MEDIATING EFFECTS OF ADRENERGIC RECEPTOR STIMULATION

Since the hormone–receptor interaction occurs on the external cell surface, this membrane-associated event usually triggers a secondary cascade of responses inside the cell to affect internal metabolic processes. Although stimulation of some receptors (such as the nicotinic acetylcholine receptor) directly alters ionic gradients by affecting the properties of membrane ion channels (Heidmann and Changeux, 1978), in many cases the primary effect of the hormone–receptor interaction is to cause a change in the level of some 'second messenger' inside the cell. This second messenger can then directly or through a further cascade process affect the activity of appropriate metabolic enzymes or the expression of particular genes.

5.4.1 β-Adrenergic receptors

β-Adrenergic receptors exert most of their intracellular and metabolic effects by altering cellular levels of cyclic AMP (adenosine 3':5'-cyclic monophosphate). This compound was first discovered as mediating the glycogenolytic effects of epinephrine (Sutherland and Rall, 1960), and has since been implicated as a second messenger mediating the actions of hormones on a wide variety of receptors (Nathanson, 1977). The most extensively studied of these is still the first to be discovered, the β-adrenergic receptor.

Cyclic AMP is synthesized from ATP by the enzyme adenylate cyclase (Sutherland and Rall, 1960). Adenylate cyclase is located on the internal face of the plasma membrane, allowing direct communication through the lipid bilayer with external membrane receptors. Stimulation of β-adrenergic receptors by hormone increases the activity of adenylate cyclase, which increases the intracellular concentration of cyclic AMP. The increased levels of cyclic AMP cause an enhanced phosphorylation of certain proteins within the cell, altering their functional state. In this way, stimulation of β-adrenergic receptors on the external cell surface can alter the activities of selected intracellular enzymes.

Occupation of β-adrenergic receptors by agonists leads to increased cyclic AMP accumulation in intact tissues and cells (Sutherland and Rall, 1960). When cells are broken by sonication or mechanical disruption, the activity of adenylate cyclase in the plasma membrane can often still be directly stimulated by activation of β-adrenergic receptors (Klainer *et al.*, 1962). This intimate link between β-adrenergic receptors and adenylate cyclase has served as a type of bioassay for these receptors, as the existence of the receptors in isolated tissue fragments can be directly inferred from the observed stimulation of adenylate cyclase by catecholamines. Unfortunately, the absence of such stimulation cannot be taken as a reliable indicator that no β-adrenergic receptors are present, since certain tissues such as mammalian brain, which respond to β-adrenergic receptor stimulation with increases in cyclic AMP accumulation when intact, lose this response when the tissue is disrupted (Chasin *et al.*, 1974). The fact that in many tissues β-adrenergic receptors stimulate adenylate cyclase activity directly in broken cell preparations has been instrumental in focusing interest on these receptors and making them amenable to study.

A great deal is now known about the molecular mechanism whereby β-adrenergic receptors stimulate adenylate cyclase activity within the plasma membrane and this will be discussed in detail in Section 5.11 (*Signal transduction by adrenergic receptors*). At this point it is sufficient to emphasize that β-adrenergic receptors and adenylate cyclase are separate molecular entities and communicate in the membrane by means of a third membrane constituent, a guanine nucleotide-binding protein (Pfeuffer and Helmreich, 1975). The observed loss of coupling between β-adrenergic receptors and adenylate cyclase in some tissues after homogenization may reflect a disruption of this process.

Although β-adrenergic receptors increase cyclic AMP production in every tissue in which they exist that has been studied, it is not yet certain that *all* of the effects of β-adrenergic receptor stimulation are mediated by increases in cyclic AMP levels. Although many of the metabolic effects of β-adrenergic receptor stimulation have been convincingly demonstrated to be mediated by cyclic AMP, for many of the mechanical and electrical responses strong evidence is still lacking. This is often due to the rapid time course of receptor-mediated electrical and mechanical events, which makes it difficult to elucidate a direct mechanistic sequence. In the heart, for example, there is strong evidence that cyclic AMP mediates the glycogenolytic effects of β-adrenergic receptor activation (Mayer, 1978). It is less certain that cyclic AMP mediates the increase in cardiac contractility caused by β-adrenergic receptor activation. For example, tazolol (Tuttle and Mills, 1975) and prenalterol (H133/22; Carlsson *et al.*, 1977) both stimulate cardiac contractility, yet neither of these compounds activate adenylate cyclase activity in any tissue so far examined, including heart (Vauquelin *et al.*, 1976; Hedberg, 1980). Both of these drugs are relatively potent in inhibiting β-adrenergic-receptor-stimulated adenylate cyclase activity. Thus, the possible involvement of cyclic AMP in mediating the increase in cardiac contractility caused by β-adrenergic receptor stimulation has not yet been clarified.

In summary, all β-adrenergic receptors so far examined have been shown to be linked to adenylate cyclase and to stimulate cyclic AMP production. Often, and perhaps always, cyclic AMP is the intracellular messenger which causes the physiological effects of the hormone–receptor interaction.

5.4.2 α-Adrenergic receptors

Robison *et al.*, (1971) suggested that the effects of α-adrenergic receptor stimulation might be mediated through inhibition of adenylate cyclase

Table 5.2 Second messengers for adrenergic receptors.

Receptor	Membrane action	Intracellular second messenger	Intracellular metabolic result
β_1	increase adenylate cyclase activity	increased cyclic AMP	increased protein phosphorylation
β_2	increase adenylate cyclase activity	increased cyclic AMP	increased protein phosphorylation
α_1	increase phosphatidylinositol turnover	increased calcium	increased protein phosphorylation, direct ionic effects on enzymes and structural proteins
α_2	decrease adenylate cyclase activity	decreased cyclic AMP	decreased protein phosphorylation

Adapted from Fain and Garcia-Sainz (1980).

activity. In a number of systems it has now been demonstrated that stimulation of α-adrenergic receptors does inhibit adenylate cyclase activity. These tissues include human platelets (Salzman and Neri, 1969) and adipocytes (Burns *et al.*, 1971), canine thyroid slices (Yamashita *et al.*, 1977), neuroblastoma × glioma hybrid cells (Sabol and Nirenberg, 1979) and bovine parathyroid cells (Brown *et al.*, 1978).

On the other hand, some α-adrenergic receptors, most notably those in the liver, do not either stimulate or inhibit adenylate cyclase activity (Exton, 1979). It has been suggested that these α-adrenergic receptors may exert their effects on carbohydrate metabolism by causing an increase in cytosolic calcium levels. However, it has been shown that α-adrenergic activation of liver glycogenolysis is not dependent on the presence of extracellular calcium (Chan and Exton, 1977). Chan and Exton (1977) found that α-adrenergic receptor stimulation raised cyclic AMP levels similarly to β-adrenergic receptor stimulation only in the absence of calcium, and proposed that the increase in cyclic AMP levels could be responsible for the changes in carbohydrate metabolism. Kneer *et al.* (1979) and Fain and Garcia-Sainz (1980) have disputed this hypothesis claiming that α-adrenergic-receptor-mediated activation of glycogen phosphorylase in the liver does not require extracellular calcium and also is not related to cyclic AMP production.

Michell (1975) has proposed that all receptors which increase cytosolic calcium levels also increase turnover of the membrane lipid phosphatidylinositol. It has been shown that stimulation of α-adrenergic receptors in a number of tissues, such as rat (Hokin and Sherwin, 1957) and rabbit (Jones and Michell, 1974) parotid gland and rat hepatocytes (Kirk *et al.*, 1977) and adipocytes (Fain and Garcia-Sainz, 1980), increases phosphatidylinositol turnover. This increase in phosphatidylinositol turnover is not dependent on the presence of extracellular calcium. Michell (1975) suggested that phosphatidylinositol breakdown may be involved in opening calcium gates, and Berridge and Fain (1979) proposed that breakdown of this compound may be involved in closing calcium gates. In any case, the evidence to date suggests that phosphatidylinositol turnover is involved in calcium gating and may be an intermediate step in the increase in cytosolic calcium caused by α-adrenergic receptor stimulation in some tissues.

Fain and Garcia-Sainz (1980) have proposed a unifying hypothesis of the second messengers involved in α-adrenergic receptor signal transduction. On examination of the literature, these authors note that where the pharmacology has been examined, those α-adrenergic receptors which inhibit adenylate cyclase activity are of the α_2-subtype, while those that alter phosphatidylinositol turnover and calcium levels are of the α_1-subtype. They have proposed that the effects of α_2-receptors are mediated by decreases in cyclic AMP levels, while the effects of α_1-receptors are mediated by increases in membrane phosphatidylinositol turnover and subsequent increases in cytosolic calcium. Such a hypothesis could explain the paradoxical effects of α-adrenergic receptor stimulation in the absence of calcium in the liver, where phosphatidylinositol and not extracellular calcium may be the important intracellular signal. Further correlation of α-adrenergic receptor subtypes with inhibition of adenylate cyclase activity and changes in phosphatidylinositol turnover and cytosolic calcium is needed to substantiate this hypothesis.

5.5 DIRECT MEASUREMENT OF ADRENERGIC RECEPTORS

The study of adrenergic receptors as discrete molecular entities has been greatly facilitated by the ability to measure these receptors directly in the absence of a functionally coupled biological response. The experimental dissociation of the initial hormone–receptor interaction from subsequent biological events has allowed a more precise examination of the molecular events involved in the binding of hormone to receptor.

The direct measurement of receptors has been accomplished by taking advantage of the specificity of the recognition site of the receptor molecule. Since a receptor is defined and classified by the relative potencies of drugs in stimulating or inhibiting a biological response, this pharmacological specificity can be used to identify the receptor directly. Drugs with a very high affinity and specificity for the receptor are radioactively labeled, and the interaction of these specific radiolabeled compounds with a tissue preparation containing the appropriate receptor molecules is examined. Bound and free radioligand are separated by appropriate techniques such as dialysis, filtration and centrifugation, and the kinetic and pharmacological characteristics of the radioligand bound to the tissue are examined. At very low concentrations of radiolabeled drug a substantial portion of the binding of the radioligand should be specifically to the receptor site, although there is also almost always some non-receptor binding. The binding of the radioligand to receptor and non-receptor sites can be distinguished by examining the saturability and pharmacological specificity of the radioligand-binding sites. If the binding sites are saturable and reversible and display the same stereospecificity and pharmacological characteristics as the receptor-mediated biological response, one can be fairly certain that the radioligand is specifically labeling the recognition site of the receptor. Kinetic and equilibrium methods can then be used to quantify the number of receptors in a given tissue sample and determine their molecular and pharmacological properties.

The first hormone receptors to be successfully labeled by a reversible radioligand-binding assay were the insulin (Cuatrecasas, 1971) and glucagon (Rodbell *et al*, 1971a) receptors. The capability of radioiodinating the natural peptide hormones for these receptors resulted in suitable radioligands with a very high specific radioactivity, and a high affinity and specificity for the receptor. Although substantial progress was made in studying the hormone–receptor interaction for these peptides (see Cuatrecasas, 1974), further studies were limited by the lack of a well-developed series of agonists and antagonists for these receptors. Problems with the purity and mono-iodinated nature of the radiolabeled peptides, as well as questions about the biological activity of these compounds caused some problems in interpretation of data (Cuatrecasas, 1974). In addition, the complexity of agonist binding to receptors (see below) made much of the data difficult to interpret.

5.5.1 Early attempts to measure specific catecholamine binding

In spite of these problems, the success of the radioligand-binding assays for glucagon and insulin receptors stimulated interest in development of radioligand-binding assays for other hormone receptors, particularly the β-adrenergic receptor. This receptor had two major advantages over other receptors which made it especially suitable for development of a radioligand-binding assay. First, a wide variety of agonists and antagonists with a marked selectivity for the β-adrenergic receptor was available, including some drugs which displayed a marked stereoselectivity. The availability of these compounds would be very useful in determining the pharmacological specificity of putative receptor sites. Secondly, the intimate link between β-adrenergic receptors and adenylate cyclase meant that activation of adenylate cyclase in crude membrane preparations could serve as an index of the biological response to β-adrenergic receptor activation. The potency of agonists and antagonists in activating and inhibiting the activation of adenylate cyclase could then be directly compared with their potency in inhibiting radioligand binding.

A number of attempts were made to develop specific radioligand-binding assays for β-adrenergic receptors using the radioactively labeled catecholamines [^{3}H]epinephrine and [^{3}H]norepinephrine. These compounds had been useful in studying enzyme, storage and transport mechanisms of adrenergic neurons (Iversen, 1967; Molinoff and Axelrod, 1971). They turned out, however, to be much less useful as radioligands for studying β-adrenergic receptors. Although [^{3}H]epinephrine and [^{3}H]norepinephrine were shown to bind to membranes derived from a variety of tissues (Dunnick and Marinetti, 1971; Lefkowitz and Haber, 1971; Lefkowitz *et al.*, 1972; Bilezikian and Aurbach, 1973; Schramm *et al.*, 1972) and this binding was blocked by other catecholamines, several observations suggested that ^{3}H-labeled catecholamines might not be specifically binding to β-adrenergic receptors. The binding was inhibited by a number of catechol-containing compounds which were not active at β-adrenergic receptors, there was no evidence of stereospecificity, and potent β-adrenergic receptor antagonists which did not contain a catechol moiety, such as propranolol, did not inhibit the binding except at extremely high concentrations. In addition, although the binding was apparently saturable it was generally not reversible, except sometimes on the addition of strong acid.

Further characterization of the binding of ^{3}H-labeled catecholamines by other authors (Cuatrecasas *et al.*, 1974; Maguire *et al.*, 1974; Wolfe *et al.*, 1974) refuted the suggestion that the observed binding represented specific binding to β-adrenergic receptors. With a few exceptions (Bilezikian and Aurbach, 1973) the binding of ^{3}H-labeled catecholamines was almost entirely irreversible. Cuatrecasas *et al.*, (1974) suggested that the binding was related to catechol *O*-methyltransferase (COMT), one of the degradative enzymes for catecholamines. They showed that several inhibitors of COMT inhibited [^{3}H]norepinephrine binding and that *S*-adenosylmethionine, a co-substrate of COMT, increased the rate of [^{3}H]norepinephrine binding. Although the relationship of ^{3}H-labeled catecholamine binding to COMT was disputed by Lefkowitz (1974), other authors presented compelling evidence that the binding of ^{3}H-labeled catecholamines represented a non-specific, probably covalent, interaction of oxidized catechol-degradation products with biological membranes (Maguire *et al.*, 1974; Wolfe *et al.*, 1974). The inhibition of oxidation by such agents as sodium metabisulphite and EDTA inhibited [^{3}H]norepine-phrine binding (Maguire *et al.*, 1974), and the time course of oxidation of [^{3}H]epinephrine closely paralleled the apparent time course of [^{3}H]epine-phrine binding (Wolfe *et al.*, 1974). In addition, [^{3}H]epinephrine bound to bovine serum albumin with properties similar to its binding to rat heart. It is clear therefore that these early attempts with ^{3}H-labeled catecholamines did not succeed in specifically labeling β-adrenergic receptors.

5.5.2 Development of radiolabeled β-adrenergic receptor antagonists

Owing to the failure of attempts to use radiolabeled catecholamine agonists to specifically label β-adrenergic receptors, a number of investigators began exploring the possibility of using radiolabeled β-adrenergic receptor antagonists. Many antagonists have two or three orders of magnitude higher affinity for β-adrenergic receptors than do agonists, and it was reasoned that this increased affinity would improve the specificity of the interaction and that the lower concentrations of radioligand needed would help reduce the binding of the compound to non-receptor sites. In addition, β-adrenergic receptor antagonists, which are generally isopropyl-substituted analogues of ethanolamine, are chemically more stable than the rapidly oxidized catecholamine agonists. Thus, problems due to covalent modification of the drug molecule and interactions with non-receptor membrane constituents might be minimized. These considerations were indeed critical, and the use of radiolabeled antagonists to label β-adrenergic receptors has been highly successful.

Although initial attempts to label β-adrenergic receptors with [³H]propranolol were unsuccessful (Potter, 1967; Vatner and Lefkowitz, 1974), Levitzki *et al.*, (1974) showed that the binding of [³H]propranolol to turkey erythrocyte membranes was saturable and reversible and was inhibited in a stereospecific manner by β-adrenergic receptor agonists and antagonists. The affinity constants of agonists and antagonists for inhibition of [³H]propranolol binding agreed well with the affinity of the compounds in activating or inhibiting adenylate cyclase activity in the same tissue preparation (Levitzki *et al.*, 1975). Although the relative amount of receptor to non-receptor binding observed in this preparation was very low (15 per cent), the high density of β-adrenergic receptors on turkey erythrocyte membranes (800 fmol/mg of protein) probably contributed to the success of these experiments. Although Nahorski (1976) also demonstrated stereospecifically displaceable [³H]propranolol binding to rat brain membranes, again the relative amount of receptor to non-receptor binding was quite low (20–45 per cent). The large amount of non-receptor binding observed with [³H]propranolol severely curtails its usefulness, and other radiolabeled antagonists with a higher affinity and/or lower non-receptor-binding characteristics have replaced [³H]propranolol in general use.

Lefkowitz and co-workers (1974) introduced [³H]dihydroalprenolol ([³H]DHA) as a radiolabeled antagonist for studying β-adrenergic receptors. This compound was synthesized from (−)-alprenolol by reducing the carbon–carbon double bond with palladium and tritium gas, resulting in a tritiated compound with a reasonably high specific activity (17–33 Ci/mmol). The specific binding of [³H]DHA to frog erythrocyte membranes was saturable and reversible, and the pharmacological characteristics of these binding sites have been extensively characterized (Mukherjee *et al.*, 1975). The relative affinities of β-adrenergic receptor agonists and antagonists for inhibiting [³H]DHA binding agreed well with their relative potencies in activating or inhibiting adenylate cyclase in this tissue. [³H]DHA has subsequently been used successfully to label β-adrenergic receptors in a variety of other tissues, including heart (Alexander *et al.*, 1975a) and brain (Alexander *et al.*, 1975b; Bylund and Snyder, 1976) and is currently widely used as a radioligand for studying β-adrenergic receptors.

The other radioligand which has come into wide use for studying β-adrenergic receptors is [¹²⁵I]iodohydroxybenzylpindolol (¹²⁵IHYP), also a high-affinity β-adrenergic receptor antagonist (Aurbach *et al.*, 1974). Brown *et al.* (1976b) showed that the binding of [125]IHYP to turkey erythrocyte membranes was saturable and reversible and stereoselectively inhibited by β-adrenergic receptor agonists and antagonists with a potency similar to that for activation and inhibition of adenylate cyclase activity in the same tissue. This compound has also proved useful in studying β-adrenergic receptors in other tissues, such as rat heart (Harden *et al.*, 1976), brain (Sporn and Molinoff, 1976) and various clonal cell lines (Maguire *et al.*, 1976a).

Both [³H]DHA and [125]IHYP have peculiar advantages and disadvantages for studying β-adrenergic receptors. [³H]DHA is optically pure, has been readily available commercially and as a tritiated compound is relatively stable when stored for long periods of time. In addition, there is relatively minimal non-receptor binding with [³H]DHA. In contrast, [125]IHYP is a racemic mixture, has a much shorter half-life (3 months) and has only recently become commercially available. There are also substantial prob-

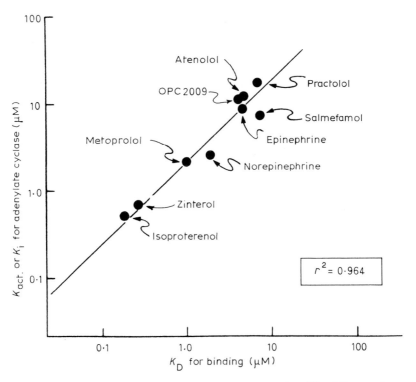

Fig. 5.1 Correlation between the K_D for the binding of [125]IHYP to turkey erythrocyte membranes and the $K_{act.}$ or K_i for activation or inhibition of adenylate cyclase in the same tissue. Reprinted by permission from Minneman *et al.* (1980a).

lems with non-receptor binding involved in the use of ^{125}IHYP, which is a fairly lipophilic compound. Conversely, ^{125}IHYP can be easily purified to theoretical specific activity (2200 Ci/mmol) compared with a much lower specific activity for [^{3}H]DHA (~50 Ci/mmol). [^{3}H]DHA (K_D = 1000 pM) also has a substantially lower affinity than ^{125}IHYP (K_D = 80 pM) for β-adrenergic receptors. The higher specific activity and affinity of ^{125}IHYP allow the use of much smaller tissue samples (up to 10-fold) compared with those needed with [^{3}H]DHA. This is an important factor when the amount of tissue is limiting, such as in studies with small brain regions. Competition curves for non-radioactive drugs can be performed at concentrations of ^{125}IHYP close to its K_D value, such that only small correction factors (i.e. 2-fold) need to be introduced to relate the apparent IC_{50} to the true K_D value for the displacing drug. Because of the lower specific activity of [^{3}H]DHA the concentration of radioligand needed is much larger relative to its K_D value, and the correction factor in determining the K_D value of competing drugs is correspondingly larger. Finally, ^{125}IHYP as a gamma-emitter can be counted directly in a gamma counter and no scintillation fluid is needed.

The problem of non-receptor binding of ^{125}IHYP can be substantially reduced by including phentolamine (final concentration 0.1 mM) in the incubation medium (Sporn and Molinoff, 1976; Minneman *et al.*, 1979b). At this concentration phentolamine inhibits non-receptor binding of ^{125}IHYP (particularly to brain membranes where non-receptor binding is extremely high) without affecting receptor binding. Phentolamine has also proved to be useful in inhibiting non-receptor binding in studies of ^{125}IHYP binding to intact C-6 glioma cells (Terasaki and Brooker, 1978).

In retrospect it is interesting to point out that the particular radioligands which were developed for study of β-adrenergic receptors had several fortuitous advantages which made the results obtained in studies of β-adrenergic receptors much less confusing than results obtained with radioligand-binding assays for other receptors. First and foremost, both of the major radioligands were antagonists. It has become abundantly clear over the past few years that the binding of agonists to the receptor is much more complicated than the binding of antagonists (see below). The use of antagonists as radiolabeled probes to study β-adrenergic receptors has allowed a clearer understanding of some of the basic properties of the receptor before the complexity of agonist binding was introduced, allowing the complexity of agonist binding to be examined in a more rational manner. Secondly, both ^{125}IHYP and [^{3}H]DHA have identical affinities for the two β-adrenergic receptor subtypes (β_1 and β_2) (Rugg *et al.*, 1978; Minneman *et al.*, 1979a), and use of either of these compounds will label the total β-adrenergic receptor population of a given tissue. For this reason discrepancies in the relative number of ^{125}IHYP and [^{3}H]DHA in different tissues have not been encountered.

Table 5.3 Radioligands used to study adrenergic receptors.

	Compound	Abbreviation	Agonist or antagonist	Subtype selectivity
α-adrenergic receptors	[^{3}H]clonidine	[^{3}H]CLON	agonist	α_2-selective
	[^{3}H]epinephrine	[^{3}H]EPI	agonist	non-selective*
	[^{3}H]norepinephrine	[^{3}H]NE	agonist	non-selective
	[^{3}H]para-aminoclonidine	[^{3}H]PAC	agonist	α_2-selective
	[^{3}H]dihydroergokryptine	[^{3}H]DHE	antagonist(?)	non-selective
	[^{3}H]WB 4101	[^{3}H]WB 4101	antagonist	α_1-selective
	[^{3}H]prazosin	[^{3}H]PRAZ	antagonist	α_1-selective
β-adrenergic receptors	[^{3}H]propranolol	[^{3}H]PRO	antagonist	non-selective*
	[^{3}H]dihydroalprenolol	[^{3}H]DHA	antagonist	non-selective
	[^{125}I]iodohydroxybenzylpindolol	^{125}IHYP	antagonist	non-selective
	[^{3}H]hydroxybenzylisoproterenol	[^{3}H]HBI	agonist	non-selective
	[^{3}H]epinephrine	[^{3}H]EPI	agonist	non-selective

References are given in the text.

* Non-selective means that the compound does not distinguish between the two receptor subtypes (i.e. either α_1 and α_2, or β_1 and β_2).

Recently, under rigidly controlled conditions, several investigators have succeeded in labeling β-adrenergic receptors with catecholamine agonists (Lefkowitz and Williams, 1977; U'Prichard *et al.*, 1978). The results of these studies will be discussed in Section 5.6.2 (Binding of agonists to β-adrenergic receptors.)

5.5.3 Radioligands for labeling α-adrenergic receptors

A variety of radioligands has been developed which have been proposed to selectively label α-adrenergic receptors. For a number of reasons, however, interpretation of the binding of these radiolabeled compounds has been more complicated than interpretation of the binding of radiolabeled antagonists to β-adrenergic receptors. There is no simple biochemical index, such as activation of adenylate cyclase by β-adrenergic receptors, which can be correlated with α-adrenergic receptor activation in homogenized tissue preparations. As discussed above, in some tissues such as platelets (Salzman and Neri, 1969) activation of α-adrenergic receptors inhibits adenylate cyclase activity, although in other tissues such as liver (Exton, 1979) this effect is not seen. Even when inhibition of adenylate cyclase activity by α-adrenergic receptors can be demonstrated, the degree of inhibition is relatively small (20–40 per cent inhibition) compared with the severalfold stimulation of adenylate cyclase activity which can be caused by β-adrenergic receptor activation, and is correspondingly harder to characterize pharmacologically. It is therefore difficult to make quantitative correlations between the pharmacological characteristics of a radioligand-binding site and an observed physiological response and show that a particular radioligand-binding site is indeed a functional receptor.

In addition, the radioligands which have been developed to study α-adrenergic receptors include both agonists and antagonists. Since the binding of agonists to α-adrenergic receptors, like binding to β-adrenergic receptors and almost all other hormone receptors, is kinetically complex and sensitive to the presence or absence of mono- and di-valent cations and guanine nucleotides (see below), small changes in experimental conditions can lead to large changes in the affinity and apparent number of binding sites for radiolabeled agonists. Thus, quantification of the number of receptors by radiolabeled agonist binding can be misleading, and it is difficult to compare the results obtained in these studies with results obtained with radiolabeled antagonist binding.

Finally, to complicate the situation further, several of the radioligands which have been developed to study α-adrenergic receptors do not have the same affinity for both α-adrenergic receptor subtypes. Thus these radioligands will label α_1- and α_2-receptors to different extents, depending on the concentration of radioligand used. This can result in misleading discrepancies in the apparent affinity of drugs for different binding sites, and make it difficult quantitatively to compare the number of binding sites labeled by each radioligand.

Despite these limitations, considerable progress has been made in developing radioligand-binding assays for α-adrenergic receptors. The radioactive compounds which have been used include the agonists [^{3}H]clonidine ([^{3}H]CLON; Greenberg *et al*., 1976), [^{3}H]epinephrine ([^{3}H]EPI), [^{3}H]norepinephrine ([^{3}H]NE; U'Prichard and Snyder, 1977) and [^{3}H]para-aminoclonidine ([^{3}H]PAC; Rouot and Snyder, 1979), and the antagonists [^{3}H]dihydroergokryptine ([^{3}H]DHE; Williams *et al*., 1976a), [^{3}H]WB 4101 (Greenberg *et al*., 1976) and [^{3}H]prazosin ([^{3}H]PRAZ; Greenglass and Bremner, 1979). The binding characteristics of each of these compounds have been examined in a number of different tissues, including both brain and peripheral organs.

[^{3}H]DHE is a potent α-adrenergic receptor antagonist which may have some partial agonist properties (Innes, 1962). This compound has been successfully used to label α-adrenergic receptors in rabbit uterine membranes (Williams *et al*., 1976a), platelets (Tsai and Lefkowitz, 1978a,b) and other tissues. The [^{3}H]DHE-binding sites had the pharmacological characteristics expected of physiological α-adrenergic receptors. However, [^{3}H]DHE also has a reasonably high affinity for dopamine and 5-hydroxytryptamine receptors in rat brain (Davis *et al*., 1977), and thus must be used with caution when attempting to label α-adrenergic receptors selectively. Since [^{3}H]DHE has similar affinities for α_1- and α_2-adrenergic receptors, it seems likely that this radioligand labels all the α-adrenergic receptors in a particular tissue preparation.

Greenberg *et al*. (1976) showed that the α_2-selective agonist [^{3}H]CLO and the α_1-selective antagonist [^{3}H]WB 4101 each interacted with different populations of specific high-affinity binding sites in a crude membrane preparation from rat brain. On the basis of the observation that α-adrenergic agonists were more potent in inhibiting [^{3}H]CLON than [^{3}H]WB 4101 binding, and that antagonists were more potent in inhibiting [^{3}H]WB 4101 than [^{3}H]CLON binding, these authors suggested that there might be two different states of the α-adrenergic receptor. One state would preferentially bind agonists and be selectively labeled by [^{3}H]CLON, while the other state would preferentially bind antagonists and be selectively labeled by [^{3}H]WB 4101. Both the 'agonist' and 'antagonist' sites could be labeled with [^{3}H]DHE (which was proposed to be a mixed agonist/antagonist), and the summation of the apparent number of [^{3}H]CLON sites and [^{3}H]WB 4101 sites was approximately equal to the apparent number of [^{3}H]DHE sites (Greenberg and Snyder, 1978; U'Prichard *et al*., 1977).

In the presence of pyrocatechol, U'Prichard and Snyder (1977) were able to observe binding of [³H]EPI and [³H]NE to membranes prepared from calf brain. The pharmacological specificity of these binding sites suggested that [³H]EPI and [³H]NE might be binding to α- but not β-adrenergic receptors in this preparation. The pharmacological characteristics of the [³H]EPI and [³H]NE sites were similar to the pharmacological characteristics of [³H]CLON but not of [³H]WB 4101 sites, suggesting that [³H]EPI and [³H]NE labeled the same 'agonist' sites as [³H]CLON (U'Prichard and Snyder, 1977).

Analysis of the regional distribution (Peroutka *et al.*, 1978) of 'agonist' and 'antagonist' sites showed that the ratio of these sites varied in different brain regions. Miach *et al.* (1978) further showed that the potent α_2-selective antagonist yohimbine interacted with the same specific binding sites as the α_2-selective agonist clonidine, and these authors suggested that the putative 'agonist' and 'antagonist'-binding sites might actually represent two non-interconvertible α-adrenergic receptor subtypes, i.e. α_1- and α_2-receptors. Examination of the specific binding of the α_1-selective antagonist [³H]PRAZ (Greenglass and Bremner, 1979; Barnes *et al.*, 1979) and the α_2-selective agonist [³H]PAC (Rouot and Snyder, 1979) support this hypothesis.

Davis *et al.* (1978) have presented evidence that the pharmacological specificity of the [³H]WB 4101-binding sites in rat brain correlate with the α-adrenergic receptor linked to adenylate cyclase in this tissue. Although this would seem to be an example of an α_1-receptor linked to adenylate cyclase, in the brain, unlike peripheral tissues, stimulation of α-adrenergic receptors leads to an increase, not decrease, in cyclic AMP accumulation. This interaction is apparently not a direct action of the receptor on adenylate cyclase, but may be mediated by prostaglandins (Partington *et al.*, 1980).

It is not yet clear whether the α-receptor selectivity of [³H]WB 4101 observed in brain membranes will also be exhibited in other tissues. Hoffman and Lefkowitz (1980) recently reported that [³H]WB 4101 binds to the entire α-adrenergic receptor population with apparently uniform affinity in rabbit uterus. Therefore [³H]WB 4101 could not be used to label α_1-receptors in this tissue.

These studies show that specific binding sites with the appropriate specificity of α_1 and α_2-receptors can be distinguished using various radioligands. [³H]PRAZ and possibly [³H]WB 4101 seem to label α_1-receptors selectively, [³H]CLON, [³H]EPI, [³H]NE and [³H]PAC seem to label α_2-receptors selectively, while [³H]DHE labels both subtypes. U'Prichard *et al.* (1979) have proposed that [³H]CLON may label more than one site, although this observation and other peculiarities observed with the binding of radiolabeled agonists in the above studies are probably not due to multiple receptor sites but rather to the inherent complexity of agonist binding. This will be discussed in more detail below.

5.5.4 Evidence from radioligand-binding assays for β-adrenergic receptor subtypes

Several studies of the pharmacological specificity of β-adrenergic receptors linked to adenylate cyclase in different tissues presented the first direct evidence that β-adrenergic receptor subtypes could also be distinguished *in vitro* on the basis of their pharmacological properties. For example, the β_2-selective agonists salbutamol and soterenol activate adenylate cyclase in membranes prepared from lung but not from heart (Burges and Blackburn, 1972) or fat cells (Lefkowitz, 1975). The β_1-selective antagonists practolol, metoprolol and paraoxprenolol inhibit β-adrenergic-receptor-stimulated adenylate cyclase activity with a greater potency in the heart and adipose tissue than in liver, trachea or lung (Lefkowitz, 1975; Murad, 1973; Petrack and Czernick, 1976; Minneman *et al.*, 1979a). These studies also demonstrate that both β_1 and β_2-receptors increase adenylate cyclase activity.

The pharmacological differences between β_1- and β_2-receptors can also be demonstrated using radioligand-binding assays. The pharmacological specificity of β-adrenergic-receptor-binding sites in tissues thought to contain mostly β_1-receptors (rat heart, calf cerebral cortex, rabbit heart, rabbit lung) has been compared with those in tissues thought to contain mostly β_2-receptors (rat lung, calf cerebellum, rat corpus luteum) (U'Prichard *et al.*, 1978; Rugg *et al.*, 1978; Minneman *et al.*, 1979a; Coleman *et al.*, 1979; Gibson *et al.*, 1979). In some of these studies, the results obtained in binding assays were directly compared with studies of adenylate cyclase activation in the same tissue (Minneman *et al.*, 1979a; Coleman *et al.*, 1979). The results of these studies suggest that the difference in the pharmacological specificity of β-adrenergic receptor subtypes lies in the physical characteristics of the recognition site of each receptor molecule. Thus the β_1 selective antagonists practolol, metoprolol, atenolol and paraoxprenolol are ten- to fifty-fold more potent in inhibiting radioligand binding to β-adrenergic receptors in tissues containing mostly β_1-receptors than in tissues containing mostly β_2-receptors. Some β_2-selective agonists, such as zinterol, salmefamol and procaterol also show *in vitro* selectivity and are more potent in inhibiting radioligand binding to β_2-receptors than to β_1-receptors. Other β_2-selective agonists such as salbutamol and soterenol, which selectively increase adenylate cyclase activity in tissues containing predominantly β_2-receptors, have similar affinities for β_1- and β_2-receptors in radioligand-binding assays. This is due to the fact that, although these drugs are selective agonists at β_2-receptors, they are fairly potent antagonists at β_1-receptors as well (Minneman *et al.*, 1979a). Since radioligand-binding assays do not readily distinguish between agonists and antagonists, these drugs appear equipotent at both receptors.

Although the β_2-selective antagonist IPS 339 is more potent in inhibiting radioligand binding to β_2-receptors than to β_1-receptors, the widely used α-methylmethoxamine congeners, butoxamine and H35/25, are equipotent at these two receptors (Minneman *et al.*, 1979c). Since these drugs appear to be β_2-selective antagonists in physiological experiments (O'Donnell and Wanstall, 1979), there is as yet no explanation for this discrepancy. A similar discrepancy has been noticed in the study of β_1-selective agonists. Although norepinephrine shows the expected greater potency in inhibiting radioligand binding to β_1-receptors than to β_2-receptors, the apparently β_1-selective agonists dobutamine, tazolol and prenalterol are equipotent in inhibiting radioligand binding to β_1- and β_2-receptors. For a further discussion of these apparent discrepancies see Minneman *et al.*, (1981).

Physiological evidence suggests that both β_1- and β_2-receptors can coexist in a single organ, and that activation of both subtypes can cause the same physiological response such as increased heart rate or tracheal relaxation (Carlsson *et al.*, 1972, 1977; O'Donnell and Wanstall, 1979). Evidence from radioligand-binding assays strongly supports this concept. Barnett *et al.* (1978) and Minneman *et al.* (1979b) showed that inhibition of [^{3}H]DHA or ^{125}IHYP binding in rat heart and lung and various brain regions by drugs showing *in vitro* selectivity between β_1- and β_2-receptors results in biphasic competition curves. It was argued that these biphasic competition curves reflected the co-existence of two β-adrenergic receptor subtypes in each tissue, each of which had an equal affinity for the radioligand but different affinities for the selective competing drug. Minneman *et al.*, (1979b) used a computer-assisted curve-peeling technique to calculate the relative proportion of each receptor subtype and the affinity of each drug for each subtype. Hancock *et al.*, (1979) introduced a computerized curve-fitting process for the same purpose, which had statistical advantages over the curve-peeling approach (see also Minneman and Molinoff, 1980).

To determine whether more than two subtypes of β-adrenergic receptor might exist in mammalian tissues, a quantitative survey of the pharmacological specificity of specific ^{125}IHYP-binding sites was performed in a variety of tissues (Minneman *et al.*, 1979c). Five tissues were found in which inhibition of specific ^{125}IHYP binding by selective drugs resulted in simple mass action competition curves, suggesting a homogeneous β-adrenergic receptor population. Two of these tissues (left ventricle of cat and guinea pig heart) showed the characteristics of β_1-receptors, while three of the tissues (rat liver and cerebellum and cat soleus muscle) showed the characteristics of β_2-receptors. Comparison of the pharmacological specificity of the homogeneous group of receptors in each of these tissues with the pharmacological specificity of β_1- and β_2-receptors calculated

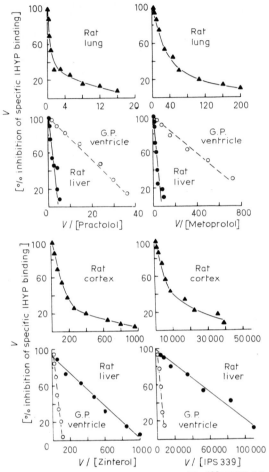

Fig. 5.2 Hofstee plots for the inhibition of specific [125]IHYP binding by β_1-and β_2- selective drugs. The inhibition of specific [125]IHYP binding by the β_1-selective drugs practolol and metoprolol (top) and the β_2- selective drugs zinterol and IPS 339 (bottom) in tissues containing both β_1- and β_2-receptors (rat lung and rat cerebral cortex), in a tissue containing only β_1-receptors [left ventricle from guinea pig (G.P.) heart] and a tissue containing only β_2-receptors (rat liver). The amount bound (V; expressed as percentage of inhibition of specific [125]IHYP binding) is plotted on the ordinate, and this value divided by the drug concentration (micromolar) is plotted on the abscissa. Note that the biphasic plots observed with rat lung and cortex indicate the existence of two receptor subtypes with different affinities for the selective competing drug, while the linear plots observed with rat liver and guinea pig ventricle indicate the existence of a homogeneous group of receptors with the same affinity for the competing drug. Reprinted by permission from Minneman *et al.* (1979c).

by computer-assisted analysis in tissues containing both receptor subtypes showed an excellent agreement (Minneman *et al.*, 1979c). These observations suggest that the pharmacological specificity of each receptor subtype is constant in a range of mammalian tissues, consistent with the hypothesis that there are only two subtypes of β-adrenergic receptor in mammalian tissues (Minneman and Molinoff, 1980).

There is as yet no evidence available as to whether β_1- and β_2-receptors can co-exist in a single cell, or whether the co-existence of these receptors within an organ is due simply to the heterogeneity of cell types within the organ. To date, every homogeneous cell population that has been examined contains a homogeneous population of either β_1- or β_2-receptors (see Minneman *et al.*, 1981).

Although this problem has not yet been extensively studied, in at least some non-mammalian tissues the kinetic properties and pharmacological specificity of β-adrenergic receptors are different from those of mammalian β_1- or β_2-adrenergic receptors. The β-adrenergic receptor of the turkey erythrocyte has been carefully compared with mammalian β_1- and β_2-receptors (Gibson *et al.*, 1979; Minneman *et al.*, 1980a). Although turkey erythrocytes contain an apparently homogeneous population of β-adrenergic receptors, these receptors have major kinetic and pharmacological differences that distinguish them from mammalian β_1- or β_2-receptors. Characteristics of the β-adrenergic receptors in frog erythrocytes (Mukherjee *et al.*, 1975) and hearts (Hancock *et al.*, 1979) also appear to be different from those observed for mammalian β_1- or β_2-receptors (Minneman *et al.*, 1979c). Extrapolation of studies of β-adrenergic receptors in non-mammalian tissues to those in mammals should therefore be approached with caution.

5.5.5 Evidence from radioligand-binding assays for α-adrenergic receptor subtypes

As discussed above, much of the confusion in the use of radioligands to label α-adrenergic receptors has arisen from the different affinities which these drugs have for α_1- and α_2-receptors. Since these radioligands have such substantially different affinities for the different receptor subtypes, they have, however, provided strong evidence in support of the existence of these subtypes (see above).

Studies in peripheral tissues allow the comparison of the potency of drugs on radioligand-binding sites and physiological responses such as contraction. U'Prichard and Snyder (1979) compared the potency of drugs in inhibiting [^{3}H]CLON and [^{3}H]WB 4101 binding to membrane preparations from rat vas deferens and rabbit duodenum with previously published values on the potency of the same drugs in affecting the contraction of these muscles. The potency of drugs in relaxing rabbit duodenum (α_2) correlated well with their potency in inhibiting [^{3}H]CLON, but not [^{3}H]WB 4101 binding in this tissue. Conversely, the potency of drugs in contracting rat vas deferens (α_1) correlated well with their potency in inhibiting [^{3}H]WB 4101 in this tissue (no specific [^{3}H]CLON binding was observed in rat vas deferens). The pharmacological specificity of the [^{3}H]CLON- and [^{3}H]WB 4101-binding sites in these peripheral tissues were also in good agreement with the pharmacological specificity of the binding sites for these compounds in brain tissue (U'Prichard and Snyder, 1979). Thus, radioligand-binding assays have supported the subdivision of α-adrenergic receptors into two subtypes α_1 and α_2.

5.6 KINETIC AND EQUILIBRIUM PROPERTIES OF ADRENERGIC RECEPTOR MOLECULES

Direct examination of the initial drug–receptor interaction with radioligand-binding assays has resulted in quantitative information on the kinetic and equilibrium properties of this interaction. This information has resulted in a greater insight into the single- or multi-step nature of this interaction and the physical driving forces involved.

5.6.1 Binding of antagonists to β-adrenergic receptors

The binding of antagonists to β-adrenergic receptors has generally been found to be a simple bimolecular interaction, probably reflecting a passive mass-action occupation of a homogeneous class of high-affinity sites. With only a few exceptions, the association of ^{125}IHYP and [^{3}H]DHA with β-adrenergic receptors is a second-order process, the dissociation of these compounds is a first-order process, and the ratio of the backward (k_{-1}) and forward (k_{+1}) rate constants approximately equals the equilibrium dissociation constant (K_D) determined from equilibrium saturation isotherms. The k_{+1} values for radiolabeled-antagonist binding to β-adrenergic receptors are generally of the order of 10^7 to 10^8 litre/mole-s, approaching diffusion control. The k_{+1} values are independent of radioligand concentration and the k_{-1} values are independent of whether dilution or competition is used as the dissociating stimulus. Scatchard (1949) plots of equilibrium saturation isotherms are linear with Hill coefficients of 1.0 (Maguire *et al.*, 1976a; Brown *et al.*, 1976a; Malbon and Cabelli, 1978; Minneman *et al.*, 1980a; Pollet *et al.*, 1980).

Some reports have suggested that there may be a small degree of complexity in the binding of antagonists to β-adrenergic receptors. Limbird *et al.* (1975) and Limbird and Lefkowitz (1976) presented evidence that the binding of [^{3}H]DHA to β-adrenergic receptors in frog erythrocyte mem-

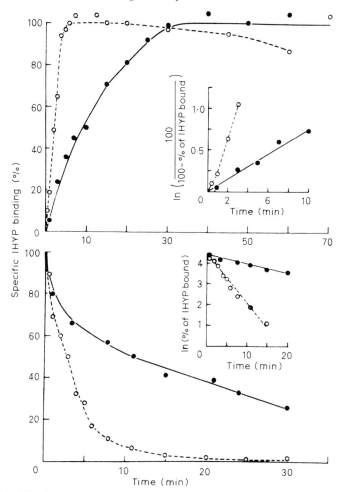

Fig. 5.3 Kinetics of association and dissociation of the binding of [125]IHYP to turkey erythrocyte (O) and rat heart (●) membranes. Upper: Association kinetics. Inset: Pseudo-first-order plot of association. Lower: Dissociation kinetics. Inset: First-order plot of dissociation. Note that both the association kinetics and dissociation kinetics for [125]IHYP binding to turkey erythrocyte membranes are much faster than for [125]IHYP binding to rat heart membranes Since both rate constants are faster, the equilibrium dissociation constant for [125]IHYP in the two tissues are very similar. Reprinted by permission from Minneman *et al.* (1980a).

branes was negatively co-operative. They showed that Scatchard plots were curvilinear and that dissociation of previously bound [³H]DHA was facilitated by the presence of unlabeled (−)-alprenolol as compared with simple dilution. Although Krawietz *et al.* (1979) obtained similar results in examining [³H]DHA binding to guinea pig heart and lung, other evidence suggests that [³H]DHA binding to β-adrenergic receptors is not cooperative. Previous (Mukherjee *et al*., 1975) and subsequent (Mukherjee and Lefkowitz, 1977; Williams and Lefkowitz, 1977) work from the same laboratory has resulted in completely linear Scatchard plots for [³H]DHA binding to frog erythrocyte membranes. Analysis of [³H]DHA binding to fat cells (Malbon and Cabelli, 1978) and frog erythrocyte membranes (Pollet *et al*., 1980) using kinetic and equilibrium methods indicated no evidence for curvilinear Scatchard plots or competition-facilitated dissociation. Pollet *et al.* (1980) suggest that the increased dissociation of [³H]DHA in the presence of unlabeled alprenolol observed previously might have been due to somewhat different binding affinities for the unlabeled and radiolabeled drug. Also, in all of these studies non-receptor binding was determined by the amount of [³H]DHA bound in the presence of 10^{-5} M-unlabeled (−)-alprenolol. Since this concentration of alprenolol is four orders of magnitude greater than its K_D value (10^{-9} M) at β-adrenergic receptors it is possible that some (non-saturable) non-receptor binding was included in the apparent receptor binding, resulting in a curvilinear Scatchard plot.

A careful examination of the binding of ^{125}IHYP to membranes from S49 lymphoma cells showed that, although Scatchard analysis was consistently linear, the kinetics of dissociation yielded evidence for two kinetic components, a very fast phase and a slow phase (Ross *et al*., 1977). If ^{125}IHYP was incubated long enough to reach equilibrium in this system, the dissociation rate was very nearly first-order, although when dissociation was examined before equilibrium had been reached a biphasic dissociation rate became apparent. These authors postulated a time-dependent isomerization of the ^{125}IHYP–receptor complex toward a thermodynamically favoured form to explain their data. Similar results were obtained in examining the binding of ^{125}IHYP to membranes from guinea-pig lung (Kleinstein and Glossman, 1978). While evidence of this kind was not seen in studies of ^{125}IHYP binding to other tissues (Brown *et al*., 1976a; Maguire *et al*., 1976a; Terasaki and Brooker, 1978; Minneman *et al*., 1980a), since pre-equilibrium dissociation kinetics were not examined in these studies, the possibility of antagonist-induced receptor isomerization cannot be ruled out.

5.6.2 Binding of agonists to β-adrenergic receptors

Because the first radioligands successfully used to label β-adrenergic receptors were antagonists, much of the initial characterization of agonist binding has been indirect, that is by monitoring the displacement of radiolabeled antagonists by unlabeled agonists. Although this procedure has severe limitations with regard to the information that can be obtained (particularly with regard to kinetics), it has allowed a preliminary understanding of the phenomenology of agonist binding without the attendant technical difficulties and limitations inherent in direct radioligand-binding assays (i.e. problems in reaching saturation, non-receptor binding, rapid dissociation, etc.). More recently Lefkowitz and colleagues have developed a radiolabeled catecholamine agonist, [^{3}H]hydroxybenzylisoproterenol ([^{3}H]HBI) which can be used to examine the agonist–receptor interaction directly (Lefkowitz and Williams, 1977; Lefkowitz and Hamp, 1977; Williams and Lefkowitz, 1977).

(a) *Effects of guanine nucleotides and cations*

The first evidence that agonist binding to β-adrenergic receptors might not always be a simple mass-action interaction was obtained in studies of the effects of guanine nucleotides on the potency of agonists in displacing radiolabeled antagonist binding. It was known that GTP was an essential cofactor for stimulation of adenylate cyclase by several different hormone receptors, including the β-adrenergic receptor (Rodbell *et al.*, 1971c; Wolff and Cook, 1973), and that guanine nucleotides accelerated the dissociation of ^{125}I-labeled glucagon from its binding sites on hepatic membranes (Rodbell *et al.*, 1971b). The effects of GTP and its non-hydrolysable analogue guanosine 5′-($\beta\delta$-imido) triphosphate (p$^{[NH]}$ppG) were examined on the inhibition by various compounds of radiolabeled antagonist binding to β-adrenergic receptors in two clonal cell lines (Maguire *et al.*, 1976b) and frog erythrocyte membranes (Lefkowitz *et al.*, 1976). GTP and p$^{[NH]}$ppG decreased the apparent potency of agonists in displacing bound radioligand by ten- to one hundred-fold, but had no effect on the potency of antagonists. The effect was specific to GTP, p$^{[NH]}$ppG and GDP and was not caused by GMP, cyclic GMP or any adenine nucleotide derivative (Maguire *et al.*, 1976b; Lefkowitz *et al.*, 1976). Guanine nucleotides also changed the shape of the competition curve for agonists, but not antagonists. In the absence of GTP, agonist competition curves were relatively broad and extended over three orders of magnitude of drug concentration, characterized by a Hill coefficient of 0.6 to 0.7. The presence of GTP caused a steepening of the agonist competition curve, so that it was apparently mass action and extended over only two orders of magnitude of drug concentration, with a Hill coefficient of 1.0. This agonist-specific effect of GTP on β-adrenergic receptor affinity has since been observed in a variety of other tissues (Hegstrand *et al.*, 1979), although it has not been seen in every tissue that has been examined. GTP had no effect on the affinity of agonists for β-adrenergic receptors in turkey erythrocytes (Brown *et al.*, 1976b), rat reticulocytes or erythrocytes (Bilezikian *et al.* (1977a) or in several areas of rat brain (Hegstrand *et al.*, 1979).

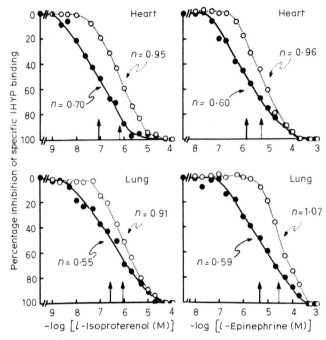

Fig. 5.4 Effect of GTP on the affinity of agonists in inhibiting specific [125]IHYP binding to membranes prepared from rat heart (top) and lung (bottom). The inhibition of specific [125]IHYP binding by *l*-isoproterenol (left) and *l*-epinephrine (right) was determined in the absence (●) and presence (○) of 300 μM-GTP. The results are expressed as the percentage inhibition of specific [125]IHYP binding. GTP had no effect on the amount of [125]IHYP bound in either preparation. Reprinted by permission from Hegstrand *et al.* (1979).

Haga *et al.* (1977a) studied the effects of GTP on agonist binding to the β-adrenergic receptors of S49 lymphoma cells and mutants of this cell line. These authors observed effects of GTP on agonist binding to β-adrenergic receptors in wild-type S49 cells. In one mutant of this cell line which contained both β-adrenergic receptors and adenylate cyclase, occupation of the β-adrenergic receptor by agonist did not increase adenylate cyclase activity. There was also no effect of GTP on agonist binding to the receptor in these uncoupled cells. The authors suggested that the effect of GTP on agonist binding to β-adrenergic receptors is a reflection of the 'coupling' between the receptor and the adenylate cyclase in the membrane, and that the lack of effect of GTP on agonist binding may indicate a 'poorly coupled' system (Maguire *et al.*, 1977).

Recently Lad *et al.* (1980) showed that stripping turkey erythrocyte membranes of residual guanine nucleotides by pretreatment with isopro-

terenol and GMP can result in an effect of guanine nucleotides on
β-adrenergic receptor agonist affinity which was not seen before the treatment. These authors postulated that guanine nucleotides may affect agonist
affinity for β-adrenergic receptors in all tissues, and that the reason that
this effect had not previously been observed in some tissues was due to
tight binding of residual guanine nucleotides in the tissue.

Magnesium ions also specifically affect agonist inhibition of radiolabeled
antagonist binding to β-adrenergic receptors (Maguire *et al.*, 1976b). Bird
and Maguire (1978) and Williams *et al.* (1978) showed that in the absence
of GTP, Mg^{2+} increases the apparent affinity of agonists for
β-adrenergic receptors. This effect can also be observed with Mn^{2+}, and to
a certain extent Ca^{2+}, but not with Sr^{2+}, Ba^{2+}, Na^+, Li^+ or La^{3+}. Mg^{2+} also
decreases the apparent Hill coefficient for agonist inhibition of radio-
labeled antagonist binding. Thus, in all respects, the effect of Mg^{2+} on
agonist binding is opposite to the effect of GTP. GTP decreases apparent
agonist affinity, while Mg^{2+} increases it. GTP removes the apparent
negative co-operativity associated with agonist binding, while Mg^{2+}
increases it. The effects of Mg^{2+} could be non-competitively blocked by the
presence of GTP, and in the S49 mutant cells in which β-adrenergic receptors and adenylate cyclase are uncoupled and there is no effect of GTP
on agonist affinity there is also no effect of Mg^{2+} on agonist affinity (Bird
and Maguire, 1978). Thus the specific effects of GTP and Mg^{2+} on agonist
affinity for β-adrenergic receptors are opposite but interrelated.

(b) *Direct characterization of β-adrenergic receptor agonist binding*

The first successful use of radiolabeled agonists to label β-adrenergic receptors specifically came with the introduction of [³H]hydroxybenzyliso- ·
proterenol ([³H]HBI) by Lefkowitz and colleagues. [³H]HBI is a
β-adrenergic receptor agonist with a high intrinsic activity and affinity for
the receptor (Kent *et al.*, 1980). Lefkowitz and Williams (1977) showed
that [³H]HBI binding to frog erythrocyte membranes, in the presence of
high concentrations of pyrocatechol to inhibit oxidation and suppress non-
receptor binding, was rapid, saturable and stereospecific. The affinity of
drugs in inhibiting the binding of [³H]HBI was identical with their affinity
in inhibiting the binding of the antagonist [³H]DHA (Lefkowitz and
Hamp, 1977). The binding of [³H]HBI was only slowly and incompletely
reversible in the absence of guanine nucleotides, although in the presence
of p[NH]ppG there was a rapid and complete dissociation of [³H]HBI
from its specific binding sites (Lefkowitz and Williams, 1977). Analysis of
saturation curves for [³H]HBI binding to frog erythrocyte membranes
showed that p[NH]ppG decreased the affinity of [³H]HBI for the
β-adrenergic receptor (Williams and Lefkowitz, 1977), probably owing to
the increased dissociation rate. p[NH]ppG did not affect the binding of the

antagonist [³H]DHA. Thus the effects of guanine nucleotides on direct agonist binding supported the indirect observations that had previously been made.

Similarly, the agonist-specific effects of Mg^{2+} which had been observed previously in studies of agonist inhibition of radiolabeled antagonist binding were also observed in direct studies of agonist binding (Williams *et al.*, 1978). Mg^{2+} and Mn^{2+}, but not Sr^{2+} or Ba^{2+}, increased specific [³H]HBI binding to frog erythrocyte membranes, but had no effect on [³H]DHA binding.

The binding of [³H]HBI to a mammalian tissue (rat lung) has also been extensively characterized (Heidenreich *et al.*, 1980), with results similar to those obtained previously in frog erythrocytes. Mg^{2+} increased and Na^+ and GTP decreased the binding of [³H]HBI to rat lung. These authors performed Scatchard (1949) analysis of equilibrium saturation isotherms of [³H]HBI binding in the absence and presence of nucleotides and ions (Heidenreich *et al.*, 1980). Scatchard analysis revealed curvilinear plots, and the total number of [³H]HBI binding sites was similar to the number of ^{125}IHYP sites. $p^{[NH]}ppG$ reduced the apparent affinity of the receptor for [³H]HBI and Scatchard plots became apparently linear with an apparent decrease in the number of [³H]HBI-binding sites. NaCl mimicked the effect of $p^{[NH]}ppG$, while $MgCl_2$ increased the affinity of the receptor by reducing the curvature of the Scatchard plot but had no effect on the apparent number of specific [³H]HBI-binding sites. Dissociation kinetics of [³H]HBI were very complicated, with at least three different rates being observed (Heidenreich *et al.*, 1980).

U'Prichard *et al.* (1978) presented evidence that under certain experimental conditions [³H]EPI also interacted specifically with β-adrenergic receptors in calf cerebellum and rat lung. Although NaCl had the same effect on [³H]EPI binding as it did on [³H]HBI binding, there were a number of discrepancies. Scatchard plots of [³H]EPI binding were linear (U'Prichard *et al.*, 1978) and there was no effect of guanine nucleotides on [³H]EPI binding (U'Prichard and Snyder, 1978a). Since the results obtained in studies of [³H]HBI binding agree with the indirect studies of agonist inhibition of radiolabeled antagonist binding, there is at present no explanation for the discrepancies observed with [³H]EPI binding.

(c) *Models to explain the complexity of agonist binding*
The above experiments demonstrate two major types of behaviour exhibited by agonists in binding to β-adrenergic receptors. The first, which occurs in the presence of Na^+ and GTP, is apparently a simple mass-action occupation of a high-affinity site. The second, which occurs in the absence of GTP and the presence of Mg^{2+}, is characterized by an apparent negative

co-operativity, reflected in a low Hill coefficient and curvilinear Scatchard plots. Similar behaviour has been observed in agonist binding to a wide variety of other hormone receptors, such as the opiate (Blume, 1978), prostaglandin E_1 (Williams and Lefkowitz, 1977), dopamine (Creese *et al.*, 1979) and glucagon (Lin *et al.*, 1977) receptors. Thus, there may be common features in the mechanism of agonist binding to each of these disparate receptors.

Several mechanisms could explain the apparent negative co-operativity of agonist binding to β-adrenergic receptors in the absence of GTP. The simplest explanation is the existence of two distinct non-interconvertible binding sites with equal affinities for antagonists and different affinities for agonists. Conversely, there could be negatively co-operative site–site interactions between receptor molecules, such that binding of agonist to one receptor molecule reduces the affinity of an adjacent receptor molecule for the agonist. Although these explanations cannot be completely ruled out, there is no evidence to support them. In addition, the complex dissociation kinetics of [^{3}H]HBI (Heidenreich *et al.*, 1980) argues against the existence of two non-interconvertible sites, and the absence of agonist-facilitated displacement of [^{3}H]HBI (Heidenreich *et al.*, 1980) argues against the existence of negative co-operativity.

Another mechanistic interpretation of the data is based on a two-step model of receptor–ligand interaction (DeHaen, 1976; Jacobs and Cuatrecasas, 1976; Boeynaems and Dumont, 1977). In this model hormone (H) binds to its receptor (R), and the hormone-receptor complex then binds to another effector molecule within the membrane (X) as follows:

$$H + R \rightleftharpoons HR$$
$$HR + X \rightleftharpoons HRX$$

If agonist-occupied receptor is able to participate in the second reaction but antagonist-occupied receptor is not, this model can explain the observed results. The participation of HR in the second reaction will continuously deplete HR from the first equilibrium, and the net result will be to increase the apparent affinity of R for H. The saturation curves for H binding to R will show an apparent negative co-operativity reflected in a curvilinear Scatchard plot.

The apparent mass-action behaviour of agonist binding to β-adrenergic receptors in the presence of GTP can be rationalized by this model in two different ways. Either in the presence of GTP the second reaction (HR binding to X) does not occur, or GTP causes a very rapid dissociation of HR from X such that there is no build-up of HRX and consequently no depletion of HR from the first reaction. In both these cases, in the presence of GTP the binding of agonist to the receptor would reflect only the first reaction, and would be apparently mass-action.

DeLean *et al.* (1980) have recently applied this model to data on [^{3}H]HBI binding to frog erythrocyte membranes with good experimental fit. Good evidence is now available that such a two-step binding reaction does occur with β-adrenergic receptors (and possibly other receptors), and that the effector molecule (X) which the hormone–receptor complex binds to is the guanine nucleotide-binding protein (Pfeuffer and Helmreich, 1975) (see below).

Since the participation of agonists in multiple equilibria leads to very complex binding kinetics, radiolabeled agonists are unsuitable for routine use in the measurement of receptors. Although pharmacological character-ization of the binding site can demonstrate that the radiolabeled agonist is occupying a specific receptor, it is difficult to be certain that characteriza-tion of all of the available receptor sites is being obtained with radiolabeled agonist binding. Under different experimental conditions the various equilibria discussed above can play a greater or lesser role, and under certain conditions the low-affinity equilibrium may be lost, owing to too-rapid dissociation kinetics. In this case alterations in components of the membrane other than the receptor molecule (such as the transducer molecule X) can lead to apparent but not actual changes in receptor density. For routine measurement of receptors it is much better to use radiolabeled antagonists, since with these compounds such considerations are not relevant.

5.6.3 Thermodynamics of binding of agonists and antagonists to β-adrenergic receptors

A specific effect of temperature on the affinity of compounds for β-adrenergic receptors was first reported by Pike and Lefkowitz (1978) who showed that agonist, but not antagonist, affinity for turkey erythrocyte β-adrenergic receptors increased at lower incubation temperatures. A detailed analysis of the effects of temperature on agonist and antagonist binding to turkey erythrocyte β-adrenergic receptors was performed by Weiland *et al.* (1979) using the principles of equilibrium thermodynamics. The standard enthalpy and entropy of the equilibrium binding of agonists and antagonists to β-adrenergic receptors was calculated from the tempera-ture dependence of the equilibrium association constant of each drug, determined indirectly by displacement of ^{125}IHYP. The results demon-strated that the physical forces causing the binding of agonists and antagon-ists were fundamentally different. The binding of antagonists was almost completely entropy-driven with little or no change in enthalpy (Weiland *et al.*, 1979). The entropy-driven nature of antagonist binding to β-adrenergic

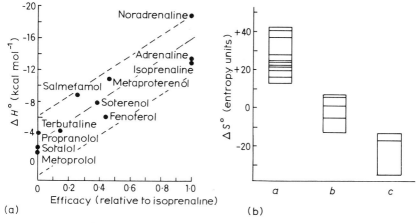

Fig. 5.5 Relationship between the equilibrium enthalpy and entropy of binding of drugs to β-adrenergic receptors in turkey erythrocyte membranes and their efficacy in activating adenylate cyclase in this preparation. Left: Efficacy was measured as the maximal activation of adenylate cyclase caused by the drug in relation to the maximal activation caused by isoproterenol. Only three representative antagonists are shown. The solid line represents a linear regression analysis of the data. The correlation coefficient is 0.916. The dashed lines show the range of values observed. Right: The changes in entropy are plotted as a function of antagonist (*a*), partial agonist (*b*) and full agonist (*c*) properties. Each horizontal line represents a ligand. Reprinted by permission from Weiland *et al.* (1979).

receptors is similar to the passive binding of other ligands to proteins, such as antigen–antibody interactions (Singer and Campbell, 1955) and the binding of organic ions to bovine serum albumin (Klotz and Urguhart, 1949). These reactions may be hydrophobic interactions driven by the increase in entropy caused by displacement of water molecules locally ordered around hydrophobic components of the ligand and binding site (Kauzmann, 1959).

The thermodynamic parameters of agonist binding to β-adrenergic receptors are substantially different from those of antagonist binding and other passive ligand–protein interactions where information transfer is not involved. The binding of agonists is enthalpy-driven with a concomitant thermodynamically unfavorable decrease in entropy. The enthalpy and negative entropy of agonist binding to β-adrenergic receptors may reflect an agonist-induced conformational change in the receptor molecule. The excellent correlation observed between the enthalpy and negative entropy involved in the binding reaction and the efficacy of partial agonists supports this concept (Weiland *et al.*, 1979). Since the observed thermodynamic parameters are net changes, they will reflect not only the binding of the agonist to the receptor but also any induced conformational changes in the receptor and in adjoining molecules which may occur. Since binding reactions in general are entropy-driven it seems likely that the initial binding of the agonist to the receptor is also associated with an increased entropy, and the net decrease in entropy and enthalpy is due to the conformational change of the receptor protein or surrounding membrane components. The net decrease in entropy would be the sum of the increase in entropy associated with initial binding and the larger decrease resulting from conformational alterations, while the net enthalpy decrease should reflect the lower enthalpy of the particular conformational state induced by agonists (Weiland *et al.*, 1979).

These studies have recently been extended to β-adrenergic receptors in mammalian tissues with similar results (Weiland *et al.*, 1980). Thus the thermodynamic analysis of agonist and antagonist binding to the β-adrenergic receptor is complementary to the kinetic and equilibrium studies described above. Antagonist binding to β-adrenergic receptors seems to be a simple entropy-driven, probably hydrophobic, bimolecular binding reaction, while agonist binding is much more complicated. The binding of agonists to β-adrenergic receptors probably induces a conformational alteration in the receptor molecule such that the agonist–receptor complex can then bind to a third transducer molecule within the membrane, the guanine nucleotide-binding protein.

5.6.4 Binding of antagonists to α-adrenergic receptors

The binding of the radiolabeled antagonists [^{3}H]DHE, [^{3}H]WB 4101 and [^{3}H]PRAZ to α-adrenergic receptors also results in linear Scatchard plots, second-order association kinetics and first-order dissociation kinetics (Williams *et al.*, 1976a; Davis *et al.*, 1977; Strittmatter *et al.*, 1977; U'Prichard *et al.*, 1977; Greenberg and Snyder, 1978; Barnes *et al.*, 1979; Miach *et al.*, 1980). In many cases, however, the agreement between the kinetically derived equilibrium constant and the equilibrium constant determined by Scatchard analysis of saturation isotherms is not good, and has been shown to vary by over tenfold in the case of [^{3}H]DHE (Williams *et al.*, 1976a; Greenberg and Snyder, 1978) and fivefold in the case of [^{3}H]PRAZ (Barnes *et al.*, 1979). Since detailed kinetic analyses such as the dependence of the pseudo-first-order rate constant on radioligand concentration, pre-equilibrium dissociation or ligand-facilitated dissociation of the binding of these compounds have not yet been performed, there is as yet no mechanistic explanation for these discrepancies, although the possibility of two-step binding must be considered (Strickland *et al.*, 1975).

5.6.5 Binding of agonists to α-adrenergic receptors

Many aspects of agonist binding to α-adrenergic receptors closely resemble agonist binding to β-adrenergic receptors. Determined indirectly by inhibition of radiolabeled antagonist binding, sodium and guanine nucleotides decrease, and magnesium increases, the affinity of agonists for α-adrenergic receptors (Tsai and Lefkowitz, 1978a,b; U'Prichard and Snyder, 1978a) in a like manner to the effects of these compounds on β-adrenergic receptors. The effect of guanine nucleotides seems to be only on the α_2-receptor, with no effect on α_1-receptors (U'Prichard and Snyder, 1978a). GTP is also required for α_2-receptor-mediated inhibition of adenylate cyclase activity (Aktories *et al.*, 1979).

Examination of direct binding of agonists to α-adrenergic receptors has yielded conflicting results. Scatchard plots of [^{3}H]CLON binding to brain membranes have been reported to be linear (U'Prichard *et al.*, 1977; U'Prichard and Snyder, 1977) or curvilinear (U'Prichard *et al.*, 1979; Rouot *et al.*, 1980), while Scatchard plots of the binding of [^{3}H]EPI, [^{3}H]NE and [^{3}H]PAC, which have been proposed to label the same sites as [^{3}H]CLON (U'Prichard and Snyder, 1977), are linear (U'Prichard and Snyder, 1978; Rouot and Snyder, 1979). Association kinetics for these radioligands are almost always second-order (U'Prichard *et al.*, 1977; U'Prichard and Snyder, 1977; Rouot and Snyder, 1979). There is less consistency in the reported dissociation kinetics, as the dissociation of [^{3}H]CLON from brain membranes has been reported to be both first-order (U'Prichard *et al.*, 1977) and biphasic (U'Prichard *et al.*, 1979); the dissociation of [^{3}H]EPI and [^{3}H]NE has been reported to be either first-order or biphasic depending on temperature (U'Prichard and Snyder, 1977), and the dissociation of [^{3}H]PAC has been reported to be biphasic (Rouot and Snyder, 1979). Thus, despite the quantity of experimental information which has been published on radiolabeled agonist binding to α-adrenergic receptors, no consistent picture has emerged. The indirect data suggest that agonist binding to α_2-receptors is similar to agonist binding to β-adrenergic receptors.

5.6.6 Thermodynamics of binding of agonists and antagonists to α-adrenergic receptors

Although no comprehensive thermodynamic analysis of α-adrenergic receptors has yet been published, available data suggest that α-adrenergic receptors will be similar to β-adrenergic receptors in this sense also. U'Prichard and Snyder (1977) reported that the affinity of agonists, but not of antagonists, for α-adrenergic receptors increases at lower incubation temperatures. This would suggest that at α-adrenergic receptors, like

β-adrenergic receptors, antagonist binding is entropy-driven while agonist binding is enthalpy-driven.

5.7 BIOCHEMICAL PROPERTIES OF ADRENERGIC RECEPTOR MOLECULES

The availability of radioligands for measuring adrenergic receptors in the absence of a biological response has also resulted in progress in the solubilization and purification of these molecules in an attempt to determine their fundamental biochemical properties. Although little progress has been made in the solubilization and purification of α-adrenergic receptors, the progress with regard to β-adrenergic receptors has been substantial. For a more complete discussion see Ross and Gilman (1980).

5.7.1 β-Adrenergic receptors and adenylate cyclase are separate molecules

Several different lines of evidence have shown that β-adrenergic receptors and adenylate cyclase are separate molecules. Adenylate cyclase activity can be chemically destroyed without affecting ligand binding to β-adrenergic receptors, and ligand binding to β-adrenergic receptors can be chemically inactivated without affecting adenylate cyclase activity (Schramm, 1976). Certain clonal cell lines genetically deficient in adenylate cyclase can have apparently normal populations of β-adrenergic receptors (Insel *et al.*, 1976). Cells containing β-adrenergic receptors but no adenylate cyclase activity can be fused with cells containing adenylate cyclase activity but no β-adrenergic receptors to obtain cells in which β-adrenergic receptors stimulate adenylate cyclase activity (Schramm *et al.*, 1977). Finally, β-adrenergic receptors and adenylate cyclase can be solubilized and separated by chromatographic techniques (Limbird and Lefkowitz, 1977; Haga *et al.*, 1977b; Vauquelin *et al.*, 1977).

5.7.2 Solubilized β-adrenergic receptors

Since β-adrenergic receptors make up only a very small fraction of total membrane protein, attempts to solubilize and purify the receptor have used tissues substantially enriched with regard to these molecules, such as frog erythrocyte membranes (Caron and Lefkowitz, 1976), turkey erythrocyte membranes (Vauquelin *et al.*, 1977), S49 lymphoma cell membranes (Haga *et al.*, 1977b) and membranes from guinea pig lung (Kleinstein and Glossman, 1978). Solubilization of receptors has been accomplished with either digitonin or Lubrol PX. When Lubrol PX is used to solubilize the receptors, the radioligand must be pre-equilibrated with the tissue before solubilization (Haga *et al.*, 1977b). When digitonin is used, the solubilized β-adrenergic receptors can still specifically bind radioligand, however (Caron and Lefkowitz, 1976; Vauquelin *et al.*, 1977; Kleinstein and Glossman, 1978), permitting a more direct examination of their pharmacological properties. Bound and free radioligand are separated by gel filtration or polyethylene glycol precipitation and filtration over glass-fiber filters.

The hydrodynamic properties of the detergent-solubilized β-adrenergic receptor from S49 lymphoma cells indicates that it is an asymmetric protein that binds fairly large amounts of detergent in solution (Haga *et al.*, 1977b), possibly reflecting a significant hydrophobic surface area (Ross and Gilman, 1980). Substantial purification (up to 2000-fold) of the β-adrenergic receptor has been reported with the use of a single or double cycle of affinity chromatography on columns of alprenolol–agarose derivatives (Vauquelin *et al.*, 1977; Caron *et al.*, 1979), preparing the way for large-scale purification of the receptor protein to study its biochemical properties.

In some cases, the binding characteristics of β-adrenergic receptors alter in an interesting manner following solubilization. When β-adrenergic receptors are solubilized with digitonin so that the pharmacological properties of the solubilized receptor can be examined directly, in some cases the solubilized receptor has a higher affinity for agonists, but not antagonists, than does the particulate receptor. This has been shown for the β-adrenergic receptor of the turkey erythrocyte (Vauquelin *et al.*, 1977; Pike and Lefkowitz, 1978) and guinea-pig lung (Kleinstein and Glossman, 1978), but not the frog erythrocyte (Caron and Lefkowitz, 1976). The rank order of potency of agonists in inhibiting radiolabeled antagonist binding to the β-adrenergic receptor is the same in the particulate and solubilized preparations, but the affinities of agonists are ten- to fifty-fold higher in the solubilized preparation. In addition, there is no effect of guanine nucleotides or divalent cations on solubilized β-adrenergic receptors (Kleinstein and Glossman, 1978).

It is interesting to relate these agonist-specific increases in affinity following β-adrenergic receptor solubilization to the thermodynamic parameters of binding to β-adrenergic receptors discussed above. Since the affinity of a drug for the receptor is a reflection of the thermodynamic driving forces involved in the binding reaction, alterations in agonist, but not antagonist, affinity for the β-adrenergic receptor following solubilization must reflect alterations in the thermodynamic driving forces of agonist, but not antagonist, binding. Although this has not yet been experimentally examined, the increase in agonist affinity following receptor solubilization could be caused by a greater thermodynamically favourable negative enthalpy involved in the binding reaction or by a smaller thermodynamically unfavourable negative entropy.

Whichever of these is the correct explanation, it seems likely that the difference in the driving forces of agonist binding between particulate and solubilized β-adrenergic receptors reflects an interaction of the agonist-receptor complex with other membrane constituents. The thermodynamically unfavourable nature of this interaction (i.e. a lowering of agonist affinity in the membrane-bound receptor) is consistent with a role in information transfer through the cell membrane.

5.8   CELLULAR LOCALIZATION OF ADRENERGIC RECEPTORS

The use of radioligand-binding assays has also resulted in new information concerning the organ and cellular localization of adrenergic receptors. Although the existence of receptors on some cell types can of course be inferred from observed alterations in the contractile or metabolic state of the cell upon receptor stimulation, it is likely that receptors also exist on other cell types and mediate functions which are presently unknown or unmeasurable. Direct localization of these receptors can pinpoint the specific cells on which they are located as possible targets for neurotransmitters and hormones, and possibly help to identify some new biological consequences of hormone and neurotransmitter release. The most exciting area for this type of approach is the central nervous system where inter-cellular communication plays such a major, but as yet little understood, role in organismal function. Localization of receptors on identified cell populations in the brain may provide clues as to what biological substrates are involved in the actions of specific psychoactive drugs. Correlation of the biological substrates with the behavioral and physiological actions of drugs might provide insights into biochemical mechanisms underlying the various behavioral and physiological states.

The direct localization of receptors with radioligand-binding assays has generally been accomplished by measuring the receptors in broken cell preparations of the particular tissue in which one is interested. More specific information on the cellular localization of the receptors within the tissue is obtained by the use of microdissection and surgical and chemical lesions to deplete or enrich tissues of identified cell populations. Biochemical separation techniques can also be used to bulk-isolate specific cell populations on which receptor density can then be measured.

Techniques for direct localization of adrenergic receptors by histofluorescent or autoradiographic techniques in intact tissues up until recently have met with only limited success. However, Kuhar and co-workers have recently developed conditions under which adrenergic receptors can be visualized by light microscopic autoradiography in slide-mounted brain sections (Palacios and Kuhar, 1980; Young and Kuhar, 1980). Techniques such as this should be of increasing importance in future receptor-localization studies.

5.8.1 Subcellular distribution of adrenergic receptors

Both α- and β-adrenergic receptors appear to be localized on cellular plasma membranes. β-Adrenergic receptors co-purify with membrane-bound adenylate cyclase activity in rat liver (Wolfe *et al.*, 1976), with plasma membranes of rat adipocytes (Williams *et al.*, 1976b) and with a synaptosomal fraction of rat brain (Bylund and Snyder, 1976; Davis and Lefkowitz, 1976). α-Adrenergic receptors are also located in particulate fractions of all tissues studied, although extensive subcellular localization has not been performed.

5.8.2 Adrenergic receptors in the periphery

The use of radioligand-binding assays to study adrenergic receptors in peripheral tissues has generally been more concerned with pharmacological specificity and regulation of receptor density than with cellular localization. Some information has been presented, however, on the relative proportions of receptor subtypes and the pre- or post-synaptic localization of these receptors.

(a) *Cardiac Adrenergic Receptors*

Both α- and β-adrenergic receptors have been identified using radioligand-binding assays in mammalian heart preparations (Alexander *et al.*, 1975a; Harden *et al.*, 1976; Ciaraldi and Marinetti, 1977; Sharma and Banerjee, 1978). The distribution of β-adrenergic receptors in various regions of dog heart was examined by Baker *et al.* (1980), who found the relative receptor density to be left atrium $>$ right atrium $>$ right ventricle $>$ septum $>$ left ventricle, which was closely related to the distribution of blood flow, but not the distribution of noradrenergic terminals. Minneman *et al.* (1979b) showed that rat heart contained both β_1- and β_2-receptors, although the predominant population (85 per cent) was β_1. The distribution of β_1- and β_2-receptors in cat and guinea pig heart was examined by Hedberg *et al.* (1980), who showed that, although the right atrium of both species contained both β_1- (75 per cent) and β_2-(25 per cent) receptors, the left ventricle contained only β_1-receptors. This is in agreement with previous physiological evidence suggesting that although both β_1- and β_2-receptors mediate positive chronotropic stimulation in the heart, only β_1-receptors mediate positive inotropic stimulation (Carlsson *et al.*, 1972, 1977). To date, the regional distribution and subtype specificity of cardiac α-adrenergic receptors has not been examined.

(b) *Pre- or post-synaptic localization*

Although there is substantial evidence for presynaptic α- and β-adrenergic receptors regulating norepinephrine release from nerve terminals in several peripheral organs (Langer, 1977; Dahlof *et al*., 1978), the results of studies with radioligand-binding assays have generally been disappointing. U'Prichard and Snyder (1979) have shown that sympathetic denervation of rat kidney, heart, vas deferens and salivary gland causes no change in the density of [^{3}H]WB 4101- or [^{3}H]CLON-binding sites, and Nahorski *et al*. (1979a) have shown that the same treatment causes no change in β_1- or β_2-receptor density in rat spleen. Although it is always possible that decreases in receptors due to degeneration of presynaptic terminals were masked by compensatory increases in receptor density (see below), these results suggest that presynaptic receptors do not make up a significant proportion of the total adrenergic receptor population of these tissues. This is perhaps not surprising in view of the very small proportion of tissue mass which is contributed by presynaptic nerve terminals.

5.8.3 Adrenergic receptors in the central nervous system

The distribution of α- and β-adrenergic receptors in various areas of the central nervous system has been examined by several groups. Examination of β-adrenergic receptor density using ^{125}IHYP and [^{3}H]DHA has resulted in good agreement between studies. β-Adrenergic receptors are relatively homogeneously distributed throughout the brain, with the highest density being found in cerebral cortex and corpus striatum, but with reasonably high levels also found in hippocampus, cerebellum, midbrain and pons-medulla (Alexander *et al*., 1975b; Sporn and Molinoff, 1976; Bylund and Snyder, 1976). The most surprising finding of these studies was that the density of β-adrenergic receptors in a particular brain region had no apparent relationship to the extent of the noradrenergic innervation. Thus a high or moderate density of β-adrenergic receptors was found in areas receiving a major noradrenergic innervation such as cerebral cortex, hippocampus and cerebellum, and also in an area receiving no apparent noradrenergic input such as the caudate. Since all brain areas contain both β_1 and β_2 receptors (Nahorski, 1978; Minneman *et al*., 1979b) it was possible that the distribution of β_1-receptors (which have the highest affinity for norepinephrine) would more closely parallel the extent of noradrenergic innervation. This was not the case, however, since the highest and lowest densities of β_1-receptors were found in the cerebral cortex and cerebellum respectively, both tissues with a dense noradrenergic input (Minneman *et al*., 1979b). The non-noradrenergically innervated caudate also had a high density of β_1-receptors comparable with the heavily innervated cerebral cortex. An interesting finding of these studies was that, although the

Table 5.4 Density of β_1- and β_2-adrenergic receptors in various regions of rat brain. Reprinted by permission from Minneman *et al.* (1979b).

	Total β-adrenergic receptors	β_1-Adrenergic receptors	β_2-Adrenergic receptors
	(fmol of IHYP bound/mg of protein)	(fmol of IHYP bound/mg of protein)	(fmol of IHYP bound/mg of protein)
cerebellum	21.7 ± 2.24	3.3 ± 0.46	18.4 ± 1.92
diencephalon	27.4 ± 1.69	19.4 ± 1.28	8.0 ± 0.67
hippocampus	38.1 ± 5.11	31.0 ± 4.18	7.1 ± 0.95
caudate	54.0 ± 3.41	41.3 ± 2.65	12.7 ± 0.93
cortex	71.3 ± 8.38	58.1 ± 6.84	13.2 ± 1.55

density of β_1-receptors varied up to twenty-fold between different brain regions, the density of β_2-receptors was reasonably homogeneous throughout the brain, prompting the suggestion that β_2-receptors may be associated with the more homogeneously distributed non-neuronal elements in the brain, such as glia or blood vessels (Minneman *et al.*, 1979b).

α-Adrenergic receptors in the brain are less homogeneously distributed than β-adrenergic receptors, although the regional distribution of α-adrenergic receptors also does not correlate with the density of noradrenergic innervation. The use of different agonist and antagonist radioligands has led to some discrepant results concerning the relative distribution of α-adrenergic receptors, with the picture being further complicated by the possibility that [³H]DHE may label dopaminergic and serotoninergic receptors as well as α-adrenergic receptors in different brain regions (Davis *et al.*, 1977). There is a high density of [³H]DHE-binding sites in the cerebral cortex, hippocampus, thalamus and hypothalamus (Davis *et al.*, 1977; Greenberg and Snyder, 1978), although the density of [³H]DHE-binding sites in the caudate has been reported to be relatively high (Greenberg and Snyder, 1978) or relatively low (Davis *et al.*, 1977). The density of [³H]DHE binding sites in the cerebellum is quite low (Davis *et al.*, 1977; Greenberg and Snyder, 1978). Although it has been proposed that [³H]WB 4101 and [³H]CLON label α_1- and α_2-receptors respectively, and that the summation of the number of [³H]WB 4101 (α_1) and [³H]CLON (α_2) sites equals the number of [³H]DHE (α_1 and α_2) sites (Greenberg and Snyder, 1978), comparison of the regional distribution of [³H]DHE sites with [³H]WB 4101 and [³H]CLON sites does not support this hypothesis. U'Prichard *et al.* (1977) and Greenberg and Snyder (1978) found approximately equivalent numbers of [³H]DHE sites and [³H]WB 4101 plus [³H]CLON sites in the cerebral cortex, hypothalamus, hippocampus, medulla-pons and the thalamus-midbrain, but in the caudate and cerebellum they found substantial differences, with more [³H]DHE sites than [³H]WB 4101 plus [³H]CLON sites found in the caudate and less in the cerebellum. Although the reasons for these various discrepancies are not obvious, they may relate either to the labeling of more than one receptor population to different extents by [³H]DHE or to problems inherent in the use of radiolabeled agonists such as [³H]CLON to quantify receptor density (see above).

(a) Pre- or post-synaptic localization

Examination of the pre- or post-synaptic localization of adrenergic receptors in the rat central nervous system has been accomplished by selective destruction of noradrenergic nerve terminals by 6-hydroxydopamine. If a significant proportion of the adrenergic receptors in a given brain region are located on presynaptic noradrenergic nerve terminals, this treatment should lead to a decrease in receptor density. Although compensatory increases in postsynaptic receptors can obscure the results, since these occur relatively slowly (Sporn *et al.*, 1977), rapid initial decreases should still be observable. The effects of this treatment on both α- and β-adrenergic receptor density in the brain, as in peripheral tissues (see above), have been generally negative (Sporn *et al.*, 1977; U'Prichard *et al.*, 1977; Skolnick *et al.*, 1978; Minneman *et al.*, 1979d), although U'Prichard *et al.* (1980) observed small decreases in [³H]CLON binding to septum and amygdala following lesion of the dorsal noradrenergic bundle. In the brain, as in peripheral tissues, no large proportion of the adrenergic receptor population in a given tissue is localized on presynaptic adrenergic nerve tissue.

(b) Localization of adrenergic receptors on neuronal or glial elements in rat caudate

The existence of a high density of both α- and β-adrenergic receptors in rat caudate, a brain region containing no noradrenergic input, has prompted the suggestion that these receptors may be located on non-neuronal elements (Sporn and Molinoff, 1976; U'Prichard *et al.*, 1977). In order to examine this possibility, the effect of kainic acid injection on the density of β-adrenergic receptors in rat caudate has been examined. Microinjection of kainic acid into rat caudate has been proposed to selectively destroy neuronal cell bodies and leave nerve terminals and axons arising from cell bodies external to this structure intact (Coyle and Schwarcz, 1976; McGeer and McGeer, 1976). Proliferation of glial cells is observed after this treatment. A potentiation of β-adrenergic-receptor-stimulated cyclic AMP accumulation in slices of rat caudate has been observed following kainic acid lesions (Minneman *et al.*, 1978). The effect of microinjection of kainic acid on β-adrenergic receptor density in rat caudate has been examined by Zahniser *et al.* (1979), Nahorski *et al.* (1979b) and Chang *et al.* (1980). Although small decreases in β-adrenergic receptor density in the caudate after kainic acid administration were observed by Nahorski *et al.* (1979b) and Chang *et al.* (1980), no alteration in β_1- or β_2-receptor density were observed by Zahniser *et al.* (1979). When decreases in neurochemical parameters are observed after chemical lesions, it is important to rule out the possibility that the observed losses are due to non-specific damage. Since kainic acid lesions leave the presynaptic dopaminergic input to the caudate intact, it is possible to validate the specificity of the lesion by measurement of tyrosine hydroxylase activity or synaptosomal [^{3}H]dopamine uptake, both of which should remain unchanged (Schwarcz and Coyle, 1976). Since this was not done in the studies by Nahorski *et al.* (1979b) and Chang *et al.* (1980), the possibility that the observed losses in β-adrenergic receptor density were due to non-specific damage cannot be ruled out. Conversely, in the study by Zahniser *et al.* (1980) where no change in β-adrenergic receptor density was observed after kainic acid administration, the effectiveness of the lesion was validated by showing that the expected 50–60 per cent decreases in five other neurochemical parameters were in fact observed. Thus it seems unlikely that a significant percentage of β-adrenergic receptors in rat striatum are associated with neuronal cell bodies or dendrites, leaving open the possibility that they may be located on glial cells in this brain area. The possible function or lack of function of such receptors is still obscure, although it is possible that they may be vestigial or alternatively that they may play a developmental role.

The effect of kainic acid administration on α-adrenergic receptor density in rat caudate has not yet been examined.

(c) *Localization of adrenergic receptors on cerebral blood vessels*
Some of the adrenergic receptors in the brain may also be located on blood vessels and play a role in control of the cerebral circulation. A particularly good candidate for a vascular localization would be the relatively norepinephrine-insensitive β_2-receptors, since localization in cerebral blood vessels on the peripheral side of the blood–brain barrier would allow them access to circulating epinephrine. Recent progress in biochemical techniques for the isolation of cerebral microvessels has enabled several groups to examine these preparations for the presence of α- and/or β-adrenergic receptors. Nathanson and Glaser (1979) and Herbst *et al.* (1979) showed that β-adrenergic-receptor-stimulated adenylate cyclase activity could be observed in purified preparations of cerebral blood vessels. Peroutka *et al.* (1980) and Harik *et al.* (1980) have examined radioligand binding to similar preparations. Both groups found a reasonably low density of

β-adrenergic receptors ([^{3}H]DHA-binding sites about one-third that of whole brain homogenate), and Peroutka *et al.*, (1980) also found some α-adrenergic receptors ([^{3}H]WB 4101 and [^{3}H]PAC about half that of whole brain homogenate), although Harik *et al.* (1980) found no [^{3}H]WB 4101 sites in their preparation. Examination of the potency of catecholamines in inhibiting [^{3}H]DHA binding from this preparation showed that the β-adrenergic receptors in cerebral microvessels are apparently of the β_1-subtype (Peroutka *et al.*, 1980), in agreement with previous physiological evidence (Sercombe *et al.*, 1977). Conversely, in an extensive examination of the pharmacological specificity of the β-adrenergic receptor linked to adenylate cyclase in cerebral microvessels, Nathanson (1980) presented strong evidence that these receptors are of the β_2-subtype. There is at present no apparent explanation for this discrepancy, although possible differences in species [Peroutka *et al.* (1980) used calf brain while Nathanson (1980) used cat brain] or experimental technique must be considered. The results of Peroutka *et al.* (1980) suggest that both α_1- and α_2-receptors exist on cerebral microvessels.

Although these studies constitute strong evidence for the existence of adrenergic receptors on cerebral blood vessels, consideration of the density of these receptors in these preparations and the amount of brain mass made up by blood vessels makes it unlikely that they constitute a measurable fraction of the total adrenergic receptors in the brain. Since the density of these receptors in a highly purified microvessel preparation is substantially less than that in a whole brain homogenate, and microvessels make up less than one per cent of the mass of the brain, the adrenergic receptors on microvessels must make up substantially less than 1 per cent of the total adrenergic receptors in the brain. Although this percentage may be higher in tissues with a low total receptor density and a dense vasculature, it seems unlikely that it will ever be very large.

(d) *Localization of β-adrenergic receptor subtypes in rat cerebellum*
Although most regions of the central nervous system contain mainly β_1-receptors, the β-adrenergic receptors in the cerebellum are predominantly of the β_2-subtype (U'Prichard *et al.*, 1978; Minneman *et al.*, 1979b). However, some β_1-receptors are found in the cerebellum and depending on the age of the animal comprise from 18 per cent (10-day-old rats) to 2 per cent (180-day-old rats) of the total number of β-adrenergic receptors (Pittman *et al.*, 1980a). In the cerebellum as in other brain areas the major adrenergic neurotransmitter is norepinephrine. Since β_2-receptors have a relatively low affinity for norepinephrine, it seems unlikely that norepinephrine acts as the natural agonist at these receptors. It is possible, therefore, that the small population of β_1-receptors in the cerebellum might be the neuronally innervated receptors in this tissue.

The noradrenergic input to the cerebellum arises from the locus coeruleus and synapses primarily in the Purkinje and molecular layers (Bloom *et al.*, 1972). Little or no catecholamine histofluorescence is observed in the granule cell layer. It has been shown using electro-physiological techniques that the spontaneous or glutamate-induced firing of Purkinje cells is substantially inhibited by iontophoretic application of β-adrenergic agonists and cyclic AMP (Siggins *et al.*, 1969). However, the uncertain nature of drug concentrations when applied by microion-tophoresis has made it difficult to determine whether these receptors are β_1- or β_2-adrenergic receptors.

Information on specific cell populations in the cerebellum has been obtained by subjecting neonatal rats to intermittent X-irradiation focused on the cerebellum (Altman and Anderson, 1973). This treatment causes a 70 per cent loss in cerebellar mass in adult rats, destroying the late-maturing granule, basket and stellate interneurons but sparing early matur-ing Purkinje neurons. Purkinje cells from X-irradiated rats have been examined both histologically and electrophysiologically and shown to have similar properties to Purkinje cells from untreated rats (Woodward *et al.*, 1974). Measurement of the total number of β-adrenergic receptors per cerebellum in 6- or 12-week-old animals subjected to neonatal X-irradiation revealed an 80 per cent decrease in the number of β-adrenergic receptors per cerebellum (Minneman *et al.*, 1980b). Analysis of receptor subtypes showed that this loss was entirely due to a decrease in the number of β_2-receptors. The number of β_1-receptors in an X-irradiated cerebellum was not different from that in control animals (Minneman *et al.*, 1980b).

The co-survival of Purkinje cells and β_1-receptors in X-irradiated cere-bella suggests that the β_1-receptors, although comprising only 2—3 per cent of the total number of β-adrenergic receptors in the cerebellum of mature rats, may be the receptors on the Purkinje neurons which receive the noradrenergic input to this tissue. Although there are very few β_1-receptors in an adult rat cerebellum (about 0.8 fmol/mg of protein or 18 fmol/cerebellum), the number of Purkinje cells is also quite low (about 300 000 cells/cerebellum; Armstrong and Schild, 1970). If all the β_1-receptors in the cerebellum were on Purkinje cells, there would be approxi-mately 36 000 receptors/cell, which is not an unreasonable number in view of the large size of these cells.

(e) *Histochemical localization of cerebral adrenergic receptors*

The first attempt at direct histochemical localization of β-adrenergic recep-tors was made by Atlas and Levitzki (1977), who developed fluorescently labeled analogues of the high-affinity β-adrenergic antagonist propranolol. The fluorescently labeled compounds retained their high affinity for β-adrenergic receptors and were used to attempt to localize these receptors *in vivo*. The drugs were injected into rats and the fluorescence pattern monitored by fluorescence microscopy on cryostat tissue slices. These compounds were shown to label specific regions and cells in the central nervous system, particularly the pyramidal cell layer of the hippocampus, the granule cell layer of the dentate gyrus, the cerebellar Purkinje layer and spinal α-motor neurons (Atlas and Melamed, 1978). Despite these promising results, careful examination of the labeling pattern of this fluorescent drug in other laboratories has indicated that the fluorescence pattern observed is not associated with β-adrenergic receptors (Hess, 1979; Barnes *et al.*, 1980). These authors showed that, contrary to the results of Atlas and Melamed (1978), prior injection of propranolol did not block the fluorescence pattern observed after injection of the labeled compounds, and Hess (1979) also showed that similar fluorescent patterns were observed in rats that had not been injected with any labeled compounds.

A more successful approach has been taken by Kuhar and co-workers, who have localized both α- and β-adrenergic receptors using light microscopic radioautographic techniques (Young and Kuhar, 1980; Palacios and Kuhar, 1980). These authors incubated slide-mounted tissue sections with specific radioligands ([^{3}H]DHA for β-, [^{3}H]WB 4101 for α_1- and [^{3}H]PAC for α_2-receptors, respectively). Under appropriate conditions and with extensive cold washes these authors showed pharmacologically that a substantial proportion of the bound radioligands (70–80 per cent) were associated with specific receptor sites. Subsequent development of the radioautographs and quantitative comparison with similar control slides incubated with competing drugs to give an estimate of non-receptor binding resulted in a light-microscopic localization of the specific binding sites for these radioligands.

High densities of β-adrenergic receptors were found in superficial layers of the cerebral cortex, throughout the caudate putamen, in the periventricular nucleus of the thalamus and in the molecular layer of the cerebellum (Palacios and Kuhar, 1980). High densities of α-adrenergic receptors were found in portions of olfactory areas, cerebral cortex, dentate gyrus, hypothalamus, thalamus, locus coeruleus, nucleus tractus solitarius and spinal cord (Young and Kuhar, 1980). The distribution of specific binding for [^{3}H]WB 4101 and [^{3}H]PAC was not always the same. For example, the locus coeruleus had substantial [^{3}H]PAC binding with very little [^{3}H]WB 4101 binding (Young and Kuhar, 1980).

The results of these radioautographic studies are in good agreement with previous biochemical studies of receptor distribution. The advantage of the radioautographic approach is that it allows the localization of receptors to be extended to much more accurately defined anatomical areas and cell layers. Thus small cell layers with a high receptor density, but very few total receptors owing to the small tissue mass, can be distinguished from much larger tissue masses which contain a low receptor density (but a large number of total receptors). This technique should therefore lead to a more precise knowledge concerning the localization of adrenergic receptors in various tissues, particularly the brain.

5.9 DEVELOPMENT OF ADRENERGIC RECEPTORS

The appearance of β-adrenergic receptors during organismal development has been studied in rat heart, cerebral cortex and cerebellum, and mouse heart (Harden *et al.*, 1977a; Chen *et al.*, 1979; Pittman *et al.*, 1980a; Baker and Potter, 1980a). Since β-adrenergic receptor density develops in parallel with isoproterenol-stimulated adenylate cyclase activity in the cerebral cortex, and isoproterenol-stimulated chronotropic responses in the mouse heart, it seems likely that appearance of the receptor permits expression of the tissue response (Harden *et al.*, 1977a; Chen *et al.*, 1979). Although there was adenylate cyclase activity present in rat cerebral cortex prior to the appearance of measurable levels of β-adrenergic receptors, at this time cyclic AMP accumulation was not affected by catecholamines (Harden *et al.*, 1977a). The presence or absence of a normal presynaptic input did not influence the time of appearance of either β-adrenergic receptors or isoproterenol-stimulated cyclic AMP accumulation, although it markedly increased receptor density and maximal levels of catecholamine-stimulated cyclic AMP accumulation (Harden *et al.*, 1977b).

The ontogenetic appearance of β-adrenergic receptors in rat or mouse heart (Harden *et al.*, 1977a; Chen *et al.*, 1979; Baker and Potter, 1980a) is much earlier than in rat cerebral cortex and cerebellum (Harden *et al.*, 1977a; Pittman *et al.*, 1980a). In the heart, β-adrenergic receptor density increases slowly during the prenatal period, continues to increase until about 3 days postnatal and then remains relatively constant throughout life (Chen *et al.*, 1979). Heart weight increases substantially as the heart matures postnatally and the total number of receptors in the heart increases correspondingly, although the density of receptors measured per unit tissue weight does not change (Baker and Potter, 1980a). These observations suggest that cell surface area may be a major factor determining the number of β-adrenergic receptors on an individual heart cell (Baker and Potter, 1980a).

There are no measurable β-adrenergic receptors in rat cerebral cortex or cerebellum until about five or six days postnatal (Harden *et al.*, 1977a; Pittman *et al.*, 1980a). During the next 2 (cerebral cortex) or 4 (cerebellum) weeks of life the density of β-adrenergic receptors in these tissues increases markedly, and subsequently maintains a fairly stable plateau. Since the developmental cues determining the development of these receptors are not yet known, it is not clear why β-adrenergic receptors in the brain develop so much later than β-adrenergic receptors in the heart.

However, there is no apparent correlation of the development of receptor density with tissue catecholamine content, and the pattern of development does not change in the absence of a presynaptic input to the receptors (Harden *et al.*, 1977b), suggesting that a catecholamine input is not critical to the development of these receptors.

The differential ontogeny of β_1- and β_2-receptors has been studied in rat cerebral cortex and cerebellum (Pittman *et al.*, 1980a). The cortex contained primarily β_1-receptors and the cerebellum contained primarily β_2-receptors throughout development. In both brain areas, β_1-receptors

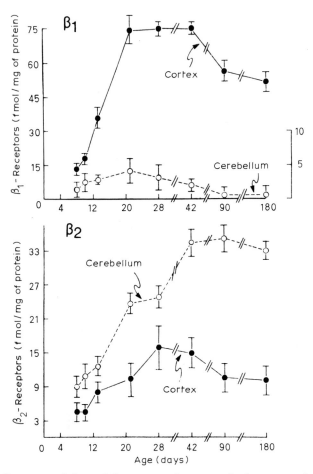

Fig. 5.6 Ontogeny of β_1- and β_2-receptors in rat cerebral cortex and cerebellum. Age is expressed as days postnatal. Note expanded scale on right side of upper panel representing fmol of β_1-receptors/mg of protein in cerebellum. Reprinted by permission from Pittman *et al.* (1980a).

reached their maximum density earlier in development than did β_2-receptors. The developmental pattern of neither receptor subtype appeared to be uniquely correlated with the ontogeny of specific cell types, although the development of β_2-receptors more closely paralleled cerebral gliogenesis and vascularization than cerebral neurogenesis. The early development of β_1-receptors was consistent with their being located primarily on neuronal elements. β_1- and β_2-receptors in the same brain area followed different developmental patterns, suggesting that they may be associated with different cellular elements responsive to different developmental cues (Pittman *et al.*, 1980a).

The developmental pattern of β_1-receptors in the rat cerebellum showed a particularly interesting pattern (Pittman *et al.*, 1980a,b). The density of cerebellar β_1-receptors increased up to postnatal day 28 and then declined markedly. Examination of the total number of β_1-receptors per cerebellum showed that this decline in density was not due to dilution of a constant receptor population by increasing tissue mass, but rather to a decrease in the total number of β_1-receptors in an individual cerebellum. There were only one-quarter as many β_1-receptors in 90-day-old rat cerebellum as there were in 28-day-old rat cerebellum (Pittman *et al.*, 1980a). Further examination showed that as the rats aged the β_1-receptors reappeared (Pittman *et al.*, 1980b) and in 14-month-old rats there were three to four times as many β_1-receptors in the cerebellum as in 3- or 6-month-old rats. Decreases in total β-adrenergic receptor density during aging have been demonstrated in several brain areas, including cerebellum (Greenberg and Weiss, 1978; Maggi *et al*, 1979; Weiss *et al.*, 1979). Decreases in the density of β_2-receptors in the cerebellum during aging were also observed by Pittman *et al.* (1980b). These decreases may reflect a gradual breakdown of biochemical processes during the aging process. β_1-Receptors in the cerebellum are the only receptor population which has so far been shown to increase during aging (Pittman *et al.*, 1980b). The physiological function or mechanism of this increase in receptor density is not yet understood, although it is not apparently related to changes in Purkinje cell firing (Rogers *et al.*, 1979) or cerebellum norepinephrine content (Pittman *et al.*, 1980b).

The pattern of development of β-adrenergic receptors has also been examined during maturation of the rat reticulocyte to the mature erythrocyte (Charness *et al.*, 1976; Bilezikian *et al.*, 1977b). Reticulocyte maturation is associated with a large decline in catecholamine-stimulated adenylate cyclase activity and a much smaller and slower decline in β-adrenergic receptor density. Thus, the maturation of the rat erythrocyte is associated with a decline in β-adrenergic receptor density and also with an uncoupling of the remaining β-adrenergic receptors from adenylate cyclase. Bilezikian *et al.* (1977a) have shown that the uncoupled β-adrenergic receptor–

adenylate cyclase system in the mature erythrocyte can be restored by guanine nucleotides, suggesting that the decreased coupling efficiency seen upon erythrocyte maturation may be related to alterations in the guanine nucleotide regulatory system.

5.10   REGULATION OF ADRENERGIC RECEPTOR DENSITY

A decrease in the normal afferent input to a tissue is usually associated with an increase in the sensitivity of that tissue to further hormonal stimulation. This phenomenon is known as supersensitivity, and was first characterized in the peripheral cholinergic (Kuffler, 1943) and adrenergic (Trendelenburg, 1963) nervous systems. Conversely, increases in the normal afferent input to a tissue are often associated with decreases in the sensitivity of the tissue to further stimulation, a phenomenon known as subsensitivity (Trendelenburg, 1963). In the adrenergic nervous system, two separate components contribute to tissue supersensitivity, a reduction in neurotransmitter inactivation by loss of presynaptic uptake processes, and a slowly developing postsynaptic alteration in the sensitivity of the target cell to hormonal stimulation. Subsensitivity appears to involve only postsynaptic elements. The use of radioligand-binding assays has allowed an examination of the possible role of alterations in receptor density in the postsynaptic component of supersensitivity and subsensitivity. The results have shown that alterations in receptor density play a major role in super- and sub-sensitive tissue responses, but that other postsynaptic alterations are also involved (Wolfe *et al.*, 1977).

Three types of phenomena have been observed. Increases in receptor density following decreased receptor stimulation have generally been characterized by a slow onset and probably involve increased synthesis of receptor protein (Sporn *et al.*, 1977). Decreases in receptor density following continuous receptor stimulation can be of two types. In some cases the decrease in receptor density following exposure to agonist is very rapid and readily reversible (Mukherjee and Lefkowitz, 1977) and probably does not involve degradation or synthesis of receptor proteins. In other cases the decrease is slower in onset and reversal (Wolfe *et al.*, 1978) and probably does involve degradation and synthesis of receptor proteins. Slowly developing increases and decreases in receptor density may well be two different manifestations of a single physiological process, the control of the density of receptor protein in the cell membrane. The rapid decrease in apparent receptor density following previous exposure to agonist ('desensitization') seems to be a completely separate phenomenon, and will be discussed separately.

5.10.1 Regulation of β-adrenergic receptor density in rat central nervous system

Alterations in the activity of the noradrenergic input has a marked effect on β-adrenergic receptor density in the brain. This phenomenon has been documented most extensively in the rat cerebral cortex.

Palmer (1972) and Kalisker *et al.* (1973) showed that depletion of brain norepinephrine by intraventricular injection of 6-hydroxydopamine increased the norepinephrine-stimulated accumulation of cyclic AMP in slices of rat cerebral cortex. Kalisker *et al.* (1973) showed that this effect was composed of two different components. An early loss of norepinephrine uptake due to destruction of noradrenergic terminals resulted in an apparent increase in norepinephrine affinity. In addition, a later postsynaptic increase in the maximal responsiveness to norepinephrine was also observed. Sporn *et al.*, (1976, 1977) confirmed and extended these findings to show that the slowly developing postsynaptic increase in norepinephrine responsiveness involved an increase in β-adrenergic receptor density. Significant increases in β-adrenergic receptor density were first seen 3 days following 6-hydroxydopamine administration and did not reach peak levels until 16 days after treatment (Sporn *et al.*, 1977). Although β-adrenergic receptor density was increased after 6-hydroxydopamine treatment, there was no change in the pharmacological characteristics of the receptor. Chronic administration of the potent β-adrenergic receptor antagonist propranolol also increased β-adrenergic receptor density in the cerebral cortex (Wolfe *et al.*, 1978; Dolphin *et al.*, 1979), showing that the increase in receptor density is probably due to a decrease in receptor occupancy by agonist.

Depletion of cerebral catecholamines by chronic reserpine treatment also increased β-adrenergic receptor density in the cerebral cortex (Dolphin *et al.*, 1979), although acute treatment with reserpine had no effect (Nahorski, 1977). It has also been reported that chronic, but not acute, amphetamine administration increases β-adrenergic receptor density in rat brain (Banerjee *et al.*, 1978).

The time course of increases in β-adrenergic-receptor-stimulated cyclic AMP accumulation closely paralleled the time course of increases in β-adrenergic receptor density in the cerebral cortex, suggesting that these two phenomena might be causally related (Sporn *et al.*, 1977). The magnitude of the increase in receptor-stimulated cyclic AMP accumulation was usually larger than the observed increase in receptor density, however (Sporn *et al.*, 1977; Nahorski, 1977; Dolphin *et al.*, 1979). Thus, other adaptive responses in addition to the increase in receptor density probably play a role in supersensitive tissue responses. These factors have not yet been rigorously identified, but may include increased adenylate cyclase, more efficient coupling between the receptor and adenylate cyclase, or alterations in the intracellular events involved in tissue responsiveness to receptor stimulation.

Several authors have now shown that chronic increases in norepinephrine availability decrease the density of β-adrenergic receptors in the cerebral cortex. Chronic administration of inhibitors of monoamine oxidase or norepinephrine uptake decreased the ability of norepinephrine to increase cyclic AMP accumulation in brain slices (Vetulani *et al.*, 1976a,b; Schultz, 1976). Banerjee *et al.* (1977) and Wolfe *et al.* (1978) showed that this loss of catecholamine-stimulated cyclic AMP accumulation was correlated with a decrease in the density of β-adrenergic receptors in the cerebral cortex. Wolfe *et al.* (1978) showed that chronic treatment of rats with the anti-depressant drugs desmethylimipramine (an inhibitor of norepinephrine reuptake), pargyline (a monoamine oxidase inhibitor) and iprindole (mechanism of action unknown) decreased β-adrenergic receptor density in rat cerebral cortex. The time course and extent of the decrease in β-adrenergic receptor density and the decrease in isoproterenol-stimulated cyclic AMP accumulation were very similar. The effect of chronic desmethylimipramine treatment was blocked by co-administration of the β-adrenergic receptor antagonist propranolol or previous sympathetic denervation by 6-hydroxydopamine treatment, showing that the effect of this drug was mediated through increased β-adrenergic receptor occupancy (Wolfe *et al.*, 1978). The effects of chronic iprindole treatment on β-adrenergic receptor density were also blocked by previous sympathetic denervation with 6-hydroxydopamine, showing that the effects of this compound were also dependent on the presence of a presynaptic noradrenergic input (Wolfe *et al.*, 1978), and might be due to a weak inhibition of neuronal uptake or to an enhanced release of norepinephrine (Hendley, 1978).

The decrease in cerebral β-adrenergic receptor density following chronic treatment with anti-depressant drugs correlates with electrophysiological observations on decreases in neuronal sensitivity to norepinephrine following this treatment. Olpe and Schellenberg (1980) showed that chronic treatment of rats with several different anti-depressants reduced sensitivity of cells in the rat cingulate cortex to inhibition by microiontophoretically applied norepinephrine.

Since rat cerebral cortex contains both β_1- and β_2-receptors, it was of interest to determine which receptor population(s) was being affected by these treatments, in order to determine which receptor subtype normally receives the noradrenergic neuronal input in the brain. Minneman *et al.* (1979d) showed that destruction of noradrenergic neurons by 6-hydroxydopamine treatment of newborn rats selectively increased β_1-

receptor density in cerebral cortex of the rats when fully grown, but had no effect on β_2-receptor density. Conversely, chronic treatment with desmethylimipramine decreased β_1-receptor density in the cerebral cortex without affecting β_2-receptor density (Minneman *et al.*, 1979d). Since the effects of these alterations in noradrenergic neurotransmission were restricted to the β_1-receptor population, it seems likely that this is the β-adrenergic receptor subtype which normally receives the noradrenergic input in the cerebral cortex. The lack of effect of these treatments on β_2-receptor density in this brain area suggests that these receptors do not have access to neuronally released norepinephrine.

Recent evidence suggests that non-catecholamine hormones can also affect the β-adrenergic receptor adenylate cyclase system in the brain. Gross *et al.* (1980) showed that β-adrenergic receptor density and cyclic AMP responsiveness were decreased in cerebral cortex from hypothyroid rats. Mobley and Sulser (1980) showed that norepinephrine-stimulated cyclic AMP accumulation in rat cerebral cortex was increased in adrenalectomized rats and that this effect was reversed by chronic corticosterone treatment. No effect was seen on β-adrenergic receptor density in the cerebral cortex of adrenalectomized animals (see also Minneman *et al.*, 1981).

5.10.2 Regulation of β-adrenergic receptor density in rat pineal

The rat pineal organ has been a useful system for studying supersensitivity and subsensitivity in the β-adrenergic receptor–adenylate cyclase system. Stimulation of β-adrenergic receptors in pineal parenchymal cells leads to an easily measurable postsynaptic response, an increased synthesis of the hormone melatonin (Axelrod *et al.*, 1969). This is caused by an enormous increase in the activity of one of the melatonin-synthesizing enzymes, serotonin *N*-acetyltransferase (SNAT; Klein *et al.*, 1970). β-Adrenergic receptors in the pineal organ are linked to adenylate cyclase (Weiss and Costa, 1968) and the induction of SNAT by β-adrenergic receptor stimulation is mediated by increased intracellular cyclic AMP (Shein and Wurtman, 1969; Minneman and Iversen, 1976). The pineal organ, therefore, provides a good system in which the effects of alterations in β-adrenergic receptor density on an easily measurable cyclic AMP-mediated postsynaptic biochemical response can be examined.

Denervation of the rat pineal causes an increase in the ability of norepinephrine to activate adenylate cyclase (Weiss and Costa, 1969) and an increase in the norepinephrine-mediated induction of SNAT (Deguchi and Axelrod, 1972). Conversely, continuous stimulation of β-adrenergic receptors in the pineal leads to a decreased responsiveness of adenylate cyclase to catecholamines (Strada and Weiss, 1974) which is accompanied by a decreased induction of SNAT (Deguchi and Axelrod, 1973).

Kebabian *et al*. (1975) showed that decreases in β-adrenergic-receptor-stimulated adenylate cyclase were correlated with a marked decrease in β-adrenergic receptor density in the pineal. The time course and magnitude of the decrease in receptor density and adenylate cyclase responsiveness were very similar, suggesting that the two were causally related.

A circadian rhythm in the sensitivity of the pineal organ to β-adrenergic-receptor-mediated induction of SNAT has also been reported (Romero and Axelrod, 1974). This is probably caused by light-induced changes in the activity of the sympathetic input to the pineal (Taylor and Wilson, 1970). This circadian rhythm in responsiveness has also been correlated with alterations in pineal β-adrenergic receptor density (Romero *et al*., 1975), showing that changes in β-adrenergic receptor density play an important role in regulating pineal sensitivity. Other evidence suggests, however, that other postsynaptic alterations, such as changes in cyclic nucleotide metabolism (Minneman, 1977; Zatz, 1978) and changes in cellular messenger RNA levels (Zatz *et al*., 1976), are also involved in regulating pineal sensitivity.

5.10.3 Regulation of β-adrenergic receptor density in peripheral tissues

Factors governing the regulation of β-adrenergic receptor density have also been studied in several peripheral organs. Glaubiger *et al*. (1978) reported that depletion of catecholamines by chronic guanethidine treatment increased β-adrenergic receptor density in rat heart. Continuous blockade of β-adrenergic receptors by chronic propranolol administration has also been reported to increase β-adrenergic receptor density in rat heart (Glaubiger and Lefkowitz, 1977) as well as human lymphocytes (Aarons *et al*., 1980). However, Baker and Potter (1980b) were unable to find any effects of chronic propranolol administration on β-adrenergic receptor density in rat heart, even using the identical injection protocol reported by Glaubiger and Lefkowitz (1977). Wolfe *et al*. (1978) observed no effect of chronic desmethylimipramine administration on β-adrenergic receptor density in rat heart and suggested that the central effects of this compound may override the peripheral inhibition of norepinephrine uptake (Wolfe *et al*., 1978). Thus whether or not β-adrenergic receptor density in the heart is regulated by the activity of the presynaptic input is still controversial.

The density of β-adrenergic receptors in rat liver is increased severalfold following bilateral adrenalectomy (Wolfe *et al*., 1976; Guellaen *et al*., 1978). This increase was correlated with a similar increase in isoproterenol-stimulated adenylate cyclase activity. Both the increase in receptor density and receptor-stimulated adenylate cyclase activity could be reversed by repeated injection of a high dose of cortisone for 2 days (Wolfe *et al*., 1976). The reversal of the adrenalectomy-induced increase in β-adrenergic receptor density by cortisone suggests that the density of these receptors in liver may be regulated by the metabolic state of the cell, not only the degree of receptor stimulation (Wolfe *et al.*, 1976).

Regulation of β-adrenergic receptor density by thyroid state has also been reported. Chronic treatment with thyroid hormones increased β-adrenergic receptor density and isoproterenol-stimulated adenylate cyclase activity in rat heart (Ciaraldi and Marinetti, 1977; Williams *et al.*, 1977; Tse *et al.*, 1980). No changes in β-adrenergic receptor density or adenylate cyclase activity were observed during hyperthyroidism in rat fat cells (Malbon *et al.*, 1978) or turkey erythrocytes (Bilezikian *et al.*, 1979). With both rat fat cells (Malbon *et al.*, 1978) and turkey erythrocytes (Bilezikian *et al.*, 1979) a decrease in isoproterenol-stimulated adenylate cyclase activity was observed during hypothyroid states, although only in turkey erythrocytes was this correlated with a fall in β-adrenergic receptor density.

5.10.4 Regulation of α-adrenergic receptor density

Considerably less information is available on the regulation of α-adrenergic receptor density than on the regulation of β-adrenergic receptor density. U'Prichard *et al.* (1979) and U'Prichard and Snyder (1978b) reported that depletion of cerebral catecholamines by 6-hydroxydopamine or chronic reserpine treatment increased the number of binding sites for [³H]CLON, [³H]WB 4101 and [³H]EPI in rat brain. Skolnick *et al.* (1978), however, saw no effect of 6-hydroxydopamine treatment on [³H]WB 4101-binding to brain membranes from two different strains of rats, although increases in β-adrenergic receptor density and α-adrenergic-receptor-stimulated cyclic AMP accumulation were observed after this treatment. U'Prichard *et al.* (1980) measured [³H]WB 4101 and [³H]CLON-binding in various rat brain areas following bilateral 6-hydroxydopamine lesions of the dorsal noradrenergic bundle. These investigators found increases in [³H]WB 4101-binding in frontal cortex, thalamus and septum, increases in [³H]CLON-binding in frontal cortex, and decreases in [³H]CLON-binding in amygdala and septum following dorsal bundle lesions. Reisine *et al.* (1980) showed that treatment of rats for 3 days with amphetamine, iprindole, or amphetamine and iprindole increased [³H]CLON-binding in rat cerebral cortex but had no effect on [³H]WB 4101-binding in this tissue.

Adrenalectomy did not affect the density of [³H]DHE-binding sites in rat liver (Guellaen *et al.*, 1978). Some hormonal factors do affect α-adrenergic receptor density, however, as Roberts *et al.* (1977) showed that treatment of rabbit uterus with oestrogen increased the number of [³H]DHE-binding sites as compared with progesterone-treated uterus. Thyroidectomized rats treated with tri-iodothyronine also had a higher density of [³H]DHE-binding sites than those that had not received tri-iodothyronine (Sharma and Banerjee, 1978).

5.10.5 Desensitization of β-adrenergic receptors

The rapid loss in the sensitivity of cells to β-adrenergic receptor stimulation following acute exposure to agonist is called 'desensitization'. This phenomenon may involve two different components, an uncoupling of β-adrenergic receptors from adenylate cyclase such that agonist occupancy of the receptor no longer leads to activation of the enzyme, and an apparent decrease in the number of β-adrenergic receptors in the cell membrane accessible to hormonal stimulation.

(a) *Decreases in β-adrenergic receptor density*

Lefkowitz and co-workers have shown that *in vitro* exposure of intact frog erythrocytes to isoproterenol causes time-dependent decreases in isoproterenol-stimulated adenylate cyclase activity and β-adrenergic-receptor-binding sites (Mickey *et al.*, 1975, 1976). The time course and drug specificity of the two processes were similar, and both were blocked by the presence of propranolol. Both processes were reversible, and subsequent incubation of the cells without agonist caused a reappearance of both the receptor sites and the isoproterenol-stimulated adenylate cyclase activity. Cycloheximide had no effect on either process, suggesting that protein synthesis was not involved.

Exposure to isoproterenol also decreased the apparent density of β-adrenergic receptors in purified plasma membranes from frog erythrocytes (Mukherjee and Lefkowitz, 1977). This agonist-induced fall in receptor number in purified membranes differed in several respects from that observed in intact cells. The fall in receptor density was much faster in isolated membranes (complete in 10 min compared with several hours for whole cells), and the addition of guanine nucleotides to the isolated membranes rapidly returned receptor number to normal, while guanine nucleotides had little effect on the loss in receptor number observed in whole cells.

Further work has supported the hypothesis that the agonist-induced loss in β-adrenergic receptor density in whole cells and isolated membranes are separate phenomena. The slower loss of receptors in whole cells may relate to redistribution and internalization of the agonist–receptor complex (Chuang and Costa, 1979) similar to that observed with many peptide receptors (see Catt *et al.*, 1979). The rapid loss of binding sites in purified membranes may not be a true loss of receptors, but may be due to persistent binding of agonist to receptor. Williams and Lefkowitz (1977) have shown that preincubation of frog erythrocyte membranes with the radiolabeled agonist [³H]HBI results in substantial 'irreversible' binding which cannot be washed out. The extent of the 'irreversible' binding of [³H]HBI accounts for the loss in radiolabeled antagonist ([³H]DHA)-binding sites in these membranes (Williams and Lefkowitz, 1977). Thus the rapid loss of [³H]DHA-binding sites is not due to receptor loss, but simply to persistent binding of agonist. This 'irreversible' binding is not truly irreversible, only very high affinity (Lefkowitz and Williams, 1977), and if the membranes could be incubated long enough to reach equilibrium with very high concentrations of [³H]DHA, the antagonist could probably competitively displace the agonist. Reducing the affinity of the receptors for agonists by the addition of guanine nucleotides (Lefkowitz and Williams, 1977) causes the tightly bound agonist to dissociate from the receptor and restores the normal number of [³H]DHA-binding sites (Mukherjee and Lefkowitz, 1977). Since guanine nucleotides are present in most living cells in concentrations sufficient to decrease the affinity of β-adrenergic receptors for agonists (as evidenced by the fact that no such rapid 'desensitization' was observed in experiments with whole cells), the rapid apparent decrease in β-adrenergic receptor number caused by agonists in purified membranes may not represent a physiological desensitization process. This phenomenon has, however, provided insights into the molecular mechanism whereby β-adrenergic receptors stimulate adenylate cyclase activity (see below).

(b) *Uncoupling of β-adrenergic receptors and adenylate cyclase*
Although a decreased responsiveness to catecholamines following agonist exposure often involves both decreased receptor number and decreased responsiveness of adenylate cyclase (Shear *et al.*, 1976; Johnson *et al.*, 1978a), the decreased responsiveness of adenylate cyclase often exceeds the loss in receptor density. The time course of the loss in adenylate cyclase responsiveness and the loss in receptor density in human astrocytoma cells have been examined by Su *et al.* (1979). After exposure to low concentrations of isoproterenol, these cells showed a loss in isoproterenol-stimulated adenylate cyclase activity and a loss in β-adrenergic receptor density. The loss in receptor-stimulated adenylate cyclase activity was much more rapid than the loss in receptor density, suggesting that these two phenomena were not causally related (Su *et al.*, 1979). In some cases (Johnson *et al.*, 1978a; Anderson and Jaworski, 1979) substantial loss of catecholamine-stimulated cyclic AMP accumulation after exposure to agonists can be observed with little loss in receptor density. These studies indicate that an initial 'uncoupling' of the receptor from adenylate cyclase often precedes any loss in receptor density.

The initial 'uncoupling' of receptor from adenylate cyclase following exposure to agonists has been studied in some detail. In some systems

(DeVellis and Brooker, 1974; Nordeen and Young, 1978), but not others (Lauzon *et al.*, 1976; Su *et al.*, 1976), the uncoupling reaction can be blocked by inhibitors of protein synthesis, suggesting that a newly synthesized protein may be involved in this phenomena. Brooker and co-workers have examined the uncoupling of β-adrenergic receptors from adenylate cyclase, which is blocked by inhibitors of protein synthesis, in a C6 glioma cell line. These cells can also be made refractory to catecholamine stimulation by treatment with cholera toxin (Nickols and Brooker, 1979). Cholera toxin has no known direct effects on β-adrenergic receptors, but irreversibly activates adenylate cyclase through a covalent modification of the guanine nucleotide-binding protein within the membrane (Cassel and Pfeuffer, 1978). The time course of refractoriness caused by cholera toxin and isoproterenol in these cells was similar (Nickols and Brooker, 1979), and refractoriness to either agent seemed to be mediated by cyclic AMP (Terasaki *et al.*, 1978). The refractoriness caused by either cholera toxin or isoproterenol could be blocked by protein-synthesis inhibitors, and in neither case could alterations in β-adrenergic receptor density be observed. These authors have postulated that increases in intracellular cyclic AMP cause an increased synthesis of a short-lived 'refractoriness protein' within the cell, which might negatively affect adenylate cyclase to block further hormonal response.

Harden *et al.* (1979) have studied a cell line in which the uncoupling of the β-adrenergic receptor and adenylate cyclase following exposure to agonist is not blocked by inhibitors of protein synthesis. An initial loss in catecholamine responsiveness in these cells is followed by a much slower loss in β-adrenergic receptor density. These authors observed a decreased affinity of agonists in inhibiting antagonist binding to β-adrenergic receptors following initial agonist exposure (Harden *et al.*, 1979). In terms of the affinity of agonists for the β-adrenergic receptor, these 'uncoupled' cells became more like S49 cells which are genetically 'uncoupled' (Haga *et al.*, 1977a) or which have been uncoupled by the use of membrane-perturbing agents such as filipin or *N*-ethylmaleimide (Howlett *et al.*, 1978). These results support the hypothesis that the first step in catecholamine-induced desensitization is an uncoupling of the β-adrenergic receptor and adenylate cyclase, possibly through modification of other membrane constituents such as the guanine nucleotide-binding protein.

5.11 SIGNAL TRANSDUCTION BY ADRENERGIC RECEPTORS

A great deal of information is now available on the mechanism by which β-adrenergic receptors stimulate adenylate cyclase activity. As discussed above, β-adrenergic receptors and adenylate cyclase are separate macromolecules. On the basis of the work particularly of Cassel and Selinger (1976, 1977a, 1978) and Gilman and co-workers (Haga *et al.*, 1977a; Ross and Gilman, 1977; Ross *et al.*, 1978; Howlett *et al.*, 1979) it is now clear that a third membrane protein is involved in the stimulation of adenylate cyclase activity by β-adrenergic receptors. This protein is probably a guanine nucleotide-binding protein (Pfeuffer and Helmreich, 1975) which may hydrolyze GTP under certain circumstances (Cassel and Selinger, 1976) and is probably the site of action for the irreversible activation of adenylate cyclase by cholera toxin (Cassel and Pfeuffer, 1978). Again, owing to the intimate link with adenylate cyclase, most of the work has so far focused on β-adrenergic receptors, and much less is known about the membrane events occurring after α-adrenergic receptor stimulation.

5.11.1 Evidence for an agonist-induced change in β-adrenergic receptor conformation

Since occupation of β-adrenergic receptors by agonists, but not by antagonists, causes a subsequent physiological response, it is reasonable to conclude that agonists must have an effect on the conformational state of the receptor molecule that can serve as the stimulus for signal transduction through the cell membrane. As discussed above, the different equilibrium thermodynamic parameters associated with binding of agonist or antagonist to β-adrenergic receptors (Weiland *et al.*, 1979) is consistent with an agonist-induced change in receptor conformation. Direct biochemical evidence has also accumulated to support this hypothesis. Limbird and Lefkowitz (1978) have shown that the apparent Stokes radius of the digitonin-solubilized β-adrenergic receptor is larger when the receptor is occupied by the agonist [^{3}H]HBI than when it is occupied by the antagonist [^{3}H]DHA. This is not due to the association of the agonist-occupied receptor with adenylate cyclase, and is still seen under conditions in which β-adrenergic receptors and adenylate cyclase are uncoupled (Limbird *et al.*, 1979). As discussed below, this agonist-induced increase in receptor size probably reflects association of the agonist-occupied receptor with the guanine nucleotide-binding protein (Limbird *et al.*, 1980).

Bottari *et al.* (1979) showed that the alkylating agent *N*-ethylmaleimide (NEM) causes a substantial decrease in the number of β-adrenergic receptor sites on turkey erythrocyte membranes when incubated in the presence of agonists, but not antagonists. Neither agonists nor NEM alone affected the number of receptor sites. Vauquelin *et al.* (1980a) showed that the effect of agonists on NEM-mediated β-adrenergic receptor inactivation was stereospecific and that the rate constant of the inactivation process correlated with the efficacy of drugs as full or partial agonists. The permissive effect of agonists on inactivation of β-adrenergic receptors by NEM was blocked by the presence of guanine nucleotides (Vauquelin *et al.*, 1980b).

These data have been interpreted to suggest that agonists cause a conformational change in the β-adrenergic receptor to expose sites on the receptor molecule which are sensitive to NEM alkylation, thereby causing receptor inactivation. This inactivation probably involves an interaction with the guanine nucleotide-binding protein, and has been interpreted as evidence that guanine nucleotide-binding sites interact with and cause structural modification of the agonist-occupied β-adrenergic receptor (Vauquelin *et al.*, 1980b).

The biochemical evidence for agonist-induced conformational changes in the β-adrenergic receptor is all consistent with a conformational change caused by the interaction of agonist-occupied receptor with the guanine nucleotide-binding protein. In the presence of guanine nucleotides (when presumably there is very little accumulation of agonist–receptor–guanine nucleotide-binding protein complex) the agonist-induced increase in receptor size is considerably reduced (Limbird and Lefkowitz, 1978), and there is no effect of NEM on receptor number in the presence of agonists (Vauquelin *et al.*, 1980b). However, in the presence of guanine nucleotides there are still fundamental differences in the thermodynamic binding forces for agonists and antagonists (Weiland *et al.*, 1980), suggesting that any agonist-induced conformational changes in the receptor molecules are probably not due solely to interaction with the guanine nucleotide-binding protein.

5.11.2 Participation of a guanine nucleotide-binding protein in stimulation of adenylate cyclase by β-adrenergic receptors

GTP is an essential cofactor in the stimulation of adenylate cyclase by many hormone receptors, including β-adrenergic receptors (Rodbell *et al.*, 1971c; Maguire *et al.*, 1977). The guanine nucleotide-binding component of the adenylate cyclase system was partially purified by Pfeuffer and Helmreich (1975) and Pfeuffer (1977) using a photo-affinity analogue of GTP to identify a heat-stable protein with a molecular weight of 42 000 in detergent extracts of pigeon erythrocytes. It had previously been observed that one particular genetic variant of S49 lymphoma cells which contained normal quantities of β-adrenergic receptors had almost no detectable adenylate cyclase activity (Bourne *et al.*, 1975). Ross and Gilman (1977) showed that incubation of membranes from these cells with Lubrol-solubilized extracts from another cell line which did not contain β-adrenergic receptors functionally reconstituted a catecholamine-stimulated adenylate cyclase activity in the S49 cells. Extracts from another S49 variant which contained normal numbers of β-adrenergic receptors and adenylate cyclase but which had no functional link between them (Haga *et al.*, 1977a) did not reconstitute this activity. Ross and Gilman (1977) suggested that the solubilized coupling factor which reconstituted the catecholamine-stimulated adenylate cyclase might be related to the guanine nucleotide-binding protein studied by Pfeuffer and Helmreich (1975). Sternweis and Gilman (1979) later showed that the catecholamine-stimulated adenylate cyclase activity of the uncoupled S49 variant could also be reconstituted by a protein which was very similar to that which was used to reconstitute the variant apparently deficient in adenylate cyclase. The S49 variant which was apparently deficient in adenylate cyclase was shown to have a substantial adenylate cyclase activity in the presence of manganese (Ross *et al.*, 1978). These authors suggested that this cell line was not only deficient in the catalytic moiety of adenylate cyclase but was also deficient in the coupling protein. These studies showed that a third membrane protein was essential for the stimulation of adenylate cyclase by β-adrenergic receptors and that this protein was probably the site of action of guanine nucleotides in this system.

The discovery that hydrolysis-resistant analogues of GTP persistently activated adenylate cyclase (Pfeuffer and Helmreich, 1975; Schramm and Rodbell, 1975) and that catecholamines stimulated GTP hydrolysis in turkey erythrocyte membranes (Cassel and Selinger, 1976, 1977a) led to the hypothesis that GTP hydrolysis might be involved in the termination of adenylate cyclase activation. Cassel and Selinger (1978) showed that activation of adenylate cyclase by β-adrenergic receptors in turkey erythrocyte membranes was associated with a release of tightly bound GDP, and that this release was facilitated by the presence of other guanine nucleotides such as GTP. These authors proposed that inactive adenylate cyclase contains tightly bound GDP, probably on the guanine nucleotide-binding protein, which is produced by hydrolysis of GTP at the regulatory site. Occupation of β-adrenergic receptors by agonists results in a release of the tightly bound GDP and replacement by GTP, thus activating adenylate cyclase. This activation is terminated by hydrolysis of GTP to GDP, thus again resulting in an inactive adenylate cyclase (Cassel and Selinger, 1978).

The guanine nucleotide-binding protein also seems to be the primary site of action for the irreversible activation of adenylate cyclase by cholera toxin. Cassel and Selinger (1977b) proposed that cholera toxin irreversibly inhibits the GTP-hydrolyzing capability at the adenylate cyclase-regulatory site, thus eliminating the adenylate cyclase turn-off reaction (GTP hydrolysis) and irreversibly activating adenylate cyclase. Because NAD^+ is required for the action of cholera toxin (Gill, 1975), Cassel and Pfeuffer (1978), Gill and Meren (1978) and Johnson *et al.* (1978b) used ^{32}P-labeled NAD^+ to show that cholera toxin catalyzed an ADP-ribosylation of certain membrane proteins, including one with a molecular weight of 42 000 similar to the GTP-binding protein isolated by Pfeuffer (1977).

Reconstitution of this ADP-ribosylated protein from toxin-treated membranes conferred an enhanced GTP-stimulated adenylate cyclase activity in untreated membranes. These experiments suggested that cholera toxin caused a covalent modification of the guanine nucleotide-binding protein, thereby inhibiting its ability to hydrolyze GTP and terminate the activation of adenylate cyclase. In this way, cholera toxin could irreversibly activate adenylate cyclase in a GTP-dependent manner. The covalent incorporation of [^{32}P]ADP-ribose into this protein from [^{32}P]NAD$^+$ has provided a convenient method for radioactively labeling the guanine nucleotide-binding

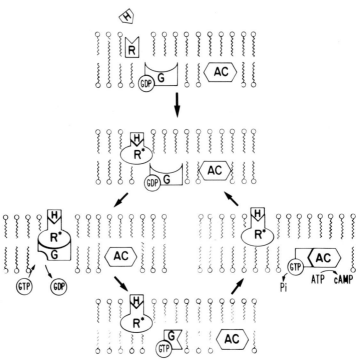

Fig. 5.7 Schematic representation of the mechanism by which β-adrenergic receptors might activate adenylate cyclase within the cell membrane. Hormone (H) binds to receptor (R) to cause a conformational change in the receptor molecule (R*), so that the HR* complex can bind to the guanine nucleotide-binding protein (G). The binding of HR* to G causes a release of tightly bound GDP from G and allows GTP to bind to G. The binding of GTP to G causes a dissociation of G from HR* and allows it to bind to adenylate cyclase (AC), thus activating the enzyme [increasing the conversion of ATP to cyclic AMP (cAMP)], and also hydrolysing GTP to release inorganic phosphate (P$_i$). The hydrolysis of GTP to GDP dissociates G from AC, allowing it to interact with HR* again. Schematic representation is based on the cyclic model of Cassel and Selinger (1978).

protein and thereby gaining a greater understanding of its functional role (see also Johnson *et al.*, 1980).

Limbird *et al.* (1980) used this method for radioactively labeling the guanine nucleotide-binding protein to show that the apparent agonist-induced increase in the size of the β-adrenergic receptor may be due to the tight binding of the agonist–receptor complex to the guanine nucleotide-binding protein. These authors showed that a protein of 42 000 molecular weight, labeled by treatment with [^{32}P]NAD$^+$ and cholera toxin, was co-eluted with the solubilized agonist-occupied β-adrenergic receptor. This co-elution was not observed when receptors were occupied by antagonists. The presence of guanine nucleotides prevented the co-elution of the labeled protein and the agonist-occupied receptor (Limbird *et al.*, 1980). These experiments provide evidence for a direct interaction of the agonist-occupied β-adrenergic receptor with the guanine nucleotide-binding protein within the membrane.

Thus, there is now strong evidence that β-adrenergic receptors activate adenylate cyclase through mediation by the guanine nucleotide-binding protein. A hypothetical mechanistic scheme based on these experiments is illustrated in Fig. 5.7 (see Cassel and Selinger, 1978). Agonists occupy β-adrenergic receptors to cause a conformational change in the receptor molecule such that the agonist–receptor complex can bind to the guanine nucleotide-binding protein within the membrane. This causes an exchange of GDP for GTP at the nucleotide-binding site, thus dissociating the GTP–guanine nucleotide-binding protein complex from the receptor. The GTP–guanine nucleotide-binding protein complex can then bind to the catalytic moiety of adenylate cyclase, thus increasing the activity of this enzyme. The guanine nucleotide-binding protein (which may be a GTPase) subsequently hydrolyzes GTP to GDP, causing a dissociation of the guanine nucleotide-binding protein from adenylate cyclase and a termination of the activation of this enzyme. Further interaction of the GDP–guanine nucleotide-binding protein complex with agonist-occupied receptors will cause a repeat of this cycle.

5.11.3 Interactions between different types of membrane receptors

One intriguing phenomenon that has recently become apparent from radioligand-binding assays has been the effect of stimulation of one type of receptor on the properties of a different type of receptor within the cell membrane. For example, stimulation of muscarinic cholinergic receptors in dog heart increases the affinity of β-adrenergic receptors for agonists but not antagonists (Watanabe *et al.*, 1978). Conversely, stimulation of β-adrenergic receptors decreases the affinity of agonists for the muscarinic cholinergic receptor in rat heart (Rosenberger *et al.*, 1980). Stimulation of α-adrenergic receptors (probably α_2) by clonidine decreased the affinity of agonists, but not antagonists, for β-adrenergic receptors in rat kidney (Woodcock and Johnston, 1980). The apparent rapid loss of β-adrenergic receptors in rat cerebral cortex caused by exposure to isoproterenol (Dibner and Molinoff, 1979) is accompanied by an increase in the apparent density of [³H]CLON-binding sites at α-adrenergic receptors (Maggi *et al.*, 1980), although, since [³H]CLON is an agonist, it is not clear whether this is truely a change in receptor number or simply a change in the characteristics of agonist binding to the receptor (see above).

These observations suggest that multiple hormone receptors within a membrane can interact in some manner. Since in the cases where this has been studied (Watanabe *et al.*, 1978; Woodcock and Johnston, 1980), this interaction is confined solely to changes in agonist, but not antagonist, affinity for the receptor, it is possible that these receptors are all competing for a common pool of guanine nucleotide-binding proteins within the membrane. The similar effects of GTP on β-adrenergic (Maguire *et al.*, 1976b), α_2-adrenergic (U'Prichard and Snyder, 1978) and muscarinic cholinergic (Rosenberger *et al.*, 1979) receptor agonist affinity supports such a possibility. The possible functional role of such interactions is still obscure.

5.11.4 Role of phospholipid methylation in signal transduction by β-adrenergic receptors

Axelrod and co-workers have presented evidence that β-adrenergic receptor stimulation increases the methylation of membrane phospholipids (Hirata *et al.*, 1979). With the use of phospholipase C, these authors presented evidence that β-adrenergic receptor stimulation increased the translocation of the methylated phospholipids from the cytoplasmic side to the outer surface of reticulocyte membranes. Phospholipid methylation also increased the fluidity of reticulocyte membranes, and Hirata *et al.* (1979) proposed that this increase in fluidity was reponsible for an observed increase in the stimulation of adenylate cyclase by β-adrenergic receptors. Hanski *et al.* (1979) also showed that increasing membrane fluidity by enrichment of membranes with *cis*-vaccenic acid also increased the stimulation of adenylate cyclase by β-adrenergic receptors. Hirata *et al.* (1979) have suggested that unoccupied β-adrenergic receptors might tonically inhibit phospholipid methylation. Occupation of these receptors by agonists might unmask phospholipid methylating activity of membrane enzymes thereby increasing membrane fluidity and thus increase the probability of interaction of the β-adrenergic receptor with its effector molecule within the membrane.

Strittmatter *et al.* (1979) presented evidence that the degree of phospholipid methylation in biological membranes can mask or unmask hidden receptors. They showed that increasing methylation of phosphatidylcholine, but not of phosphatidylethanolamine, increased the apparent number of β-adrenergic-receptor-binding sites in rat reticulocyte membranes. Mallorga *et al.* (1980) showed that phospholipid methylation may also be involved in the agonist-induced uncoupling ('desensitization') in C6 glioma cells. Treatment of these cells with phospholipase A_2 inhibitors, such as mepacrine or tetracaine, blocked the uncoupling of β-adrenergic receptors and adenylate cyclase caused by isoproterenol exposure. Activators of phospholipase A_2, such as phorbol esters or mellitin, themselves rapidly uncoupled these cells in the absence of isoproterenol. Mallorga *et al.* (1980) proposed that the uncoupling of β-adrenergic receptors and adenylate cyclase caused by exposure to β-adrenergic agonists might be mediated by products of phospholipase A_2 activity, such as lysophosphatidylcholine, arachidonic acid or its prostaglandin metabolites (see Hirata and Axelrod, 1980).

Although these experiments suggest that phospholipid methylation may be involved in the membrane actions of β-adrenergic receptors, it is possible that this interaction is complex. For example, Bakardjieva *et al.* (1979) found that increasing membrane fluidity of Chang liver cells by phospholipid enrichment interfered with, rather than facilitated, coupling between β-adrenergic receptors and adenylate cyclase, and also caused a large loss in β-adrenergic-receptor-binding sites. These authors hypothesized that the increase in membrane fluidity caused an increased redistribution and internalization of the receptor molecules.

5.11.5 Signal transduction by α-adrenergic receptors

There is much less information available concerning the mechanism by which agonist occupation of α-adrenergic receptors results in a subsequent cellular response. As discussed above, it has been suggested that α_2-receptors are negatively linked to adenylate cyclase, and α_1-receptors cause increases in phosphatidylinositol turnover and calcium transport (Fain and Garcia-Sainz, 1980). It is interesting that the effects of guanine nucleotides on the binding of agonists to α_2-receptors, but not to α_1-receptors, are very similar to their effects on the binding of agonists to β-adrenergic receptors (Tsai and Lefkowitz, 1978a; U'Prichard and Snyder, 1978a). Since the effects of guanine nucleotides on agonist binding to β-adrenergic receptors seem to be mediated through the guanine nucleotide-binding protein (Haga *et al.*, 1977a), this suggests that α_2-receptors may also interact with this protein to alter adenylate cyclase activity. Since α_2-receptors inhibit adenylate cyclase while β-adrenergic receptors activate this enzyme, there must, however, be some fundamental differences between these interactions.

5.12 CONCLUSION

The use of radioligand-binding assays has revolutionized the study of receptors. Prior to the introduction of this technique, receptors were considered as hypothetical molecules mediating an observed cellular response, and were studied by pharmacologists and physiologists with indirect methods. The ability to measure receptors directly with the use of radioligand-binding assays has resulted in evidence for the existence of discrete receptor molecules, and has allowed an examination of the molecular events involved in receptor-mediated information transfer through the cell membrane. This in turn has brought receptors to the attention of scientists in different disciplines, such as biochemistry and cell biology, who have become interested in studing the molecular nature of receptors and their importance in the regulation of cell function.

The study of β-adrenergic receptors has progressed rapidly, owing both to their intimate link with adenylate cyclase and the high-affinity radiolabeled antagonists which were developed to study them. The kinetic and equilibrium properties of agonist and antagonist interactions with these receptors are now fairly well understood. Information on the biochemical nature of β-adrenergic receptors is also becoming available, and future efforts will undoubtedly be aimed at purifying and sequencing these molecules to ultimately reconstitute a receptor-mediated response using completely defined components of the system. Information has also become available on the heterogeneity of receptor subtypes and the regulation of receptor density and cellular sensitivity by hormonal input. More precise localization of β-adrenergic receptors to specific cell populations should pinpoint target cells where hormones may exert as yet unknown actions.

A major upswing in the study of α-adrenergic receptors will probably be observed in the next few years. In the past, the study of α-adrenergic receptors has lagged behind the study of β-adrenergic receptors, owing partly to the lack of an easily measured biochemical response to α-adrenergic receptor stimulation and partly to the fact that some of the radioligands originally developed to study these receptors were agonists. These problems are rapidly being overcome as investigators examine the possibility of measuring membrane phosphatidylinositol turnover as a biochemical index of α_1-receptor occupation (Fain and Garcia-Sainz, 1980), and experiment with radiolabeled antagonists such as yohimbine to label α_2-receptors selectively (Wolfe, 1980). Thus, the next few years will probably witness a large increase in information concerning α-adrenergic receptors, similar to that which has occurred over the past few years with β-adrenergic receptors.

As the techniques for studying receptors as discrete molecular entities have become increasingly sophisticated, more and more attention has been focused on the biochemical properties of these molecules. One should always keep in mind, however, that the physiological importance of these molecules lies in their role as mediators of intercellular information transfer. The function of a receptor molecule is to receive a chemical message which has been sent by another cell, and cause the target cell to respond in an appropriate manner. Studies of receptors in homogenized tissue preparations and homogeneous cultured cell populations remove much of the biological complexity involved in the fundamental role of these molecules, and as such have major disadvantages. The specificity of the receptor molecule lies not only in the hormones to which it is capable of responding, but also which hormones have access to it *in vivo*. Similarly, the response to receptor stimulation depends not only on the effector molecules within the cell membrane, but also on the biological mechanisms within the cell capable of responding to receptor signal transduction. The sensitivity of the cell to hormonal stimulation is regulated not only by alterations in receptor density or receptor–effector coupling within the membrane, but also on the internal metabolic state of the cell, the input to other receptors on the same cell, and the general metabolic state of the organism as reflected in the oxygenation and ionic and nutrient composition of the extracellular fluid. Ideally, one would ultimately hope to be able to utilize the biochemical information obtained in studies of purified membranes and cell cultures in studies of more relevant physiological situations, in order to obtain a better understanding of the *in vivo* role of these important molecules.

REFERENCES

Aarons, R.D., Nies, A.S., Gal, J., Hegstrand, L.R. and Molinoff, P.B. (1980), *J. Clin. Invest.,* 65, 949–957.

Ahlquist, R.P. (1948), *Am. J. Physiol.,* **153.**, 586–600.

Aktories, K., Schultz, G. and Jakobs, K.H. (1979), *FEBS Lett.,* **107**, 100–104.

Alexander, R.W., Williams, L.T. and Lefkowitz, R.J. (1975a), *Proc. Natl. Acad. Sci. USA.,* **72.**, 1564–1568.

Alexander, R.W., Davis, J.N. and Lefkowitz, R.J. (1975b), *Nature (London),* **258**, 437–440.

Altman, J. and Anderson, W.J. (1973), *J. Comp. Neurol.,* **149**, 123–152.

Anderson, W.B. and Jaworski, C.J. (1979), *J. Biol. Chem.,* **254**, 4596–4601.

Ariens, E.J. and Simonis, A.M. (1976), in *Beta-Adrenoceptor Blocking Agents* (eds. P.R. Saxena and R.P. Forsyth), North-Holland Publishing Co., Amsterdam, pp 3–27.

Armstrong, D.H. and Schild, R.F. (1970), *J. Comp. Neurol.,* **139**, 449–456.

Arnold, A. and McAuliff, J.P. (1969), *Arch. Int. Pharmacodyn.,* **179**, 381–387.

Arnold, A., McAuliff, J.P., Colella, D.F., O'Connor, W.V. and Brown, Th.G. (1968), *Arch. Int. Pharmacodyn.*, **176**, 451–457.

Atlas, D. and Levitzki, A. (1977), *Proc. Natl. Acad. Sci. USA.*, **74**, 5290–5294.

Atlas, D. and Melamed, E. (1978), *Brain Res.*, **150**, 377–385.

Aurbach, G.D., Fedak, S.A., Woodard, C.J., Palmer, J.S., Hauser, D. and Troxler, F. (1976), *Science*, **186**, 1223–1224.

Axelrod, J., Shein, H.M. and Wurtman, R.J. (1969), *Proc. Natl. Acad. Sci. USA.*, **62**, 544–549.

Bakardjieva, A., Calla, H.J. and Helmreich, E.J. (1979), *Biochemistry*, **18**, 3016–3023.

Baker, S.P. and Potter, L.T. (1980a), *Br. J. Pharmacol.*, **68**, 65–70.

Baker, S.P. and Potter, L.T. (1980b), *Br. J. Pharmacol.*, **68**, 8–10.

Baker, S.P., Boyd, H.M. and Potter, L.T. (1980), *Br. J. Pharmacol.*, **68**, 57–63.

Banerjee, S.P., Kung, L.S., Riggi, S.J. and Chanda, S.K. (1977), *Nature (London)*, **268**, 455–456.

Banerjee, S.P., Sharma, V.K., Kung, L.S. and Chanda, S.K. (1978), *Nature (London)*, **271**, 380–381.

Baraban, J.M. and Aghajanian, G.K. (1980), *Neuropharmacology*, **19**, 355–363.

Barnes, P., Karliner, J., Hamilton, C. and Dollery, C. (1979), *Life Sci.*, **25**, 1207–1214.

Barnes, P., Koppel, H., Lewis, P., Hutson, C., Blair, I. and Dollery, C. (1980), *Brain Res.*, **181**, 209–213.

Barnett, D.B., Rugg, E.L. and Nahorski, S.R. (1978), *Nature (London)*, **273**, 166–168.

Berridge, M.J. and Fain, J.M. (1979), *Biochem. J.*, **178**, 59–69.

Berthelsen, S. and Pettinger, W.A. (1977), *Life Sci.*, **21**, 595–606.

Bevan, P., Bradshaw, C.M. and Szabadi, E. (1977), *Br. J. Pharmacol.*, **59**, 635–641.

Bickerton, R.K. (1963), *J. Pharmacol. Exp. Ther.*, **142**, 99–110.

Bilezikian, J.P. and Aurbach, G.D. (1973), *J. Biol. Chem.*, **248**, 5575–5583.

Bilezikian, J.P., Spiegel, A.M., Gammon, D.E. and Aurbach, G.D. (1977a), *Mol. Pharmacol.*, **13**, 786–795.

Bilezikian, J.P., Spiegel, A.M., Brown, E.M. and Aurbach, G.D. (1977b), *Mol. Pharmacol.*, **13**, 775–785.

Bilezikian, J.P., Loeb, J.N. and Gammon, D.E. (1979), *J. Clin. Invest.*, **63**, 184–192.

Bird, S.J. and Maguire, M.E. (1978), *J. Biol. Chem.*, **253**, 8826–8834.

Black, J.W., Crowther, A.F., Shanks, R.G., Smith, L.H. and Dornhorst, A.C. (1964), *Lancet*, **1**, 1080–1081.

Bloom, F.E., Hoffer, B.J. and Siggins, G.R. (1972), *Biol. Psychiat.*, **4**, 157–177.

Blume, A.J. (1978), *Proc. Natl. Acad. Sci. USA.*, **75**, 1713–1717.

Boeynaems, J.M. and Dumont, J.E. (1977), *Mol. Cell. Endocrinol.*, **7**, 33–47.

Bottari, S., Vauquelin, G., Durieu, O., Kluthchko, C. and Strosberg, A.D. (1979), *Biochem. Biophys. Res. Commun.*, **86**, 1311–1318.

Bourne, H.R., Coffino, P. and Tomkins, G.M. (1975), *Science*, **187**, 750–752.

Bowman, W.C. and Nott, M.W. (1969), *Pharmacol. Rev.*, **21**, 27–72.

Brittain, R.T., Farmer, J.B., Jack, D., Marin, L.E. and Simpson, W.T. (1968), *Nature (London)*, **219**, 862–863.

Brown, E.M., Aurbach, G.D., Hauser, D. and Troxler, F. (1976a), *J. Biol. Chem.*, **251**, 1232–1238.

Brown, E.M., Fedak, S.M., Woodard, C.J., Aurbach, G.D. and Rodbard, D. (1976b), *J. Biol. Chem.*, **251**, 1239–1246.

Brown, M., Hurwitz, S.H. and Aurbach, G.D. (1978), *Endocrinology*, **103**, 893–899.

Burges, R.A. and Blackburn, K.J. (1972), *Nature (London) New Biol.*, **235**, 249–250.

Burns, J.J., Colville, K.I., Lindsay, L.A. and Salvador, R.A. (1964), *J. Pharmacol. Exp. Ther.*, **144**, 163–171.

Burns, T.W., Langley, P.E. and Robison, G.A. (1971), *Ann. N.Y. Acad. Sci.*, **185**, 115–128.

Bylund, D.B. and Snyder, S.H. (1976), *Mol. Pharmacol.* **12**, 568–580.

Cambridge, D., Davey, M.J. and Massingham, R. (1977), *Br. J. Pharmacol.*, **59**, 514P.

Cannon, W.B. and Rosenblueth, A. (1937), *Autonomic Neuroeffector Systems*, Macmillan, New York.

Carlsson, E. and Hedberg, A. (1977), *Acta Physiol. Scand. Suppl.*, **44**, 47.

Carlsson, E., Ablad, B., Brandstrom, A. and Carlsson, B. (1972), *Life Sci.*, **11**, 953–958.

Carlsson, E., Dahlof, C-G., Hedberg, A., Persson, H. and Tangstrand, B. (1977), *Naunyn-Schmiedeberg's Arch. Pharmacol.*, **300**, 101–105.

Caron, M.G. and Lefkowitz, R.J. (1976), *J. Biol. Chem.*, **251**, 2374–2384.

Caron, M.G., Srinivasan, Y., Pitha, J., Kociolek, K. and Lefkowitz, R.J. (1979), *J. Biol. Chem.*, **254**, 2923–2927.

Cassel, D. and Pfeuffer, T. (1978), *Proc. Natl. Acad. Sci. USA*, **75**, 2669–2673.

Cassel, D. and Selinger, Z. (1976), *Biochim, Biophys. Acta*, **452**, 538–551.

Cassel, D. and Selinger, Z. (1977a), *J. Cyclic Nucleotide Res.*, **3**, 11–22.

Cassel, D. and Selinger, Z. (1977b), *Proc. Natl. Acad. Sci. U.S.A.*, **74**, 3307–3311.

Cassel, D. and Selinger, Z. (1978), *Proc. Natl. Acad. Sci. U.S.A.*, **75**, 4155–4159.

Catt, K.J., Harwood, J.P., Aguilera, G. and Dufau, M.L. (1979), *Nature (London)*, **280**, 109–116.

Cedarbaum, J.M. and Aghajanian, G.K. (1977), *Eur. J. Pharmacol.*, **44**, 375–385.

Chan, T.M. and Exton, J.H. (1977), *J. Biol. Chem.*, **252**, 8645–8651.

Chang, R.S.L., Tran, V.T. and Snyder, S.H. (1980), *Brain Res.*, **190**, 95–110.

Charness, M.E., Bylund, D.R., Beckman, B.S., Hollenberg, M.D. and Snyder, S.H. (1976), *Life Sci.*, **19**, 243–250.

Chasin, M., Mamrak, F. and Sulser, F. (1974), *J. Neurochem.*, **22**, 1031–1038.

Chen, F.M., Yamamura, H.I. and Roeske, W.R. (1979), *Eur. J. Pharmacol.*, **58**, 255–264.

Chuang, D-M., and Costa, E. (1979), *Proc. Natl. Acad. Sci. U.S.A.*, **76**, 3024–3028.

Ciaraldi, T. and Marinetti, G.V. (1977), *Biochem. Biophys. Res. Commun.*, **74**, 984–990.

Coleman, A.J., Paterson, D.S. and Somerville, A.R. (1979), *Biochem. Pharmacol.*, **28**, 1003–1010.

Coyle, J.T. and Schwarcz, R. (1976), *Nature (London)*, **263**, 244–246.

Creese, I., Usdin, T.B. and Snyder, S.H. (1979), *Mol. Pharmacol.*, **16**, 69–76.

Cuatrecasas, P. (1971), *Proc. Natl. Acad. Sci. U.S.A.*, **68**, 1264–1266.

Cuatrecasas, P. (1974), *Annu. Rev. Biochem.*, **43**, 169–214.

Cuatrecasas, P., Tell, G.P., Sica, V., Parikh, I. and Chang, K-J. (1974), *Nature (London)*, **247**, 92–97.

Cubeddu, L.X., Barnes, E., Langer, S.Z. and Weiner, N. (1974), *J. Pharmacol. Exp. Ther.*, **190**, 431–450.

Dahlof, C., Ljung, B. and Ablad, B. (1978), *Eur. J. Pharmacol.*, **50**, 75–78.

Dale, H.H. (1907), *J. Physiol. (London)*, **34**, 163–206.

Davis, J.N. and Lefkowitz, R.J. (1976), *Brain Res.*, **113**, 214–218.

Davis, J.N., Strittmatter, W., Hoyler, E. and Lefkowitz, R.J. (1977), *Brain Res.*, **132**, 327–336.

Davis, J.N., Arnett, C.D., Hoyler, E., Stalvey, L.P., Daly, J.W. and Skolnick, P. (1978), *Brain Res.*, **159**, 125–135.

Deguchi, T. and Axelrod, J. (1972), *Proc. Natl. Acad. Sci. U.S.A.*, **69**, 2208–2211.

Deguchi, T. and Axelrod, J. (1973), *Proc. Natl. Acad. Sci. U.S.A.*, **70**, 2411–2414.

DeHaen, C. (1976), *J. Theoret. Biol.*, **58**, 383–400.

DeLean, A., Stadel, J.M. and Lefkowitz, R.J. (1980), *J. Biol. Chem.* **255**, 7108–7117.

DeVellis, J. and Brooker, G. (1974), *Science*, **186**, 1221–1223.

Dibner, M.D. and Molinoff, P.B. (1979), *J. Pharmacol. Exp. Ther.*, **210**, 433–439.

Dillier, N., Laszlo, J., Muller, B., Koella, W.P. and Olpe, H.-R. (1978), *Brain Res.*, **154**, 61–74.

Dolphin, A., Adrien, J., Hamon, M. and Bockaert, J. (1979), *Mol. Pharmacol.*, **15**, 1–15.

Dungan, K.W., Cho, Y.W., Gomoll, .A.W., Aviado, D.M. and Lish, P.M. (1968), *J. Pharmacol. Exp. Ther.*, **164**, 290–301.

Dunlop, D. and Shanks, R.G. (1968), *Br. J. Pharmacol.*, **32**, 201–218.

Dunnick, J.K., Marinetti, G.V. (1971), *Biochim, Biophys. Acta*, **249**, 122–134.

Edvinsson, L. and Owman, C. (1974), *Circ. Res.*, **35**, 835–849.

Exton, J.H. (1979), *J. Cyclic Nucleotide Res.*, **5**, 277–287.

Fain, J.N. and Garcia-Sainz, J.A. (1980), *Life Sci.*, **26**, 1183–1194.

Furchgott, R.F. (1972), *Handb. Exp. Pharmacol.*, **33**, 283–335.

Gibson, R.E., Rzeszotarski, W.J., Komai, T., Reba, R.C. and Eckelman, W.C. (1979), *J. Pharmacol. Exp. Ther.*, **209**, 153–161.

Gill, D.M. (1975), *Proc. Natl. Acad. Sci. U.S.A.*, **72**, 2064–2068.

Gill, D.M. and Meren, R. (1978), *Proc. Natl. Acad. Sci. U.S.A.*, **75**, 3050–3054.

Glaubiger, G. and Lefkowitz, R.J. (1977), *Biochem. Biophys. Res. Commun.*, **78**, 720–725.

Glaubiger, G., Tsai, B.S., Lefkowitz, R.J. , Weiss, B. and Johnson, E.M., Jr. (1978), *Nature (London)* **273**, 240–242.

Govier, W.C. (1968), *J. Pharmacol. Exp. Ther.*, **159**, 82–90.

Greenberg, D.A. and Snyder, S.H. (1978), *Mol. Pharmacol.*, **14**, 38–49.

Greenberg, D.A., U'Prichard, D.C. and Snyder, S.H. (1976), *Life Sci.*, **19**, 69–76.

Greenberg, L.H. and Weiss, B. (1978), *Science*, **201**, 61–63.

Greenglass, P. and Bremner, R. (1979), *Eur. J. Pharmacol.*, **55**, 323–326.

Gross, G., Brodde, O.-E. and Schumann, H.-J. (1980), *Eur. J. Pharmacol.*, **61**, 191–194.

Guellaen, G., Yates-Aggerbeck, M., Vauquelin, G., Strosberg, D. and Hanoune, J. (1978), *J. Biol. Chem.*, **253**, 1114–1120.

Haga, R., Ross, E.M., Anderson, H.J. and Gilman, A.G. (1977a), *Proc. Natl. Acad. Sci. U.S.A.*, **74**, 2016–2020.

Haga, R., Haga, K. and Gilman, A.G. (1977b), *J. Biol. Chem.*, **252**, 5778–5782.

Hancock, A.A., DeLean, A.L. and Lefkowitz, R.J. (1979), *Mol. Pharmacol.*, **16**, 1–9.

Hanski, E., Rimon, G. and Levitzki, A. (1979), *Biochemistry*, **18**, 846–853.

Harden, T.K., Wolfe, B.B. and Molinoff, P.B. (1976), *Mol. Pharmacol.*, **12**, 1–15.

Harden, T.K., Wolfe, B.B., Sporn, J.R., Perkins, J.P. and Molinoff, P.B. (1977a), *Brain Res.*, **125**, 99–108.

Harden, T.K., Wolfe, B.B., Sporn, J.R., Poulos, B.K. and Molinoff, P.B. (1977b), *J. Pharmacol. Exp. Ther.*, **203**, 132–143.

Harden, T.K., Su, Y-F. and Perkins, J.P. (1979), *J. Cyclic Nucleotide Res.*, **5**, 99–106.

Harik, S.I., Sharma, V.K., Wetherbee, J.R., Warren, R.H. and Banerjee, S.P. (1980), *Eur. J. Pharmacol.*, **61**, 207–208.

Hedberg, A. (1980), Private communication.

Hedberg, A., Minneman, K.P. and Molinoff, P.B. (1980), *J. Pharmacol. Exp. Ther.*, **213**, 503–508.

Hegstrand, L.R., Minneman, K.P. and Molinoff, P.B. (1979), *J. Pharmacol. Exp. Ther.*, **210**., 215–221.

Heidenreich, K.H., Weiland, G.A. and Molinoff, P.B. (1980), *J. Cyclic Nucleotide Res.*, **6**, 217–230.

Heidmann, T. and Changeux, J.-P. (1978), *Annu. Rev. Biochem.*, **47**, 317–357.

Hendley, E. (1978), *Soc. Neurosci. Abstr.*, **4**, 494.

Herbst, T.J., Raichle, M.E. and Ferrendelli, J.A. (1979), *Science.*, **204**, 330–332.

Hess, A. (1979), *Brain Res.*, **160**, 533–538.

Hirata, F. and Axelrod, J. (1980), *Science.*, **209**, 1082–1090.

Hirata, F., Strittmatter, W.J. and Axelrod, J. (1979), *Proc. Natl. Acad. Sci. U.S.A.*, **76**, 368–372.

Hoffer, B.J., Siggins, G.R. and Bloom, F.E. (1971), *Brain Res.*, **25**, 523–534.

Hoffman, B. and Lefkowitz, R.J. (1980), *Biochem. Pharmacol.*, **29**, 1537–1541.

Hokfelt, T., Fuxe, K., Goldstein, M. and Johansson, O. (1974), *Brain Res.*, **66**, 235–251.

Hokin, L.E. and Sherwin, A.L. (1957), *J. Physiol. (London)*, **135**, 18–29.

Howlett, A.C., Van Arsdale, P.M. and Gilman, A.G. (1978), *Mol. Pharmacol.*, **14**, 531–539.

Howlett, A.C., Sternweis, P.C., Macik, B.A., Van Arsdale, P.M. and Gilman, A.G. (1979), *J. Biol. Chem.*, **254**, 2287–2295.

Ignarro, L.J. and Titus, E. (1968), *J. Pharmacol. Exp. Ther.*, **160**, 72–80.

Innes, I.R. (1962), *Br. J. Pharmacol. Chemother.*, **19**, 120–128.

Insel, P.A., Maguire, M.E., Gilman, A.G. , Bourne, H.R., Coffino, P. and Melmon, K.L. (1976), *Mol. Pharmacol.*, **12**, 1062–1069.

Iversen, L.L. (1967), *The Uptake and Storage of Noradrenaline in Sympathetic Nerves*, Cambridge University Press, Cambridge.

Jacobs, S. and Cuatrecasas, P. (1976), *Biochem. Biophys. Acta*, **433**, 482–495.

Johnson, G.L., Wolfe, B.B., Harden, T.K., Molinoff, P.B. and Perkins, J.P. (1978a), *J. Biol. Chem.*, **253**, 1472–1480.

Johnson, G.L., Kaslow, H.R. and Bourne, H.R. (1978b), *J. Biol. Chem.*, **253**, 7120–7123.

Johnson, G.L., Kaslow, H.R., Farfel, Z. and Bourne, H.R. (1980), *Adv. Cyclic Nucleotide Res.*, **13**, 1–37.

Jones, L.M. and Michell, R.H. (1974), *Biochem. J.*, **142**, 583–590.

Kalisker, A., Rutledge, C.O. and Perkins, J.P. (1973), *Mol. Pharmacol.*, **9**, 619–629.

Kauzmann, W. (1959), *Adv. Protein Chem.*, **14**, 1–63.

Kebabian, J.W., Zatz, M., Romero, J.A. and Axelrod, J. (1975), *Proc. Natl. Acad. Sci. U.S.A.*, **72**, 3735–3739.

Kent, R.S., DeLean, A. and Lefkowitz, R.J. (1980), *Mol. Pharmacol.*, **17**, 14–23.

Kirk, C.J., Verrinder, T.R. and Hems, D.A. (1977), *FEBS Lett.*, **83**, 267–271.

Klainer, L.M., Chi, Y-M., Freidberg, S.L., Rall, T.W. and Sutherland, E.W. (1962), *J. Biol. Chem.*, **237**, 1239–1243.

Klein, D.C., Berg, G.R. and Weller, J.L. (1970), *Science*, **168**, 979–980.

Kleinstein, J. and Glossman, H. (1978), *Naunyn Schmiedebergs Arch. Pharmacol.*, **305**, 191–200.

Klotz, I.M. and Urguhart, J.M. (1949), *J. Am. Chem. Soc.*, **71**, 847–851.

Kneer, N.M., Wagner, M.J. and Lardy, H.A. (1979), *J. Biol. Chem.*, **254**, 12160–12168.

Krawietz, W., Weinsteiger, M., Pruchniewski, M. and Erdmann, E. (1979), *Biochem. Pharmacol.*, 2999–3007.

Kuffler, S.W. (1943), *J. Neurophys.*, **6**, 99–110.

Lad, P.M., Nielsen, T.B., Preston, M.S. and Rodbell, M. (1980), *J. Biol. Chem.*, **255**, 988–995.

Lands, A.M., Arnold, A., McAuliff, J.P., Luduena, F.P. and Brown T.T. (1967a), *Nature (London)*, **214**, 597–598.

Lands, A.M., Luduena, F.P. and Buzzo, H.J. (1967b), *Life Sci.*, **6**, 2241–2249.

Langer, S.Z. (1974), *Biochem. Pharmacol.*, **23**, 1793–1800.

Langer, S.Z. (1977), *Br. J. Pharmacol.*, **60**, 481–497.

Lauzon, G.J., Kulshrestha, S., Starr, L. and Bar, H. (1976), *J. Cyclic Nucleotide Res.*, **2**, 99–114.

Lefkowitz, R.J. (1974), *Biochem. Biophys. Res. Commun.*, **58**, 1110–1118.

Lefkowitz, R.J. (1975), *Biochem. Pharmacol.*, **24**, 583–590.

Lefkowitz, R.J. and Haber, E. (1971), *Proc. Natl. Acad. Sci. U.S.A.*, **68**, 1773–1777.

Lefkowitz, R.J. and Hamp, M. (1977), *Nature (London)*, **268**, 453–454.

Lefkowitz, R.J. and Williams, L.T. (1977), *Proc. Natl. Acad. Sci. U.S.A.*, **74**, 515–519.

Lefkowitz, R.J., Haber, E. and O'Hara, D. (1972), *Proc. Natl. Acad. Sci. U.S.A.*, **69**, 2828–2832.

Lefkowitz, R.J., Mukherjee, C., Coverstone, M. and Caron, M.G. (1974), *Biochem. Biophys. Res. Commun.*, **60.**, 703–709.

Lefkowitz, R.J., Mullikin, D. and Caron, M.G. (1976), *J. Biol. Chem.*, **251**, 4684–4692.

Levitzki, A., Atlas, D. and Steer, M.L. (1974), *Proc. Natl. Acad. Sci. U.S.A.*, **71**, 2773–2776.

Levitzki, A., Sevilia, N., Atlas, D. and Steer, M.L. (1975), *J. Mol. Biol.*, **97**, 35–53.

Levy, B. (1966), *J. Pharmacol. Exp. Ther.*, **151**, 413–422.

Limbird, L.E. and Lefkowitz, R.J. (1976), *J. Biol. Chem.*, **251**, 5007–5014.

Limbird, L.E. and Lefkowitz, R.J. (1977), *J. Biol. Chem.*, **252**, 799–802.

Limbird, L.E. and Lefkowitz, R.J. (1978), *Proc. Natl. Acad. Sci. U.S.A.* **75**, 228–232.

Limbird, L.E., De Meyts, P. and Lefkowitz, R.J. (1975), *Biochem. Biophys. Res. Commun.*, **64**, 1160–1168.

Limbird, L.E., Hickey, A.R. and Lefkowitz, R.J. (1979), *J. Biol. Chem.*, **254**, 2677–2683.

Limbird, L.E., Gill, D.M. and Lefkowitz, R.J. (1980), *Proc. Natl. Acad. Sci. U.S.A.*, **77**, 775–779.

Lin, M.C., Nicosia, S., Lad, P.M. and Rodbell, M. (1977), *J. Biol. Chem.*, **252**, 2790–2792.

Maggi, A., Schmidt, M.J., Ghetti, B. and Enna, S.J. (1979), *Life Sci.*, **24**, 367–374.

Maggi, A., U'Prichard, D.C. and Enna, S.J. (1980), *Science*, **207**, 645–647.

Maguire, M.E., Goldman, P.H. and Gilman, A.G. (1974), *Mol. Pharmacol.*, **10**, 563–581.

Maguire, M.E., Wiklund, R.A., Anderson, H.J. and Gilman, A.G. (1976a), *J. Biol. Chem.*, **251**, 1221–1231.

Maguire, M.E., Van Arsdale, P.M. and Gilman, A.G. (1976b), *Mol. Pharmacol.*, **12**, 335–339.

Maguire, M.E., Ross, E.M. and Gilman, A.G. (1977), *Adv. Cyclic Nucleotide Res.*, **8**, 1–83.

Malbon, C.C. and Cabelli, R.J. (1978), *Biochim. Biophys. Acta*, **544**, 93–101.

Malbon, C.C., Moreno, F.J., Cabelli, R.J. and Fain, J.N. (1978), *J. Biol. Chem.*, **253**, 671–678.

Mallorga, P., Tallman, J.F., Henneberry, R.C., Hirata, F., Strittmatter, W.J. and Axelrod, J. (1980), *Proc. Natl. Acad. Sci. U.S.A.*, **77**, 3341–3345.

Mayer, S.E. (1978), *Beta Adrenergic Blockade: A New Era in Cardiovascular Medicine* (ed. E. Braunwald), Excerpta Medica, Amsterdam, pp 25–37.

Mayer, S.E. (1980), in *The Pharmacological Basis of Therapeutics* (eds. A.G. Gilman, L.S. Goodman and A. Gilman), MacMillan, New York, pp 56–90.

Mayer, S.E. and Moran, N.C. (1960), *J. Pharmacol. Exp. Ther.*, **129**, 271–281.

McGeer, E.G. and McGeer, P.L. (1976), *Nature (London)*, **263**, 517–519.

Miach, P.J., Dausse, J.-P. and Meyer, P. (1978), *Nature (London)*, **274**, 492–494.

Miach, P.J., Dausse, J-P, Cardot, A. and Meyer, P. (1980), *Naunyn Schmiedeberg's Arch. Pharmacol.*, **313**, 23–26.

Michell, R.H. (1975), *Biochim. Biophys. Acta*, **415**, 81–147.

Mickey, J., Tate, R. and Lefkowitz, R.J. (1975), *J. Biol. Chem.*, **250**, 5727–5729.

Mickey, J., Tate, R., Mullikin, D. and Lefkowitz, R.J. (1976), *Mol. Pharmacol.*, **12**, 409–419.

Minneman, K.P. (1977), *Mol. Pharmacol.*, **13**, 735–744.

Minneman, K.P. and Iversen, L.L. (1976), *Science*, **192**, 803–805.

Minneman, K.P. and Molinoff, P.B. (1980), *Biochem. Pharmacol.*, **29**, 1317–1323.

Minneman, K.P., Quik, M. and Emson, P.C. (1978), *Brain Res.*, **151**, 507–521.

Minneman, K.P., Hegstrand, L.R. and Molinoff, P.B. (1979a), *Mol. Pharmacol.*, **16**, 21–33.

Minneman, K.P., Hegstrand, L.R. and Molinoff, P.B. (1979b), *Mol. Pharmacol.*, **16**, 34–46.

Minneman, K.P., Hedberg, A. and Molinoff, P.B. (1979c), *J. Pharmacol. Exp. Ther.*, **211**, 502–508.

Minneman, K.P., Dibner, M.D., Wolfe, B.B. and Molinoff, P.B. (1979d), *Science*, **204**, 866–868.

Minneman, K.P., Weiland, G.A. and Molinoff, P.B. (1980a), *Mol. Pharmacol.*, **17**, 1–7.

Minneman, K.P., Pittman, R.N., Yeh, H., Woodward, D.J. and Molinoff, P.B. (1980b), *Brain Res.*, in press.

Minneman, K.P., Pittman, R.N. and Molinoff, P.B. (1981), *Annu. Rev. Neurosci.*, **4**, 419–461.

Mobley, P.L. and Sulser, F. (1980), *Nature (London)*, **286**, 608–609.

Moises, H.C., Woodward, D.J., Hoffer, B.J. and Freedman, R. (1979), *Exp. Neurol.*, **64**, 493–515.

Molinoff, P.B. and Axelrod, J. (1971), *Annu. Rev. Biochem.*, **40**, 465–500.

Moran, N.C. (1975), *Handb. Physiol.–Endocrinol. Sect. 7*, **6**, 447–472.

Moran, N.C. and Perkins, M.E. (1958), *J. Pharmacol. Exp. Ther.*, **124**, 223–237.

Mukherjee, C. and Lefkowitz, R.J. (1977), *Mol. Pharmacol.*, **13**, 291–303.

Mukherjee, C., Caron, M.G., Coverstone, M. and Lefkowitz, R.J. (1975), *J. Biol. Chem.*, **250**, 4869–4876.

Murad, F. (1973), *Biochim. Biophys. Acta*, **304**, 181–187.

Nahorski, S.R. (1976), *Nature (London)*, **259**, 488–489.

Nahorski, S.R. (1977), *Mol. Pharmacol.*, **13**, 679–689.

Nahorski, S.R. (1978), *Eur. J. Pharmacol.*, **51**, 199–209.

Nahorski, S.R., Barnett, D.B., Howlett, D.R. and Rugg, E.L. (1979a), *Naunyn Schmiedeberg's Arch. Pharmacol.*, **207**, 227–233.

Nahorski, S.R., Howlett, D.R. and Redgrave, P. (1979b), *Eur. J. Pharmacol.*, **60**, 249–252.

Nathanson, J.A. (1977), *Physiol. Rev.*, **57**, 157–256.

Nathanson, J.A. (1980), *Life Sci.*, **26**, 1793–1799.

Nathanson, J.A. and Glaser, G.H. (1979), *Nature (London)*, **278**, 567–569.

Nickerson, M. (1949), *Pharmacol. Rev.*, **1**, 27–101.

Nickerson, M. and Goodman, L.S. (1947), *J. Pharmacol. Exp. Ther.*, **89**, 167–185.

Nickols, G.A. and Brooker, G. (1979), *J. Cyclic Nucleotide Res.*, **5**, 435–477.

Nordeen, S.K. and Young, D.A. (1978), *J. Biol. Chem.*, **253**, 1234–1239.

O'Donnell, S.R. and Wanstall, J.C. (1979), *Naunyn Schmiedeberg's Arch. Pharmacol.*, **308**, 183–190.

Olpe, H.R. and Schellenberg, A. (1980), *Eur. J. Pharmacol.*, **63**, 7–13.

Palacios, J.M. and Kuhar, M.J. (1980), *Science*, **208**, 1378–1380.

Palmer, G.C. (1972), *Neuropharmacology*, **11**, 145–149.

Partington, C.R., Edwards, M.W. and Daly, J.W. (1980), *Proc. Natl. Acad. Sci. U.S.A.*, **77**, 3024–3028.

Peroutka, S.J., Greenberg, D.A., U'Prichard, D.C. and Snyder, S.H. (1978), *Mol. Pharmacol.*, **14**, 403–412.

Peroutka, S.J., Moskowitz, M.A., Reinhard, J.F., Jr. and Snyder, S.H. (1980), *Science*, **208**, 610–612.

Petrack, B. and Czernik, A.J. (1976), *Mol. Pharmacol.*, **12**, 203–207.

Pfeuffer, T. (1977), *J. Biol. Chem.*, **252**, 7224–7234.

Pfeuffer, T. and Helmreich, E.J.M. (1975), *J. Biol. Chem.*, **250**, 867–876.

Pike, L.J. and Lefkowitz, R.J. (1978), *Mol. Pharmacol.*, **14**, 370–375.

Pittman, R.N., Minneman, K.P. and Molinoff, P.B. (1980a), *Brain Res.*, **188**, 357–368.

Pittman, R.N., Minneman, K.P. and Molinoff, P.B. (1980b), *J. Neurochem.*, **35**, 273–275.

Pollet, R.J., Standaert, M.L. and Haase, B.A. (1980), *Proc. Natl. Acad. Sci. U.S.A.*, **77**, 4340–4344.

Potter, L.T. (1967), *J. Pharmacol. Exp. Ther.*, **155**, 91–100.

Powell, C.E. and Slater, I.H. (1958), *J. Pharmacol. Exp. Ther.*, **122**, 480–488.

Reisine, T.D., U'Prichard, D.C., Wiech, N.L., Ursillo, R.C. and Yamamura, H.I. (1980), *Brain Res.*, **188**, 587–592.

Roberts, J.M., Insel, P.A., Goldfien, R.D. and Goldfien, A. (1977), *Nature (London)*, **270**, 624–625.

Robison, G.A., Butcher, R.W. and Sutherland, E.W. (1971), *Cyclic AMP*, Academic Press, New York, Chapter 6.

Rodbell, M., Krans, H.M., Pohl, S.L. and Birnbaumer, L. (1971a), *J. Biol. Chem.*, **246**, 1861–1871.

Rodbell, M., Krans, H.M.J., Pohl, S.L. and Birnbaumer, L. (1971b), *J. Biol. Chem.*, **246**, 1872–1876.

Rodbell, M., Birnbaumer, L., Pohl, S.L. and Krans, H.M.J. (1971c), *J. Biol. Chem.*, **246**, 1877–1882.

Rogers, J., Silver, M.A., Shoemaker, W.J. and Bloom, F.E. (1979), *Soc. Neurosci. Abstr.*, **5**, 10.

Romero, J.A. and Axelrod, J. (1974), *Science*, **184**, 1091–1092.

Romero, J.A., Zatz, M., Kebabian, J.W. and Axelrod, J. (1975), *Nature (London)*, **258**, 435–436.

Rosenberger, L.B., Roeske, W.R. and Yamamura, H.R. (1979), *Eur. J. Pharmacol.*, **58**, 255–257.

Rosenberger, L.B., Yamamura, H.I. and Roeske, W.R. (1980), *Eur. J. Pharmacol.*, in press.

Ross, E.M. and Gilman, A.G. (1977), *Proc. Natl. Acad. Sci. U.S.A.*, **74**, 3715–3719.

Ross, E.M. and Gilman, A.G. (1980), *Annu. Rev. Biochem.*, **49**, 533–564.

Ross, E.M., Maguire, M.E., Sturgill, T.W., Biltonen, R.L. and Gilman, A.G. (1977), *J. Biol. Chem.*, **252**, 5761–5775.

Ross, E.M., Howlett, A.C., Ferguson, K.M. and Gilman, A.G. (1978), *J. Biol. Chem.*, **253**, 6401–6412.

Rouot, B.R. and Snyder, S.H. (1979), *Life Sci.*, **25**, 759–774.

Rouot, B.M., U'Prichard, D.C. and Snyder, S.H. (1980), *J. Neurochem.*, **34**, 374–384.

Rugg, E.L., Barnett, D.B. and Nahorski, S.R. (1978), *Mol. Pharmacol.*, **14**, 996–1005.

Russell, M.P. and Moran, N.C. (1980), *Circ. Res.*, **46**, 344–352.

Sabol, S.L., and Nirenberg, M. (1979), *J. Biol. Chem.*, **254**, 1913–1920.

Salzman, E.W. and Neri, L.L. (1969), *Nature (London)*, **224**, 609–610.

Scatchard, G. (1949), *Ann. N.Y. Acad. Sci.*, **51**, 600–672.

Schramm, M. (1976), *J. Cyclic Nucleotide Res.*, **2**, 347–358.

Schramm, M. and Rodbell, M. (1975), *J. Biol. Chem.*, **250**, 2232–2237.

Schramm, M., Feinstein, H., Naim, E., Lang, M. and Lasser, M. (1972), *Proc. Natl. Acad. Sci. U.S.A.*, **69**, 523–527.

Schramm, M., Orley, J., Eimerl, S. and Korner, M. (1977), *Nature (London)*, **268**, 310–313.

Schultz, J. (1976), *Nature (London)*, **261**, 417–418.

Schumann, H.J., Endoh, M. and Wagner, J. (1974), *Naunyn Schmiedeberg's Arch. Pharmacol.*, **284**, 133–148.

Schwarcz, R. and Coyle, J.T. (1976), *Brain Res.*, **127**, 235–249.

Segal, M. and Bloom, F.E. (1974), *Brain Res.*, **72**, 99–114.

Sercombe, R., Aubineau, P., Edvinsson, L., Mamo, H., Owman, C. and Seylaz, J. (1977), *Pflügers Arch.*, **368**, 241–244.

Sharma, V.K. and Banerjee, S.P. (1978), *J. Biol. Chem.*, **253**, 5277–5279.

Shear, M., Insel, P., Melmon, K.L. and Coffino, P. (1976), *J. Biol. Chem.*, **251**, 7572–7576.

Shein, H.M. and Wurtman, R.J. (1969), *Science*, **166**, 519–520.

Siggins, G.R., Hoffer, B.J. and Bloom, F.E. (1969), *Science*, **165**, 1018–1020.

Singer, S.J. and Campbell, D.H. (1955), *J. Am. Chem. Soc.*, 4851–4855.

Skolnick, P., Stalvey, L.P., Daly, J.W., Hoyler, E. and Davis, J.N. (1978), *Eur. J. Pharmacol.*, **47**, 201–210.

Smith, C.B. (1963), *J. Pharmacol. Exp. Ther.*, **142**, 163–170.

Sporn, J.R. and Molinoff, P.B. (1976), *J. Cyclic Nucleotide Res.*, **2**, 149–161.

Sporn, J.R., Harden, T.K., Wolfe, B.B. and Molinoff, P.B. (1976), *Science*, **194**, 624–626.

Sporn, J.R., Wolfe, B.B., Harden, T.K. and Molinoff, P.B. (1977), *Mol. Pharmacol.*, **13**, 1170–1180.

Starke, K., Montel, H., Gayk, W. and Merker, R. (1974), *Naunyn Schmiedeberg's Arch. Pharmacol.*, **285**, 133–150.

Starke, K., Borowski, E. and Endo, T. (1975), *Eur. J. Pharmacol.*, **34**, 385–388.

Sternweis, P.C. and Gilman, A.G. (1979), *J. Biol. Chem.*, **254**, 3333–3340.

Stone, T.W. (1976), *Naunyn Schmiedeberg's Arch. Pharmacol.*, **278**, 333–340.

Strada, S.J. and Weiss, B. (1974), *Arch. Biochem. Biophys.*, **160**, 197–204.

Strickland, S., Palmer, G. and Massey, V. (1975), *J. Biol. Chem.*, **250**, 4048–4052.

Strittmatter, W.J., Davis, J.N. and Lefkowitz, R.J. (1977), *J. Biol. Chem.*, **252**, 5472–5477.

Strittmatter, W.J., Hirata, F. and Axelrod, J. (1979), *Science*, **204**, 1205–1207.

Su, Y-F., Cubeddu, L. and Perkins, J.P. (1976), *J. Cyclic Nucleotide Res.*, **2**, 257–270.

Su, Y-F., Harden, T.K. and Perkins, J.P. (1979), *J. Biol. Chem.*, **254**, 38–41.

Sutherland, E.W. and Rall, T.W. (1960), *Pharmacol. Rev.*, **12**, 265–299.

Taylor, A. and Wilson, R. (1970), *Experientia.*, **26**, 267–269.

Terasaki, W.L. and Brooker, G. (1978), *J. Biol. Chem.*, **253**, 5418–5425.

Terasaki, W.L., Brooker, G., DeVellis, J., Inglish, D., Hsu, C-Y., and Moylan, R.D. (1978), *Adv. Cyclic Nucleotide Res.*, **9**, 33–52.

Trendelenburg, U. (1963), *Pharmacol. Rev.*, **15**, 225–276.

Tsai, B.S. and Lefkowitz, R.J. (1978a), *Mol. Pharmacol.*, **14**, 61–68.

Tsai, B.S. and Lefkowitz, R.J. (1978b), *Mol. Pharmacol.*, **14**, 540–548.

Tse, J., Wrenn, R.W. and Kuo, J.F. (1980), *Endocrinology*, **107**, 6–16.

Tuttle, R.R. and Mills, J. (1975), *Circ. Res.*, **36**, 185–196.

U'Prichard, D.C. and Snyder, S.H. (1977), *J. Biol. Chem.*, **252**, 6450–6453.

U'Prichard, D.C. and Snyder, S.H. (1978a), *J. Biol. Chem.*, **253**, 3444–3452.

U'Prichard, D.C. and Snyder, S.H. (1978b), *Eur. J. Pharmacol.*, **51**, 145–155.

U'Prichard, D.C. and Snyder, S.H. (1979), *Life Sci.*, **24**, 79–88.

U'Prichard, D.C., Greenberg, D.A. and Snyder, S.H. (1977), *Mol. Pharmacol.*, **13**, 454–473.

U'Prichard, D.C., Bylund, D.B. and Snyder, S.H. (1978), *J. Biol. Chem.*, **253**, 5090–5102.

U'Prichard, D.C., Bechtel, W.D., Rouot, B.M. and Snyder, S.H. (1979), *Mol. Pharmacol.*, **16**, 47–60.

U'Prichard, D.C., Reisine, T.D., Mason, S.T., Fibiger, H.C. and Yamamura, H.I. (1980), *Brain Res.*, **187**, 143–154.

Vatner, D. and Lefkowitz, R.J. (1974), *Mol. Pharmacol.*, **10**, 450–456.

Vauquelin, G., Lacombe, M.L., Guellaen, G., Strosberg, A.D. and Hanoune, J. (1976), *Biochem. Pharmacol.*, **25**, 2605–2608.

Vauquelin, G., Geynet, P., Hanoune, J. and Strosberg, A.D. (1977), *Proc. Natl. Acad. Sci. U.S.A.*, **74**, 3710–3714.

Vauquelin, G., Bottari, S. and Strosberg, A.D. (1980a), *Mol. Pharmacol.*, **17**, 163–171.

Vauquelin, G., Bottari, S., Andre, C., Jacobsson, B. and Strosberg, A.D. (1980b), *Proc. Natl. Acad. Sci. U.S.A.*, **77**, 3801–3805.

Vetulani, J., Stawarz, R.J., Dingell, J.V. and Sulser, F. (1976a), *Naunyn Schmiedeberg's Arch. Pharmacol.*, **293**, 109–114.

Vetulani, J., Stawarz, R.J. and Sulser, F. (1976b), *J. Neurochem.*, **27**, 661–666.

von Euler, U.S. (1956), *Noradrenaline: Chemistry, Physiology, Pharmacology and Clinical Aspects*, Thomas, Springfield, Illinois.

Watanabe, A.M., McConnaughey, M.M., Strawbridge, R.A., Fleming, J.W., Jones, L.R. and Besch, H.R., Jr. (1978), *J. Biol. Chem.*, **253**, 4833–4836.

Weiland, G.A., Minneman, K.P. and Molinoff, P.B. (1979), *Nature (London)*, **281**, 114–117.

Weiland, G.A., Minneman, K.P. and Molinoff, P.B. (1980), *Mol. Pharmacol.* **18**, 341–347.

Weiss, B. and Costa, E. (1968), *J. Pharmacol Exp. Ther.*, **161**, 310–319.

Weiss, B. and Costa, E. (1969), *J. Pharmacol. Exp. Ther.*, **168**, 146–152.

Weiss, B., Greenberg, L. and Cantor, E. (1979), *Fed. Proc. Fed. Am. Soc. Exp. Biol.*, **38**, 1915–1921.

Wikberg, J.E.S. (1978), *Nature (London)*, **273**, 164–166.

Williams, L.T. and Lefkowitz, R.J. (1977), *J. Biol. Chem.*, **252**, 7207–7213.

Williams, L.T., Mullikin, D. and Lefkowitz, R.J. (1976a), *J. Biol. Chem.*, **251**, 6915–6923.

Williams, L.T., Jarett, L. and Lefkowitz, R.J. (1976b), *J. Biol. Chem.*, **251**, 3096–3104.

Williams, L.T., Lefkowitz, R.J., Watanabe, A.M., Hathaway, D.R. and Besch, H.R., Jr. (1977), *J. Biol. Chem.,* **252**, 2787–2789.

Williams, L.T., Mullikin, D. and Lefkowitz, R.J. (1978), *J. Biol. Chem.* **253**, 2984–2989.

Wolfe, B.B., (1980), Private communication.

Wolfe, B.B., Zirrolli, J.A., and Molinoff, P.B. (1974), *Mol. Pharmacol.,* **10**, 582–596.

Wolfe, B.B., Harden, T.K. and Molinoff, P.B. (1976), *Proc. Natl. Acad. Sci. U.S.A.,* **73**, 1343–1347.

Wolfe, B.B., Harden, T.K. and Molinoff, P.B. (1977), *Annu. Rev. Pharmacol. Toxicol.,* **17**, 575–604.

Wolfe, B.B., Harden, T.K., Sporn, J.R. and Molinoff, P.B. (1978), *J. Pharmacol. Exp. Ther.,* **207**, 446–457.

Wolff, J. and Cook, G.H. (1973), *J. Biol. Chem.,* **248**, 350–355.

Woodcock, E.A. and Johnston, C.I. (1980), *Nature (London),* **286**, 159–160.

Woodward, D.J., Hoffer, B.J. and Altman, J. (1974), *J. Neurobiol.,* **5**, 283–304.

Yamashita, K., Yamashita, S. and Ogata, E. (1977), *Life Sci.,* **21**, 607–612.

Young, W.S., III and Kuhar, M.J. (1980), *Proc. Natl. Acad. Sci. U.S.A.,* **77**, 1696–1700.

Zahniser, N.R., Minneman, K.P. and Molinoff, P.B. (1979), *Brain Res.,* **178**, 589–595.

Zatz, M. (1978), *Life Sci.* **21**, 1267–1276.

Zatz, M., Romero, J.A. and Axelrod, J. (1976), *Biochem. Pharmacol.,* **25**, 903–906.

Index